MOUNTAIN SEARCH AND RESCUE TECHNIQUES

Typesetting by the Library Systems Group, Boulder, Colo.
Text set in Century Schoolbook type by Videocomp

MOUNTAIN SEARCH

and

RESCUE TECHNIQUES

by

W. G. May

Illustrated by Linda Boley

Rocky Mountain Rescue Group, Inc.
Boulder, Colo.
1973

Published and distributed by

ROCKY MOUNTAIN RESCUE GROUP, INC.
P. O. BOX Y
BOULDER, CO 80302

A member organization of the
Mountain Rescue Association

First Edition

September, 1972

Cover Design by Linda Boley

Manufactured in the U. S. A.

Library of Congress Catalog Card Number: 72-92728

Copyright © 1972 by W. G. May

Copyright © 1973 by Rocky Mountain Rescue Group, Inc.

9 8 7 6

Proceeds from the sale of this book benefit the RMRG

TABLE OF CONTENTS

PART III

APPENDICES

LIST OF ILLUSTRATIONS

FOREWORD

The beginnings of this manual surely date back nearly a quarter of a century to the time when the Rocky Mountain Rescue Group was founded. In my wanderings through this book, I was impressed not only by the sophistication that twenty-five years has brought to mountain rescue, but also by the many familiar techniques we tested and put to use way back then. Bill May says in his introduction that it has been too long in being put down. The result appears to be well worth the prolonged gestation.

The nostalgia I've felt browsing through this book has elements of both pain and pleasure. Pain is being forced to acknowledge the vintage of my own participation in R.M.R.G., to face the many years that have passed since and my present status more as a potential rescuee than rescuer. The pleasure comes of pride, not only in having participated in the beginnings of R.M.R.G., but also in seeing how far it has come. I recall our original scrutiny of the carabiner brake, the many discussions as to how it should be applied and finally the day we first put it to the test. I don't remember whether that occurred during 1948 or 1949, but the rest of the details are fairly vivid. We were lowering a Stokes litter down the face of the Third Flatiron. The "victim" had to be cajoled into the basket and tied securely (see Fig. 22-1) lest he depart. The only real flaw in the operation was brought home to us by the sound of sirens screaming up toward the Bluebell shelter; we had neglected to inform the Sheriff that it was just a practice.

The author in his introduction to this book describes the somewhat masochistic dedication that characterizes the volunteer mountain rescuer. I suppose that is so, and Bill May exemplifies the type well, for the effort involved in preparing this account of rescue techniques tested precisely those traits. The result is destined to be almost too useful, for the frequency of mountain accidents seems to be enjoying the same headlong growth that is typical of so many aspects of existence these days. One wonders how long volunteer rescue groups will be able to keep pace with the demand for their services.

Can education or regulation reverse this growth in mountain morbidity or mortality? Education may help. Regulation probably won't much. It is certainly not worth the cost and effort or the encroachment on the freedom of men to wander in the hills. Mountain rescuers should be aware of this fact. Too often the rescuer, particularly if his mountaineering becomes limited solely to rescue activity, loses sight of the fact that he is there to serve others. He must not view mountaineering as a game to be played with rules designed to suit the convenience of the rescuer.

Which brings me back to Bill's introduction. Having been in the game for several years, he sees "no tangible reasons" why anyone should enjoy rescue work. Yet, the answer is not so difficult. Mountain rescue is essentially mountaineering. A few different elements exist: the intensity, drama, and genuine altruism of saving lives; the special skills and technical expertise demanded. More could be added, but the sum is still the same. The mountaineer who commits himself to rescue does so in no small part for the pleasure he derives from it. He should recognize and accept the reward he gets in return for the time he gives, the energy he consumes, and the risks he takes. He should also recognize that if the time comes when rescue is no longer fun, he no longer has to do it. He can tuck his boots away in a deep closet and relegate this book to a high, sufficiently inaccessible shelf. Till then, though, he should find what's written here of value in developing his capabilities as a rescuer, and thereby heightening the pleasure to be had from helping others.

Tom Hornbein (Group Leader, RMRG, 1951-1952)
Seattle, Washington
August 1, 1972.

ACKNOWLEDGMENTS

The author is indebted to a large number of people for assisting in writing, editing and producing this book. Dave Lewis, Jonathan Hough, George Hurley, Guy Burgess, Dean Bowyer, and Walt Fricke made lengthy criticisms of many of the chapters. Many comments were received from others, including Joe O'Laughlin, Don Lewis, and Asa Ramsay from the Rocky Mountain Rescue Group, and Harry Ledyard, Hal Dunn and Lindon Wood from the Alpine Rescue Team. Various other people too numerous to name individually have passed along appreciated suggestions.

The following persons were major contributors to individual chapters: Ted Koeberle, attorney, Ch. 5; Walt Fricke, Ch. 11; Asa Ramsay, Ch. 12; Helen Phillips, Ch. 16; and Jonathan Hough, Ch. 33. Lewis Dahm contributed information on helicopters, and Skip Greene, on snowmobiles. Chapter 21 was criticized by Dick Parker, M.D., and Ch. 34 by Mike Koenig of the National Transportation Safety Board.

The large job of doing the illustrations fell to Linda Boley. Some figures in rough drafts were drawn by Elaine Pilz and Charlotte Bull. Duane Ball supplied the curves for the Wind Chill Chart, and Lorne Matheson calculated the Daylight Hours Chart.

The technical production of the book using computers for optical character recognition, editing and typesetting was masterminded by Mike Stone of the Library Systems Group, Boulder, Colo. Thanks goes to Dave Lewis for suggesting that the job be done this way in the first place. Linda Boley contributed much practical knowledge on layout and production of the book. The typing for optical scanning was done by Carolyn Hedrick, Sue Hoffman, and Amy Christopher. Dave Lewis prepared the tapes for the editing program which was written by Bill Waite and run by John Gammie and Dean Bowyer. Editing and proofreading of the full manuscript was done by Dave Lewis, Mary Anna Dahm, Dean Bowyer, Helen Stiles, and Bob Kinne. Sue St. John and Mike Haynes edited many chapters, and several other RMRG members criticized individual chapters. Dave Lewis found a vast number of errors using highly sophisticated but easily applied computer techniques. He also used the computer to efficiently locate key words from which the index was constructed. Any mistakes (misteaks?) are still the responsibility of the author.

Dave Lewis put the tapes in final form for typesetting. The final pasteup was supervised by Linda Boley.

Major efforts of Tom Jones provided the financial base for the publication of the book. Al DeMuth gave legal advice.

Special thanks are due Tom Hornbein for writing the Foreword.

The assistance of IBM in typesetting is gratefully acknowledged.

ROCKY MOUNTAIN RESCUE GROUP

Several mountain accidents and searches occurring near Boulder, Colorado, between 1945 and 1947 clearly indicated the need for an organized volunteer search and rescue capability. The Rocky Mountain Rescue Group was organized in the fall of 1947 to meet this need. RMRG has served the public continuously since then.

RMRG is a Colorado nonprofit corporation, exempt from income tax under Sec. 501-C-3 of the Internal Revenue Code, and a member of the Mountain Rescue Association. Its membership of about 80 is derived from the Boulder community; about half are students at the University of Colorado. RMRG is funded by the City of Boulder, Boulder County, The Associated Students of the University of Colorado, and private donations, in roughly equal (and barely adequate) amounts.

The Group holds training meetings twice a month throughout the year. Each meeting is usually followed by a weekend field operation. At these sessions prospective members are taught the basic rescue skills, and new rescue techniques are discussed, tried, and refined. Recent search and rescue operations are critiqued in detail at the training meetings. The field sessions range from training in a particular skill or technique to full-scale practice missions and demonstrations of new developments. In addition, the membership meets quarterly for elections of new members, directors, and officers. The Board of Directors meets monthly with committee chairmen and interested members to conduct Group business. In 1971, the membership expended 4600 man-hours at these training and business meetings.

Throughout its 25 years, the RMRG has pioneered many new techniques of mountain rescue. In recent years it has developed and proven methods of long face evacuations that are now applied routinely. Its backpackable rescue cable winch is unique in its safety and versatility and is undergoing continued trial and improvements.

The Group responds to calls for assistance in rock climbing and mountaineering accidents, and mountain search and rescue operations generally. Most missions are conducted in Boulder County and several adjacent mountain counties, but the Group is occasionally called to more distant areas in Colorado, and other states. RMRG maintains close liaison with the various agencies involved with search and rescue, and with other search and rescue organizations. This liaison is accomplished both directly and via regional rescue associations and a State Search and Rescue Board. In 1971, the Group received 122 calls for assistance, expending 6349 man-hours in response. 1972 has been much busier.

The Group's headquarters are in the University Memorial Center, Room 30. Its mailing address is Box Y, Boulder, Co 80302. Calls for assistance are usually directed through the Boulder County Sheriff.

THE MOUNTAIN RESCUE ASSOCIATION

The Mountain Rescue Association is a nonprofit volunteer public service organization dedicated to the saving of lives through rescue and public safety education. The MRA creates a central source through which the efforts and activities of the member units may be coordinated to promote mountain safety more effectively and to provide integrated mountain rescue service. The services of the individual unit are increased by bringing together teams that will provide additional manpower and capabilities. Agencies responsible for search and rescue may turn to the Mountain Rescue Association as a source of mountain rescue knowledge and techniques to augment their local capabilities.

Through publications like the association's Newsletter, Equipment Information Bulletins, seminars, conferences and training workshops, the MRA promotes the free exchange of rescue techniques and procedures. It disseminates advances in equipment, and when possible promotes a standardization that will improve the rescue operations. The Mountain Rescue Association endeavors to work closely with all rescue groups, agencies, mountaineering clubs and outing groups, in an effort to keep constantly informed of advancements that are in the common interest. The MRA encourages exchange of ideas and inquiries from all groups even though they are not eligible or interested in membership.

Mountain Rescue Association
P.O. Box 9
Altadena, Ca 91001

INTRODUCTION

Introduction to Mountain Search and Rescue. The need for trained and skilled mountain rescuers has grown through the years, sometimes by leaps and bounds. An individual who considers taking up volunteer mountain rescue must recognize the need for great dedication in addition to possessing a somewhat masochistic, patient and a bit crazy personality. He should be prepared for sleepless nights, sizable loss of otherwise free time, hard tiring work, sometimes large personal expense and often not even a "thank you" from the rescued upon completion of a difficult mission. There is seldom any glory in mountain rescue, and publicity seekers should look elsewhere for their kicks. The author of this book, still in mountain rescue after several years of activity, can offer no tangible reasons why anyone would seem to enjoy the work.

Introduction to this Book. This book was written as a training manual for prospective members of the Rocky Mountain Rescue Group. The need for some up-to-date written material has been present for years but suddenly became urgent when our rescue mission load increased greatly and many new prospective members needed training. Most of the notes were written during the author's term as training officer of the RMRG.

We strongly feel that good mountain rescuers are first mountaineers, then trained in rescue. The nonclimber will not readily understand the technical aspects of rescue, whereas the experienced climber can very quickly become a skilled mountain rescuer. Thus the reader is expected to have some mountaineering/technical climbing/hiking background, but occasionally some elementary aspects of mountaineering are presented, because there appeared to be a need in our training program for such material.

No one can become a skilled mountain rescuer by just reading or memorizing a book. Extensive practice is essential, and practices applying the rescue techniques should be difficult enough that actual missions can be carried out with confidence.

Throughout rescue a general attitude of safety should be present. Thus some of the techniques described herein may strike the climber as overly cautious in minimizing the subjective dangers. The lives of rescuers should not be unduly endangered. For example, an entire rescue party might easily be wiped out by an avalanche or stroke of lightning; there is never justification for putting the rescue team into an area of severe objective danger.

The existing literature in mountain rescue, some of which is cited below, was found to be inadequate because of lack of thoroughness, outmoded techniques and equipment, or inappropriateness for mountain rescue in Colorado. The techniques in this book emphasize the use of nylon rope rather than steel cable, not because of a lack of skill or experience with cable but because of the familiarity of nylon to the climber and hence ease in training a climber in rescue techniques; the use of steel cable is discussed where appropriate. Rock evacuation methods are discussed more fully than corresponding techniques on snow because of the frequency of rock accidents near Boulder, Colorado, the home of RMRG.

Hardly mentioned are the major and difficult problems of mountain rescue leadership. There are a number of reasons for this omission. The novice rescuer has problems enough becoming highly skilled in the individual and team aspects of technical mountain rescue without being simultaneously burdened with leadership. Further, a leader must know the individual's techniques thoroughly before he can be a successful team or mission leader. It is very difficult to put in writing the problems and solutions of leadership. To the author's knowledge the best job yet done in this direction is the booklet by Paul Williams.

Pertinent references are cited at the end of many chapters. Those given below contain much of value to mountaineers and mountain rescuers and will be cited again from time to time.

REFERENCES

Mountain Search and Rescue Operations, Grand Teton Natural History Association, 1958.

Mountain Rescue Techniques, Wastl Mariner, 1963.

Mountain Rescue Leadership, Paul Williams, MRA.

Mountaineering; The Freedom of the Hills, Harvey Manning, ed., Seattle Mountaineers (ed. 2, 1967).

Safety in the Mountains, Federated Mountain Clubs of New Zealand, 1967.

Mountaineering, Alan Blackshaw, 1965 (Penguin).

Manual of Ski Mountaineering, David Brower, Sierra Club.

WARNING

Mountain search and rescue expertise is not automatically bestowed upon all those who read this book. There is no substitute for training, experience and judgment.

Many steps have been taken and many hours spent to assure accuracy; however, the book by necessity must reflect familiar or particular circumstances. Different or unfamiliar situations may require different techniques or combinations of techniques. It is hoped that this book will contribute to mountain safety. It will do so only if the reader recognizes the limitations of the text and is willing to spend the time necessary to acquire considerable skill, insight and judgment in the rescue techniques.

TO CHARLENE QUICK

PART I

The first part of this book is concerned with some general aspects of mountaineering and mountain rescue. The mountaineering chapters are presented as a review, to indicate the background knowledge and experience expected of the reader, and to emphasize topics particularly important for the mountain rescuer. A variety of subjects of general interest to mountain rescuers is given to provide the background for understanding the techniques presented later.

Considerable detail is given concerning some standard "tools" of the rescuer; the chapter on rope includes information seldom found in the mountaineering literature, and the communications chapter includes details of radio procedure. Even though cable systems have been used for some very impressive rescue operations, recognized standards and techniques are only now being established, and the cable chapter is somewhat less detailed than the others.

CHAPTER 1

GENERAL MOUNTAINEERING

This chapter is little more than an outline of some general mountaineering and climbing skills which are assumed as background for understanding the remainder of the text. The intent is not to teach these skills here, but to present some very brief reminders and general references. The beginning mountain rescuer is in the best position to learn rescue techniques if he already has expertise in the skills of this chapter, but some expert mountain rescuers have learned their climbing and mountaineering along with rescue. Every well-rounded mountain rescuer must also be a climber/mountaineer.

HEAT LOSS MECHANISMS

The four major mechanisms of heat loss from a body are by radiation, convection, conduction, and vaporization of water. We briefly discuss each of these.

Radiation. Heat lost from a body by radiation is roughly proportional to the temperature difference between the body and the surroundings. If the human body is covered with any clothing, the temperature difference between the body skin and the clothing in contact is small, and thus the radiation heat loss from the body itself (except from bare skin) is negligible. However, radiation from the outer surface of the clothing may be sizable but is reduced by having the surface temperature of the clothing minimized by wearing thick insulation and by taking measures as discussed in the chapter on Survival. The now well-known "Survival blanket" or "Space blanket" (a thin sheet of metallized Mylar) does an admirable job of essentially eliminating radiation heat loss from a person by reflecting the body heat back to the body, but this sheet does almost nothing towards reducing conductive losses, which may be sizable.

Forced Convection (Wind). Heat loss due to motion of air past a body is very significant. The wind chill chart reproduced below shows that a gentle wind gives cooling equivalent to a significant drop in temperature in still air. Even a single layer of clothing greatly reduces the convection heat loss from bare skin in a breeze. The best way to reduce such heat loss is to get the body clothed well and behind a shelter to block the wind.

Conduction. The total heat flow by conduction through a substance will depend on the thermal conductivity of the material, the thickness of insulation, and the temperature difference. The important principle "Thickness equals Warmth" arises because the thermal conductivities of most (dry) materials used for clothing are about the same. These insulators conduct heat largely through the air which is trapped in the material rather than through the material itself; thus a given thickness of down, wool, or cotton each conducts heat about equally well. More insulation can be achieved only by increasing thickness, not by changing material. The choice of material is determined by other considerations, such as ability to pass water vapor, insulating qualities when wet, durability, compressibility, etc. For example, down-filled clothing gives the most warmth for its weight when dry but is quite expensive and is useless when wet. The best material for inner clothing is wool, since wool retains its insulating qualities much better when wet due to small wicking than do other materials.

Moisture. The body loses a great deal of heat (desirably) when working hard by sweating and vaporizing water. Even when at rest, the body is continually vaporizing water through pores and breathing. The main implication of this heat loss mechanism is the possibility of causing insulation to become wet and less effective.

CLOTHING

The amount of insulation worn will have to be adjusted when the rate of physical exertion is changed, as from inactivity to rapid climbing. This is conveniently done without removing much clothing by simply unzipping or unbuttoning various layers. Thus for versatility in such adjustments, clothing should open at the front for ventilation; a pullover sweater is a poor choice. The experienced mountaineer will start a period of heavy physical exertion slightly underclothed, knowing that his body will soon be generating much heat. Exposing the ears or hands will do an effective job of cooling (sometimes too rapidly in

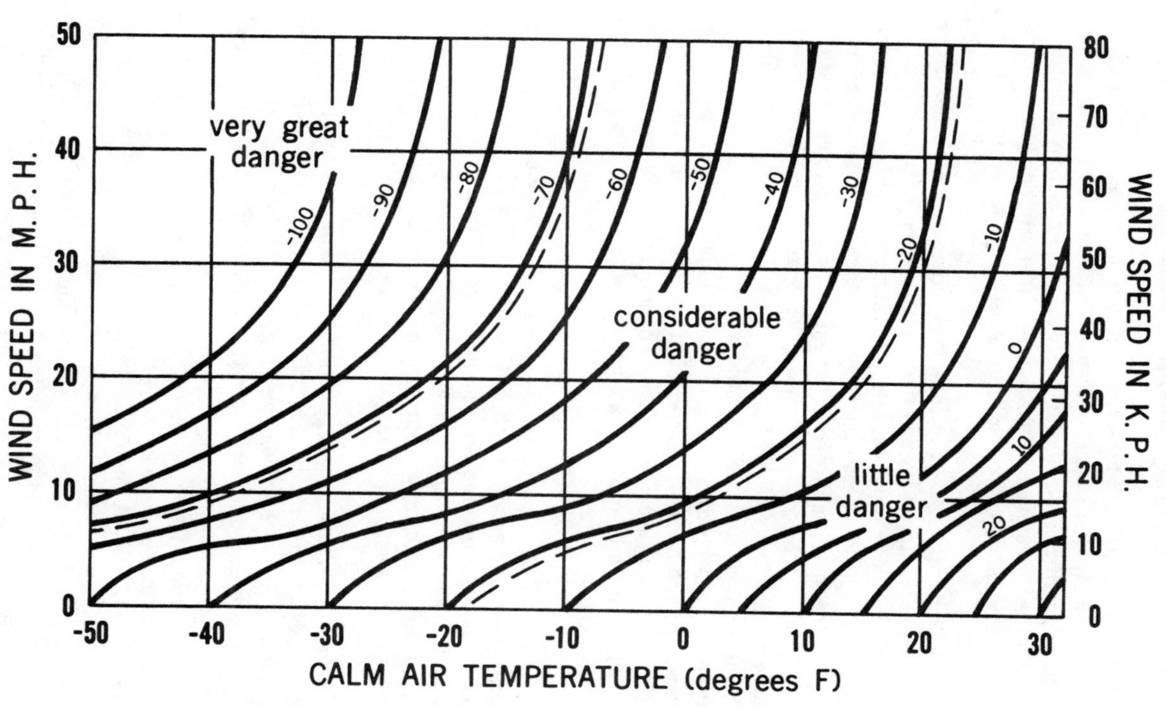

Fig. 1-1. Effective temperature on exposed skin (wind chill danger of freezing). The levels of danger are for properly clothed persons.

a wind). In the winter or above timberline it is very dangerous to be dressed so warmly that sweating occurs, since then clothing gets wet and soon thereafter becomes cold; ventilation is extremely important in cold weather. Removal or addition of undergarments outdoors in the winter can usually be avoided by a little forethought.

Outer Garments. Except in rain, it is generally most satisfactory to have the outer upper layer a lightweight nylon parka with hood, windproof and water repellent but not waterproof, so body moisture can escape. The hood is very important since a great deal of heat is lost through the head, especially from the ears. A wool watch cap or stocking cap which can be converted into a face mask is cheap and useful in bad weather. Army or Air Force wool twill trousers are excellent for the outer layer and are available at low cost.

Mittens are much warmer than gloves and always should be carried in the winter and above timberline, but for dexterity in cold weather and particularly in a wind, lightweight gloves will be needed. The hands will tend to be colder if gloves are worn inside large mittens than if removed.

Rainwear. A large poncho is inexpensive and very useful for rain protection and as a ground cloth, but a cagoule does a much better job of protecting the individual from a driving rain. Plastic outer clothing is cheap but generally does not withstand the punishment given in mountaineering and may stiffen and break in cold weather; coated nylon is much superior and more expensive.

Footwear. The various types of climbing and mountaineering boots were each designed for a different purpose. Klettershoes, lightweight and relatively flimsy, have very stiff lug soles glued on and are usually sized for a tight uncomfortable fit so that the foot has complete control of the boot. The same style of shoe may be used for trail walking, if fitted comfortably. However, this style of boot is usually suede and is difficult to waterproof, and unless well made tends to fall apart if given rugged off-trail use. A mountaineering boot, ankle high, with few seams and of rugged construction, is fitted for comfort while wearing usually two or three pairs of socks. It may be used for fifth class climbing, and can be waterproofed and used on snow with or without crampons. Work boots are a poor substitute for mountaineering boots because they are considerably less rugged, often do not have lug soles and are usually nearly impossible to waterproof adequately due to the large number of seams.

For winter use the mountaineering boot must be worn with sufficiently *few* pairs of socks that circulation in the feet is not impaired. The principle of "Thickness equals Warmth" applies to footwear; thus, the only boot which is warm is also large. Double leather boots are commonly used for winter mountaineering but are poor for summer use because they are clumsy and too warm. Double rubber boots with thick insulation are used in very cold and wet weather but are not suitable for any technical climbing. Mukluks are good for snowshoeing in the coldest weather, but are useless for temperatures near freezing or above.

Wool socks should be worn for warmth, since the feet will sweat and get the socks damp, and only wool retains reasonable insulating qualities when wet. Effort should be made to keep the feet dry, not only by using a good waterproofing compound on the boots but also by wearing gaiters to prevent entry of snow into the boots.

SHELTER

Insulation around the body during sleep is usually provided by a sleeping bag (or half bag and parka) placed on insulation for protection from the ground cold and dampness. The sleeping bag, usually down-filled to provide the maximum of insulation at a minimum of weight and bulk when packed, must be protected from moisture. Sleeping while wearing wet clothes can lead to a wet sleeping bag due to condensation of escaping water vapor within the bag itself. Also, a bag may get wet from exposure to the elements, even in the absence of precipitation. Protection from wind, cold and moisture is provided by some form of shelter, which may be primitive and/or improvised as discussed in Ch. 2, or may be luxurious, as a tent or cabin.

FOOD AND WATER

Water is an essential part of mountaineering. A person is dehydrated far more easily when climbing at high elevation than when relaxing in town. Water losses from the body may be very large—several quarts per day, even in the absence of noticeable perspiration. The effects of dehydration in the mountains can be serious, quickly leading to severe illness and inability to continue travel. During the summer, water may be found in plentiful supply in some mountain ranges, but is nearly unavailable in other areas, and then advantage must be taken of every opportunity to drink and fill canteens with potable water. In the winter, water may occasionally be found by digging through snow covering a stream or by chopping through ice on a lake, but more often must be carried and protected from the cold, perhaps by insulating a canteen in a sleeping bag. For extended winter mountaineering a stove is essential to melt snow for water.

Food eaten in the mountains during a day hike is often either easy to digest for quick energy (carbohydrates) or concentrated (high fat content) and durable. The efficient mountaineer will have food accessible to eat at any time while travelling without stopping. On a longer trip, thought must be given to weight, variety, ease of digestion and cooking.

MISCELLANEOUS EQUIPMENT

The usual items which are found in every mountaineer's pack include goggles or good sunglasses with headband to prevent loss, food, canteen (full), small personal first aid kit, compass, and lengths of parachute cord. Most climbers also carry such miscellany as matches and candle, headlamp or flashlight, signalling mirror, pocket knife, pencil (not pen) and paper, sun cream, etc.

All items of personal equipment, particularly climbing gear and outer clothing, should be marked with the owner's name, initials, or personal color code. A climber should not feel that simply because all other climbers have their gear marked, one can leave his own gear unmarked and hence distinguish it from other gear.

TECHNICAL CLIMBING

No text can hope to teach the knowledge, skill and judgment needed in technical rock climbing. Areas in which expertise is developed by the climber include such skills as balance climbing, chimneying, jamming, use of the rope for safety (tie-ins, waist loops or seat slings, belaying), rappelling, placement of points of protection, (pitons, nuts, slings) and aid climbing. It is more difficult to understand snow and ice climbing and the associated necessary skills including step chopping, cramponing, ice ax belays and arrests, protection, and judgment of conditions.

The novice will quickly learn the elements such as tie-ins, belaying on rock or snow, rappelling, and some ice ax techniques. These basics will be assumed known by the reader of succeeding chapters. However, each of these areas includes subtleties which can be appreciated only after considerable experience. Skilled technical climbers will already be familiar with much of the information in the chapters on equipment, anchors, and ascending fixed lines.

DANGERS

Mountaineering is potentially quite dangerous, with hazards arising from various sources both objective and subjective.

Weather. One danger is bad weather. The ferociousness of stormy weather above timberline is not appreciated by the uninitiated, but it is obviously best to avoid such experience by the best course of action in impending bad weather: retreat to shelter below timberline. What is an easy climb, or even a casual stroll, in good weather may be impossible in bad weather, due to cold, wetness, lack of visibility, wind, or lightning. The cooling power of wind on flesh was already shown in Fig. 1-1. A person begins to lean into a wind of about 40 knots (75 km/h) and cannot walk in an 80 knot (150 km/h) wind. Blowing rain or snow is extremely chilling and also makes navigation difficult. Lightning, an obvious hazard, is discussed more thoroughly in Ch. 3.

Rockfall. Rockfall can come about from the freezing and thawing of water in cracks, or may be caused by a person. In any case, a climbing route is often chosen to avoid dangers of rockfall by staying on ridges or obviously "clear" faces and out of steep, narrow, loose gullies. The quantity of rock debris at the base of a prospective route is often an indicator of the rockfall danger.

Snow and Ice. Negotiation of a snow field, glacier or icefall also presents hazards. Avalanche, discussed in Ch. 18, is a danger that is sometimes obvious, otherwise insidious. Usually crevasses in a glacier will be evident, and snowbridges over hidden crevasses should come as no surprise. Likewise, the danger of falling snow blocks or ice in an icefall should be evident, and the time of day and weather are major factors in this form of objective danger.

The combination of snow fields and warm weather can present another insidious danger. In the early morning, the snow may be covered by a solid crust, easy to walk on. But by early afternoon, the snow may have softened to the point where travel is essentially impossible without snowshoes or skis.

Fatigue. A given situation may be more or less dangerous to an individual depending significantly on the physical and mental capabilities of the person at the time. Potential dangers from a fall on a technically difficult climb are obvious, but perhaps more important are the hazards due to mental and physical fatigue or darkness (Fig. 1-2) as are often encountered during a descent.

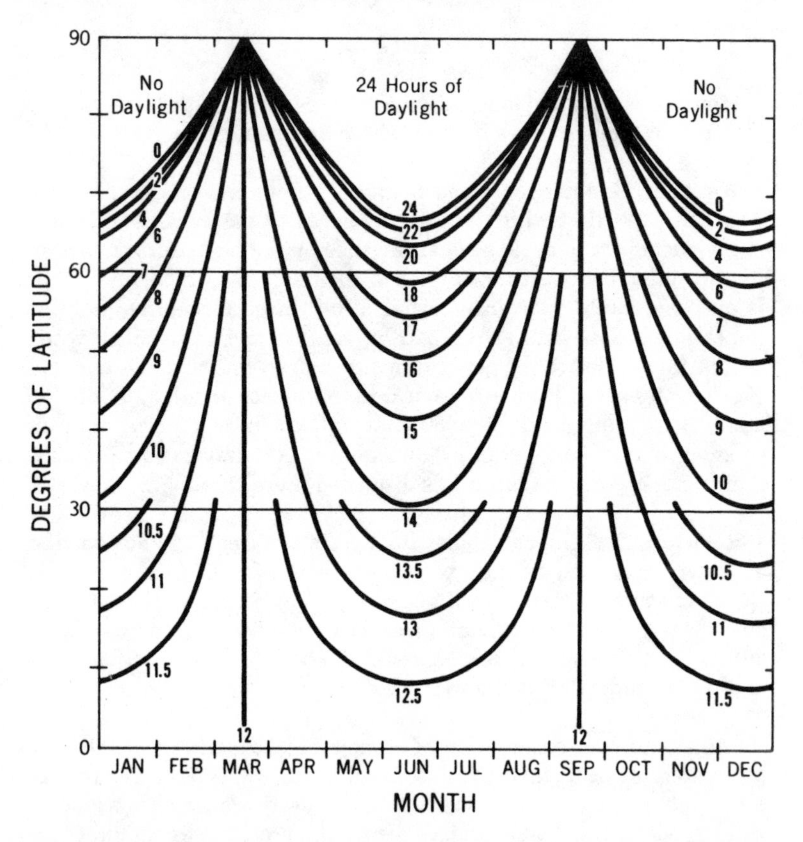

Fig. 1-2. Showing contours of constant hours of daylight (sunrise to sunset) as a function of latitude and day of the year.

REFERENCES

1. *Mountaineering: The Freedom of the Hills*, H. Manning, ed.
2. *Mountaineering*, A. Blackshaw.

CHAPTER 2

SURVIVAL TECHNIQUES

Survival can be divided into two parts: technique and attitude, or will to live. Technique is the adaptation of normal mountaineering procedures to inconvenient situations, that is, the ability to improvise, and is the main subject of this chapter. The importance of having the will to live has been shown frequently. One well-known example involved two climbers improperly equipped stranded on a large rock wall in very bad weather. They both survived quite well under trying circumstances, maintaining the will to live, until the rescuers made voice contact. At that time it seemed that both climbers felt that they were rescued and need not continue to struggle to live. Both died within minutes. Confidence in one's survival technique supports the will to live by reducing fear and panic. Techniques of survival involve primarily the conservation of body heat. The various important forms of heat transfer are well known to be radiation, convection, and conduction, with moisture vaporization of some significance. We will consider separately clothing and shelter and how insulation against each form of heat loss can be achieved. The various discussions will be brief because these topics are rather well covered in the standard mountaineering references. The techniques are important for mountain rescuers because such techniques may be used in bivouacs during missions or in caring for an injured victim until assistance arrives to perform the evacuation.

Another aspect of survival, that of food intake over a long period of time, will be ignored here because a mountain rescue team is normally only a few hours from civilization.

The overall survival picture can be summarized by the five words *Will, Wits, Warmth, Wind, Water.*

CLOTHING

The general principles of clothing were discussed in Chapter 1. The most important points mentioned there were that the clothing must be dry and must be of adequate thickness.

The extremities are excellent radiators and can be chilled readily, thus they should be covered fully to conserve heat in a survival situation. A hood on a parka is nearly essential for controlling heat dissipated by the head. Mittens are much warmer than gloves and should always be available in winter. Extra socks substitute for mittens in a survival situation. The feet are often the first part of the body to become severely chilled. If a person has stopped moving, his feet may be kept warm by removing the boots and adding extra socks (dry ones), and then keeping the feet out of the boots but well insulated from the ground, for example in a pack, and wiggling the toes.

SHELTER

The techniques of improvising shelters are discussed at length in mountaineering texts and will only be summarized here. The keys to success in improvisation are the cleverness and experience of the improviser.

Some shelters require a great deal of physical exertion to build. This activity will cause the builder's clothes to become wet from perspiration. Use of ponchos, rain chaps, etc., worn instead of (not over) clothing will save clothes from getting wet, and dry clothes will be available after the work is over. Extreme care must be exercised since wet clothing will create a serious warmth problem.

Shelters are best built not too large, and individuals should huddle close together to best conserve body heat. Insulation between the body and the ground or snow underneath is essential in survival. Preventing heat from being conducted out of the body into the ground is very important for anyone sitting or lying on cold ground or snow, and *thickness* of insulation must be provided, by sitting on mittens, pack, boots, or rope, for example, and not on relatively compressible material such as down. A foam pad or piece of Ensolite (T.M.) is best to provide the necessary thickness. An air mattress is a poor substitute since air can leak out or can circulate inside, and a plastic air mattress may become brittle and break at low temperatures. Natural materials such as pine boughs can be used; a 6 inch (15 cm) thick layer providing excellent insulation. (Consideration should be given to the ecology in cutting branches.)

A waterproof ground cloth must be used to prevent moisture from the underlying ground or snow from dampening insulation under a person sitting or lying on the ground. This ground cloth can be a very lightweight plastic sheet such as a drycleaning bag, which can always be carried in the bottom of the pack and while providing no insulation itself is of large value because it keeps the other insulators dry and effective. Without such a sheet, water vapor can be transferred upwards and condensed in the insulation.

Use of Nature. Nature often provides a shelter or can be used to advantage to improve man-made shelters described below. The rescuer should be aware of wind and weather patterns on a small scale. For example, a large boulder surrounded by snow except for a moat might appear to be a good sheltered spot, but the moat exists because the wind keeps it blown clear and thus the spot may be cold. Often small ridges, boulders, or logs can be used to advantage for protection from the wind. Because of radiation cooling to the sky on a calm clear night, it will be much colder under the stars than under a tree or rock overhang since such objects can reflect heat back to the body. Also, low spots such as small depressions or major valleys may be cold since cold air settles.

Tree Pit or Fallen Tree. In forested areas with deep snow, a large pit nearly clear of snow may often be found around the trunk of a large evergreen tree or under a partly fallen tree. The pit may be completely out of sight due to snow having built up to the branches over the pit itself. A small effort searching for such a shelter may prove very worthwhile overall. In fact, hikers on snowshoes may occasionally fall into such "traps" accidentally.

Snow Trench. A trench large enough for one or two persons to lie down in can be dug readily and quickly in a snowdrift with ski tail, snowshoe, cook pot, etc. When roofed over with snowshoes, skis, pine branches or poncho, the trench can be very cozy. Additional warmth may be achieved by digging a narrow pit along the bottom next to the long side of the main pit, letting cold air settle into the second pit.

Snow is a good insulator, and thus it keeps the ground near the freezing point even when air temperatures are much lower. If the trench or pit around a tree can be dug to ground level, some added warmth may be achieved.

Snow block or Rock Wall. Above timberline or in an open area with a strong wind, considerable protection from the wind can be achieved easily by building a low wall to windward of a person in prone position. In blowing snow, snow will collect on the lee side of the wall, and a person sleeping there will find himself covered with a snowdrift, which will in itself provide insulation. A plastic tube tent or poncho is useful in keeping the snow out of the clothing. A related structure may be constructed very rapidly on a steep lee-side snow slope by simply digging out a level place and roofing it over with a tarp.

Snow Caves. With suitable snow conditions, a large and exceptionally comfortable shelter, the snow cave, can be built. Good, deep, compacted snow is often found on the lee side of a ridge, lake or just downhill and downwind from a large open area. In crudest form, the cave is simply a room cut into the snowbank. The most basic refinement is to have the top of the entrance below floor level for added warmth, letting the heat generated by the body rise above the entrance and be trapped inside. A more complete discussion of the numerous techniques of construction may be found in the references.

Due to the fine insulating qualities of snow, a person inside can neither hear shouts of nor be heard by someone outside, although the footsteps of someone walking by are clearly heard inside. Thus if the people holed up expect to be found by others walking by, they must very clearly mark the cave outside with something that cannot accidentally be buried by falling snow.

Igloos and Snow block Houses. Igloos and snow block houses provide very good shelters, but they do require some practice, time and suitable tools for construction. A major advantage of the block construction over the cave is that the builders do not exert themselves so much and thus do not tend to become wet. A structure which is half snow cave or trench and half blocks may be the optimum. The details of techniques may be found in the references.

A shelter related to the snow cave and block house is the mound house, which is built on a flat field when there is not sufficient depth or quality of snow for another type of shelter. The technique is simply to heap up snow into a mound, into which the house is dug just as a cave is made. The method is successful even in rather powdery snow if the roof height is about as large as the diameter of the cave and if some time is allowed for the snow mound to consolidate before digging. The snow should not be packed after piling up.

Poncho Shelter. A poncho is frequently used in conjunction with some other form of shelter, but it may be used by itself in the form of a tent or lean-to windbreak. If one or two ponchos are used to form a tent with one or both ends open, the openings may be partly sealed with packs or other material.

Lean-To. A lean-to is the classic shelter used in wooded areas, and may be quickly improvised for rain protection or for a reflector for a fire by assembling some logs or branches and covering with a poncho.

OTHER CONSIDERATIONS

Aside from clothing and shelter, body warmth can be conserved by doing the obvious things such as building a fire and reflector. Survivors huddling together between the fire and reflector will get the most benefit from the fire and will tend to keep each other warm.

As is well known, a body which is active generates heat, and the person stays warm with little insulation. A resting body requires much more insulation. Any activity including shivering will help to keep the body warm.

A body needs to burn food to generate heat, but if a person eats a large meal he may feel cold shortly thereafter because blood which would otherwise be circulating providing body warmth will go to the stomach in digestive processes. However, a small amount of food eaten before sleeping will help a person feel warm.

A tired body tends to get cold readily. If a person is approaching complete exhaustion, he should get some rest to improve chances for survival rather than go to full exhaustion and collapse. (See the discussion of hypothermia in the first aid chapter.)

REFERENCES

1. *Mountaineering: The Freedom of the Hills*, H. Manning, ed.
2. *Manual of Ski Mountaineering*, D. Brower, Sierra Club, 1962.
3. *Man in a Cold Environment*, A. C. Burton and O. G. Edholm, E. Arnold (Publ.) Ltd., 1955.
4. *Outdoor Survival Skills*, L. D. Olsen.

CHAPTER 3

LIGHTNING

It is important to mountaineers to have a knowledge of lightning, how its hazards arise, and possible means of protection. This knowledge is even more important to mountain rescuers who may be in a danger area with less mobility than a climber.

Lightning is more prevalent in some areas than others, and is likely to be quite seasonal. For example, local lightning is commonplace during summer afternoons in the Colorado Rockies, and is less frequent in the Washington Cascades. Lightning may occur at any time of the year (though rarely in winter) in any mountain range. Depending on topography, electrical storms may be unpredictable, approaching unwary climbers from behind local clouds or nearby peaks.

Most climbers have experienced the obvious signs of electrical activity: hair standing on end, buzzing sounds as if bees were flying around, or even sparks from the ice ax or packframe. These signs do not guarantee that lightning is about to strike, but the prudent mountaineer will take preventive measures under such conditions as rapidly as possible.

In the paragraphs below, we discuss the physical origins of lightning and its most important hazards and suggest some protective measures. The section on lightning physics provides a basis for understanding the protective measures, but these technical details may be passed over on first reading.

PHYSICS OF LIGHTNING

Lightning arises from a separation of electrical charges, either between clouds, or between cloud and earth. This separation of charge occurs when there are strong vertical updrafts of air acting on rain drops, resulting in tremendous electrical potential differences. The strong upward air currents may occur due to unequal solar heating of neighboring areas, such as over freshly plowed fields and lakes. This thermal mechanism causes updrafts and resulting thunderheads and electrical activity over plains and other nonmountainous areas, but may also act in the mountains, in differential heating of air over valley floors and mountain ridges due to different ground cover. Lightning storms of this thermal origin will normally occur during the afternoon. Another mechanism creating vertical updrafts of particular interest to mountaineers is the very presence of the mountain slopes forcing otherwise horizontally moving air to flow upwards. A major change of weather such as a front moving through can cause a thunderstorm at any time of day. With appropriate moisture content in the air, electrical charge separation and consequent potential differences will result. Strong and obvious vertical development of clouds indicates a high probability of lightning.

Normally air is a good insulator, but in the presence of sufficiently large potential gradients, it will ionize, or break down, and conduct electrical currents quite well. The lightning flash is, crudely speaking, the flow of the separated electrical charges back together, again along ionized air. Since potential gradients are largest near high and relatively sharp points, breakdown of the air and lightning will most likely occur in such locations.

The two most important dangers from lightning are the direct hit and the ground currents. The first of these, as mentioned above, is most likely to occur at a sharply pointed feature such as a mountain summit, a sharp ridge or minor summit pinnacle at the end of a ridge. A tree or a standing person is another likely target. Furthermore, a relatively small object such as a person is less likely to be hit when in a large concave terrain feature such as a bowl than on a convex surface such as a knoll or large bench. The current which flows in the lightning bolt does not dissipate itself at the point of direct hit, but tends to flow along the easiest paths of electrical conduction on the surface of the ground. These ground currents will be strongest near the point of direct hit, rapidly diminishing in intensity with distance; but even well away from the direct hit, the ground currents can be deadly.

PROTECTION

Direct Hit. We now consider protection from the direct hit. Obviously the best solution is to be completely off the mountain. Assuming that this is impossible, advantage can be taken of the presence of a nearby prominent pinnacle or other likely spot of direct stroke. Lightning will tend to hit the pinnacle rather than a person near the pinnacle if the pinnacle is five to ten times or more the person's height and if the horizontal distance from the person to the peak is about half the pinnacle height, as sketched in Fig. 3-1. If the "potential" victim gets too close under the peak, his body may be an alternate path to that of the ground for the very strong ground currents. If he gets into a cave, as in Fig. 3-2, he may be sitting in a spark gap and thus be exposed for a minor direct hit if the currents prefer to take the direct path through the air across the mouth of the cave rather than the longer path along the ground. Also, if the person moves far from under the pinnacle, (more than its height), the direct hit might just as likely strike the victim as the pinnacle. A climber might find relative safety just down below a sharp ridge as well as near a peak or pinnacle or gendarme. The theory behind a lightning rod on a roof is related to the above, that is, it is hoped that the lightning may strike the rod rather than the roof, and the currents would then be conducted safely to ground. Furthermore, a sharp projection may serve to discharge gradually the charge-holding cloud over it without a lightning bolt actually striking, but the mountaineer should never count on this.

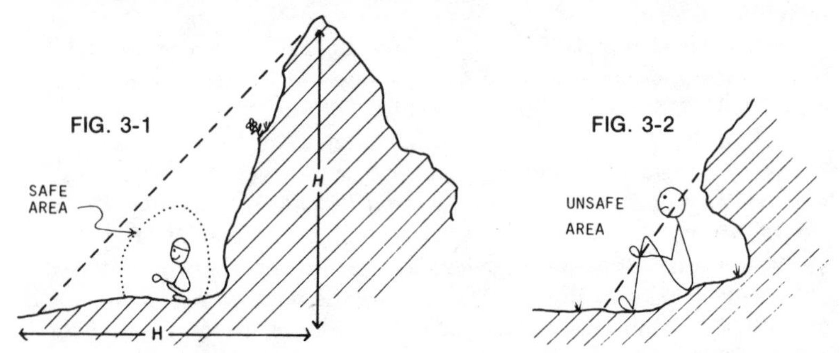

Fig. 3-1. Showing location relatively safe from lightning. If the pinnacle height H is too small, then the ground currents at the person may be fatal. **Fig. 3-2.** Showing location with high lightning danger.

If a group of persons is in a region of high lightning danger, individuals should not wait out the storm huddled together. The survival of one person whose heart or breathing has been stopped by a stroke of lightning will depend critically on prompt action by companions, and it is quite unlikely that all of a group of separated persons will be knocked unconscious simultaneously.

Ground Currents. To avoid injury from ground currents, the climber should first of all stay out of the "easy" paths of current. Such easy paths include anything wet, and particularly wet lichen-covered rock, cracks and crevices filled with water, and wet earth. Other "easy" paths include wet ropes, cables, etc., along the ground. Also, short straight paths through the air may be "easy" compared to longer paths along the ground itself. The body is an "easy" path, and thus a climber should not get in the situation shown in Fig. 3-2, or in a similar one, sitting in a depression in the ground across which currents might jump through the person.

Electrical currents are forced through the body by potential differences that are developed along the path of the ground currents. Thus, to minimize current through the body, one's feet should be kept close together, and the climber should be facing along, rather than across, the most likely direction of ground current flow. His hands should be kept off the ground to prevent current from flowing directly through the vital organs as discussed below. The person sitting as in Fig. 3-2 is more susceptible to injury than if he were squatting on his feet alone, Fig. 3-1.

Ground currents will be quite small along a dry path, and thus it appears that a safe place might be under an overhang or in a cave. The danger of being at the mouth of a cave was mentioned above—a direct spark may occur across the cave opening and pass through the body. There is also danger in being near an interior cave wall, because it is quite possible that an easy path for current exists through the ground to the cave interior, for example along a drainage crevice. It is then possible for a discharge to occur from the entrance of this crevice into the cave through a person to the floor of the cave. A small cave may give a false sense of security.

The best measure to take against being injured by lightning in the mountains is to be off the mountain; thus a speedy descent during an impending lightning storm is appropriate. Such descent is likely to involve rappelling, which may be exceedingly dangerous in electrical activity and rain because a wet rope is a very easy path for current. The potential difference between the rappeller and the rock at his feet may be essentially the potential developed along the ground over the distance from the rappel anchor to the rappeller, and a large current may be easily passed along the ropes through the body. Even a minor shock may be indirectly fatal, if it causes the rappeller to fall out of his rappel. Thus rappelling involves a calculated risk. It speeds descent and escape from a danger area, but greatly increases hazards in the process.

A climber in a location exposed in the climber's sense of the word but moderately safe from severe lightning hazards could experience a minor shock which would cause him to fall. Thus he should be tied into a secure anchor. Since his tie-in rope to the anchor point will be a conductor to some extent, the rope should lie *across* rather than *along* possible paths of ground currents to prevent a large potential from developing between the anchor point and the position of the climber. The rope should certainly not go to a chest sling, which would cause any currents to flow through the heart and spinal cord (see next section).

Any measure taken to prevent injury from lightning will involve minimization of potential differences from one part of the body to another. Thus the best body position is a crouch, in a location as in Fig. 3-1. The feet should be kept close together, and preferably on a small dry rock or other insulator such as a pack or rope, and the hands kept off the ground (IMPORTANT). A metal packframe may be used to great advantage by laying it on the ground and squatting on it—any currents would tend to pass through the metal rather than the body. An ice ax certainly should not be worn on a pack on the back pointing up, but there is no reason to throw away the ax or other small metal objects including climbing hardware, since these items may be needed later, and they do not "attract" lightning when in a pack or on the body. A lightning discharge is much more likely to occur from the body itself than from a small object worn on the person.

Physiology. Electrical currents through the body may cause not only burns but also involuntary muscle contraction, stoppage of the heart, improper functioning of the brain and any other consequent malfunctioning of the body such as cessation of breathing. The extent of the damage depends on the amplitude and duration of the current and on the path of the flow through the body. When a person is struck directly, the currents are likely to be so large that no matter what the path through the body may be, the results are fatal, but ground currents are much weaker, and the particular current path through the body makes a significant difference. For example, current from hand to hand will pass through the heart, spinal cord and vital organs and may be fatal; but the same current from foot to knee of the same leg is not so bad. First aid may include heart massage, artificial respiration, treatment for traumatic shock, hypothermia and burns.

REFERENCES

1. "Lightning Hazards to Mountaineers," E. Peterson, *American Alpine Journal* Vol. 13, pp. 143-154, 1962.

2. *Mountaineering: The Freedom of the Hills*, chapter on mountain weather.

CHAPTER 4

INDIVIDUAL RESPONSIBILITIES

Preparing for the Mission. Generally, an individual rescuer should prepare his equipment for a mission immediately upon return from any climb or mission, to be ready for the next call.

The individual must choose personal equipment for the circumstances. This means not depending on scrounging gear from the other team members in the field, but rather carrying the bare minimum (food, headlamp, clothing, technical gear, etc.) plus a reasonable supply of extras to cover contingencies. Furthermore, the member must not carry a great excess of personal gear, for example, an ice ax for a rock mission. Excess weight will be a burden which will slow him down. He should count himself out if he cannot properly equip himself, for conditions such as winter weather above timberline. If in doubt, he should ask a leader.

Each individual must possess the talents needed for the circumstances. For example, some people may be fine technical rescuers, but would make very poor members of a search team, and first rate searchers, who are mentally conditioned and disciplined to keep trying even under discouraging circumstances, may not be technical climbers. Any prospective member of a team which might cross technical terrain must be honest with himself in evaluating his own abilities. He should be able to carry confidently rescue equipment and personal gear over fourth class rock, and rapidly ascend fixed lines over fifth class terrain. Furthermore, he must be able to tie in to an anchor or belay using his own slings, to do a hot seat (dulfersitz) rappel, and do these things quickly and surely, without being checked by anyone, in a freezing rain or blizzard, wearing mittens on numb hands at night. (This is not meant to be a joke, but is completely serious.)

An individual must decide for himself whether or not he is prepared to be a member of a rescue team in the field. Even if he decides that he is capable of adding to the strength of a team, he must be prepared to be overruled by a team leader. This is always the team leader's prerogative. An individual may be pulled off a team by a leader for any reason, for example, to maintain the overall balance of strength among the various teams.

Even if the individual is suitably equipped and skilled, he must be in proper physical condition at the time. The individual who is always at the tail end of the line on the hike to the scene probably has slowed down the entire team. The person who cannot keep up is worse than no asset, he is a liability. He may be lost catching up, or if he must return to base, for safety another team member will accompany him; thus the team is weaker than if the slow person had stayed back in the first place. Someone slow but steady should count himself out of the fast "bash" team, but can go in with search or support teams, carrying more needed gear, or he can be of assistance on a carryout.

Finally the individual must not let his enthusiasm color his honest evaluation of himself. On the other hand, the thoughts presented here are not meant to scare off hesitant volunteers. These people should indeed step forward for a team position and explain their lack of experience and knowledge to the team leader. The leader will in all likelihood welcome such people on the team and will check to be sure that they are properly equipped. The only way that a newcomer will gain experience and knowledge is by doing.

The Member in the Field. The team member follows the instruction of the team leader. If an individual thinks that a leader erred, he should tactfully inquire, because the leader may have additional information which he has not had time to explain to the team. However, the team leader is human and could have made a mistake which can only be pointed out by a team member. The ultimate responsibility for safety and well-being rests with the individual, thus the leaders should be informed by the individual who seems to be getting into an unsafe or questionable situation, such as soloing fourth or fifth class rock or working above timberline in a blizzard. Also, team members should look after and assist each other. It is up to the individual to use his best judgment to decide when he is getting in too deep and to back off and request a belay or other appropriate assistance. Again, enthusiasm should not be allowed to distort good judgment.

Individuals should not grumble among themselves or complain about being assigned to what appears at the time to be a useless or not very glamorous task. Complaining does no good and is demoralizing to others.

The team member's responsibility is to add to the team's effectiveness. If an individual does not understand what is expected of him, he should ask; if for any reason he should be unable to carry out the assignment, he must so report to the team leader.

On a search, the individual must be mentally disciplined never to break continuity on a line search, always to remain alert even after hours or days of fruitless searching in bad weather, and never to stray away from the team. He must be forgiving to a somewhat irritable team leader on a long tiring mission, remembering that the leaders are often physically and mentally tired because of lack of sleep and the strain of responsibilities.

Once a victim is found on a search, individual rescuers should not be overanxious to get moving. There may be a good reason for a delay, such as first aid or determining a better route out. These reasons may not be evident to the individual team members.

An individual carrying a litter should be strong enough to go his full term; otherwise he will break the continuity of the arduous task. There are other ways a team member can be useful, such as carrying spare gear, or scouting and clearing a route ahead and directing the litter team along the best route. These functions are fully as important as carrying the litter itself. Where possible the individual should do these things before he has to be asked, but he should be sure that his actions are indicated by the situation and that he is capable of performing the tasks properly. If not, he should wait for directions.

When a team includes members competent and capable of assuming a leadership role, the team leader becomes the "first among equals." The leader will in all likelihood discuss important decisions with these "equals."

After the Mission. Everyone should be careful about loose talk concerning the mission. Information releases are to come from the leaders or appropriate agencies, not by hearsay to diligent reporters at the next table in a restaurant.

Other Thoughts. Most of the above thoughts paint a rather oppressive picture of the individual in a team. This is not meant to be the case. The successful mountain rescue group is made up not of sheep but of *individuals*, each of whom pushes himself hard and *always uses good judgment*. A *thinking* team member can contribute to the effectiveness of an operation, but nevertheless ill-conceived action can be disastrous.

CHAPTER 5

LEGAL ASPECTS OF MOUNTAIN RESCUE

Mountain search and rescue activities raise many questions of legal liability. There is very little definite law in the area because of the fortunate lack of lawsuits and almost no legal precedents. It appears quite unlikely that volunteer mountain rescuers would be held liable for any reasonable act resulting in further injuries during the course of a rescue.

Individual Obligations and Liabilities. An individual coming upon an injured stranger in the mountains is not under legal obligation to give aid, but he may feel morally obligated to assist. This is in contrast to the situation where the person is a member of a party in which an accident has occurred.

If an individual does render aid, he should do it carefully because he may be held liable for any further harm which he may do to the victim. In any event, the victim must be in "no worse" condition as a result of the individual's attention than he would have been if the "rescuer" had done nothing at all. The skills and training of the rescuer would be considered in judging whether additional harm incurred by the victim was due to negligence. For example, an untrained layman performing first aid might not be held liable for doing a poor job whereas an physician might be. In other words, the standard of care that an individual is held to is that of a reasonable and prudent person with the same level of training and experience as the "rescuer" had. A judgment should take into account other factors such as location, weather, stress due to the situation being a sudden emergency, and available equipment. The Good Samaritan statutes enacted in many states excuse physicians from liability for their actions during emergencies except in the case of clear gross negligence. In Colorado, and most states, the "Good Samaritan statutes" only apply to doctors, nurses, and other medically trained personnel, and do not apply to the rescue groups, even though highly trained in mountain rescue. A layman skilled in rescue also would not be held liable for added harm done to a victim except for, again, gross negligence or a clearly reckless disregard for an injured party's safety.

The converse situation, also of interest, is the liability of the person being rescued to the rescuer in the case that the rescuer is injured during the course of the rescue. The legal principle, sometimes called the "Rescue Doctrine," applies in such cases. It is assumed as a matter of law that when a party has created an emergency, others will come to his aid. When they do so the person creating the emergency can be held responsible for the rescuers' injuries, even though they may have placed themselves in a hazardous position which would under other circumstances be considered contributory negligence, unless the acts of the rescuer are extremely reckless or unwarranted. The "Rescue Doctrine" may or may not apply in cases involving only property and not a human life.

Yet another form of liability can arise: that of a rescuer for damages to the person or property of a third party. Probably the same general principles discussed above would apply, that is, there would be a reduced standard of care expected of a person acting under an emergency situation. If an individual rescuer is acting with reason under Federal direction, he would be relieved of personal responsibility for such acts, which come under a statute applying to the federal agency. Similarly, if the individual is acting under the supervision of a state or local governmental agency, the liability would be determined by the appropriate state statute. In many states the Doctrine of Sovereign Immunity is rapidly being wiped out. In Colorado, for example, the concept of governmental immunity or sovereign immunity has essentially been eradicated as of July 1, 1972. This means that any branch of the government is now as liable for acts of negligence as an individual would be if acting on a private basis. For this reason, many state agencies have taken steps to insure themselves against acts of negligence by their employees and volunteers. If an individual is acting under the direction of a volunteer rescue unit, governmental immunity would not apply. Individual rescuers, including students, are well advised to carry a standard tenant's or homeowner's insurance policy which includes protection against personal liability and theft of equipment. The cost of such a policy is not large. If the rescuer is charged with gross negligence, he should immediately contact his insurance company for representation by them. If he should ignore such a charge and is not insured, a judgment will be taken against him for money damages. In that event, the rescuer can only resolve the matter by paying off the judgment or having it discharged in bankruptcy.

The subject of liability of the rescuer for trespassing on another individual's private property in the United States is that the property owner has the right to hold the property secure and inviolate from trespass by outsiders. The courts through the years have eroded this concept in many ways. As a result, with such inroads as the "attractive nuisance" doctrine wherein the courts have stated that if there is something on a person's property such as a swimming pool or a mine shaft which would normally attract the attention of a child or a trespasser, the landowner may be held liable for any damages which occur to the trespasser, such as drowning or falling in the mine shaft, if the landowner does not take appropriate steps to protect the trespasser from the attractive nuisance. In the case of crossing another's property in an effort to effect a mountain rescue, the rescuer as a practical matter will either be able to cross that property because there is nothing more than a barbed wire fence setting it aside from the public land, or he will not be able to cross the property and will have to go around it because there is a more impressive deterrent to crossing it such as an eight-foot chain link fence which is electrified or a shotgun in the hands of a threatening landowner. If the rescuer is reasonably able to cross the land without the foregoing type of deterrents, and causes damage to the land, the courts would then probably look to the type of damage which was caused. For example, if in crossing the land, the rescuers trample down all of the baby trees that the landowner had carefully planted and tended, the rescuer might be held liable for the replacement value of the trees, or if the rescuer in effecting this trespass had smashed through the front and back wall of the landowner's house, again this would probably be considered compensable negligence in the act of trespass. On the other hand, if the rescuer committed no more than reasonable waste, such as clearing down timber from a mountain trail or trampling down the normal number of wild flowers as the rescue group crossed the property, the courts in all probability would excuse the trespass in view of the emergency condition which caused it in the first place. Other elements which must be considered include whether or not there was a reasonable alternative route which would avoid the complaining landowner's property, the apparent urgency of the rescue as it appeared at the time of the trespass and not afterwards when the situation could be evaluated from the cool serenity of 20-20 hindsight.

The Rescue Group and Its Relationship to the Law. Volunteer rescue units normally work under the authority of one or another branch of a state organization, often the County Sheriff, but also the

State Patrol, Police, Park Service, and others. In Colorado, there are no statutes directly requiring any governmental agency to perform a mountain rescue; such duties are only implied by general responsibilities including public safety and welfare. Although a rescue may be undertaken at the request of anyone, the volunteer rescue group should always inform the appropriate agencies in whose jurisdiction the rescue takes place. Occasionally, a rescue team competently performing its job may be caught between two or more authorities claiming legal jurisdiction. The rescuers should attempt to complete the mission quietly, settling political or jurisdictional hassles later.

Since a mountain rescue group by the implication inherent in its name is assumed to be able to perform mountain rescue operations competently, it may be held liable if a victim sustains further injuries while in its care, if the victim is not cared for using standards expected of trained rescue personnel. A unit competent at first aid and rescue techniques may be judged negligent for failure to carry or use proper equipment during a mission. However, most probably liability would be found only in the case of gross negligence.

In the case of third party liability, the outcome of a case attempting to hold the rescue unit liable would depend in detail on the nature of the organization for which the individual who caused the damages is acting. In the case of volunteer rescue groups the organization may be held responsible for the acts of its members, particularly if the act of the individual was reasonably necessary in carrying out the orders from the group leadership. For this reason, every rescue group is well advised to be incorporated according to the laws of the state in which it is headquartered, for liability reasons, and also should carry corporate liability insurance and Workman's Compensation insurance covering injuries sustained by rescuers on missions or practices. A group may also carry insurance against loss or theft of equipment, particularly small valuable items such as radios.

Death. Proof and cause of death are quite important from a legal point of view. Many life insurance policies include a double indemnity clause in the case of accidental death, and hence the cause of death is of great monetary importance to the companies and the heirs of the deceased. Distinction between accident and suicide is important and essential. Proof of death is normally made by a physician's or coroner's certificate, but if a mountaineering accident occurs in remote territory where body evacuation is impractical, proof may be given satisfactorily by witnesses who examined the body or who observed the victim fall thousands of feet or be buried by an avalanche. Observations of witnesses (other members of the climbing party) should be recorded promptly. In the case of an unrecoverable body and no strong evidence of death such as a witnessed accident, the victim might have to be considered missing, and estate settlement would have to wait for perhaps as long as seven years. Therefore, any evidence that can be accumulated by the rescue members will be extremely helpful to the authorities, and all other persons related to the deceased both legally and by blood. Rescuers are not, however, obligated to move a victim known to be dead to civilization or even to find the body if such action puts the rescuers in serious danger.

All climbers and mountain rescuers should be aware that law enforcement agencies and the local District Attorney's Office will be concerned with possible crime. Thus the scene of any accident (usually fatal) which could involve crime (homicide, drug traffic) should be preserved for law authorities. There is usually no need to hurry to do anything in the case of a fatality. A body in no danger of loss or further damage (as might occur in an avalanche) should be moved only upon the request of the county coroner or his deputy, who is the only person who can give legal approval to move a body. A district Attorney can forbid a body from being moved, but cannot give approval. In most mountaineering fatalities, the coroner will not desire to go to the scene and will approve the moving of the body to him.

All of the victim's personal belongings should be left on his person or collected and inventoried in the presence of two witnesses to avoid later questions by relatives. The belongings must be turned over to the coroner, not to even close relatives.

However, if possible, photographs of the body and the relevant area should be taken. If they are, the coroner should be advised accordingly. Photographs of a body should never be released for publication, since a close relative of the victim may sue for invasion of privacy.

Rescuers have no responsibility for determining or announcing the identity of a body. That is the coroner's job. There is no duty by members of a climbing party to tell next of kin of the death. In fact, a death message is best delivered by an authority or by a close family friend or clergyman.

If a fatal accident occurs during an expedition in a remote mountain range in a foreign country, both local and United States laws may apply for various aspects of the case; however, the local authorities must be given the opportunity to exercise their jurisdiction if they choose to do so.

News Media. Frequently reporters will be actively seeking information. The names of victims who are minors should not be released to news reporters unless the parents have been notified of the accident, no matter what the extent of the injuries may be. Names of the deceased must not be released by the rescuing party. The safest course of action for any member of the rescue group is to refer persistent reporters to the rescue team leader or publicity officer, who, if in doubt himself, will refer the reporter to the legal authority. Rescuers should be polite to the reporters, who are just trying to do their job.

During one long search mission, the news media at the request of mission leaders staged a press conference. The person interviewed was a minor who had some significant evidence which could have indicated foul play. He was asked leading questions and was observed for suspicious reactions. The legal implications of this type of situation are volatile at least, and should be avoided if possible.

Product Liability. There are currently no cases on whether the manufacturer or retailer of mountaineering equipment may be held liable for injury caused by failure of faulty equipment such as breakage of a crampon, piton hammer, etc., but the law is expanding rapidly in this field, and if there is a case involving equipment failure, the careful retrieval and custody of the broken parts are absolutely necessary in order to successfully bring a product liability case before an insurance company for damages.

CHAPTER 6

PERSONAL EQUIPMENT

The mountain rescuer needs the same personal equipment as a climber plus some additional special purpose gear. Some of those items which are of particular importance to rescue are discussed below. Some basic aspects of equipment were discussed in Chapter 1.

Footwear. Sturdy lug (Vibram, T.M.) sole boots which fit well are almost mandatory. These are useful on trail, rock or snow. Tight-fitting klettershoes are not suitable for any rescue work except for technical rock missions close to the road. Boots used in winter rescue should be very warm because rescue may involve lengthy periods of relative inactivity during which the feet tend to get cold.

Clothing. The rescuer is likely to be called upon in the worst weather, and thus should be equipped with more cold weather and rain gear than might otherwise be carried. Outer clothing should be brightly colored for visibility. This is particularly important in mountain rescue. Gloves are useful on most rescues for belaying, rappelling, and litter carrying. Leather gloves which do not stiffen after being wet (e.g. deerskin) are particularly good.

It is useful to have a mountain rescue patch or group identification clearly visible on some article of clothing to allow easy access past legal authorities to the scene of an accident.

Hardhats. High-strength hardhats should be mandatory for rescue personnel working in any steep mountain terrain. These protect the head in case of a fall of the rescuer or of falling objects. "Construction worker" style hardhats are virtually worthless. The rescuer should purchase a high-strength hardhat with crushable foam liner, and which meets Snell Foundation specifications for ski racing or surf-boarding. Use of a hardhat in rescue is perhaps more important than in climbing. One reason is the increased danger of rockfall in rescue for a variety of causes. The rescue party may not be free to choose its own path to the scene and may have to go into areas of rockfall danger. The rescue team is usually rather large, and the probability of rockfall increases as the number of people goes up. Ropes are sometimes tied together in a litter lowering, and a knot tends to dislodge loose rock. Load carriers or litter bearers are less able to be careful about knocking rock loose than are climbers. Another reason is the safety education point of view, since bystanders will see the rescuers wearing hardhats. Finally, identification of the wearer is made easier if his name is on his hardhat.

Headlamps. The headlamp should be a mandatory item for all missions. Rescues which are begun during daylight have a habit of not being completed until after dark, and the rescuers should always be prepared for night operations. A hand-held flashlight is nearly useless in technical rescues. The batteries used should operate at low temperatures and thus should not be the normal carbon-zinc type, even with industrial rating. Nickel-cadmium rechargeable batteries work at low temperatures but are very expensive and seem not to be charged at critical times. Highly recommended are the alkaline batteries, with Eveready (T.M.) seeming to give better service than other brands. These alkaline batteries work reasonably well in the cold, and the headlamp battery pack can be kept warm by being carried inside the clothing in very cold weather. The batteries last much longer than the carbon-zinc type, but die rather suddenly. They may recover some life after being shut off for awhile. Heat will destroy any battery, thus batteries stored in a hot car parked in the sun will die in a matter of weeks.

Most important for the battery life is the bulb used. The headlamp is usually initially equipped with a bright high current (.5 amp) bulb (No. 425 if screw type, 4 cell) which drains the batteries very quickly. A less powerful bulb puts out an adequate amount of light, and the battery life is far longer with a low current bulb. Thus the bulb in a newly purchased headlamp should be immediately replaced with a very low current (.15 amp) type (No. 502 screw type, 4 cell). The .3 amp bulb (No. 27) is a poor second best. A spare bulb, easily carried in the bulb housing behind the reflector, should be taped in place to keep it from rattling and to protect it from possible breakage.

Because the flashlight is easily turned on accidentally when carried in the pack and not in use, some means should be used to prevent the batteries from being inadvertently drained. This problem is solved by using a piece of cardboard to block the passage of current, or in a four cell lamp by reversing two of the batteries. If the batteries are not new, a full spare set should be carried.

Packs. Each rescuer in the field should have his own pack to carry his spare clothing, headlamp, food, and other miscellaneous equipment and reserve gear. In choosing a pack, it should be kept in mind that a pack partly full is much more comfortable to wear than a small one too full. A highly visible color is better than camouflage green not only so the individual who sets it down can find it readily, but also so the wearer can be seen by other rescuers. The pack should be kept with its owner. Too many rescuers find out the hard way that their packs seem to be not available when most wanted if someone other than the owner carries the pack.

Ice Ax and Crampons. The casual mountain hiker may carry an ice ax as a handy walking stick but never use it for serious belaying or self-arrest. In contrast, the rescuer may use his ax to belay a litter being lowered on snow. Thus the rescue ax should be of top quality with a very strong shaft, metal preferred. The details of the design of the ax head are relatively insignificant for rescue work; that is, the shape of the adze and blade are a matter of taste. The head of the ax should not be of the cheap stamped or cast variety, since it may be necessary to drive the ax into hard snow using a hammer. Furthermore, an ax with a carabiner hole is of no special virtue in mountain rescue since the head would break off of a wooden shaft with only about a 200 pound (90 kg) load if the carabiner hole were used. (The carabiner hole would not be used for anchoring heavy loads but otherwise may be quite useful.)

The length of a climber's ax will depend on the nature of his climbing. Thus for general glacier travel, a relatively long ax, useful for probing crevasses and as a walking stick, will be chosen, whereas a very short ax will be used for technical ice climbing. The first is preferred for rescue because of its greater security in giving belays and its increased safety in self-arrests. (See American Alpine Club "Accident Reports" 1971, p. 4.) However, the shorter ax is more convenient to carry.

Style of crampons is mostly a matter of taste, except that instep crampons are of limited use, but better to have than none on an icy slope. The stamped Army surplus crampons, all of which break easily, are to be completely avoided. Crampons should fit the boot well and should be secured with a binding that does not pinch the toes.

Technical Climbing Gear. Each rescuer should have as a minimum on all rescues: rappel gear, waist loop/seat sling with (locking) carabiner, and a sling and 'biner to tie into a belay stance or onto a litter during a scree evacuation. The only aluminum carabiners which open wide enough to be clipped onto the outer rail of a Stokes litter are the old Army ovals, almost unavailable now, and some very large Stubai (T.M.) D's. A wide web sling is very useful while carrying a litter on the trail to transfer weight from the arms, which tire quickly, to the shoulders. Some team members may carry a full array of fifth and sixth class climbing gear as dictated by circumstances and their own expertise.

Snowshoes and Skis. For over-snow travel skis may be excellent in appropriate circumstances, such as on terrain known to be gently rolling and open or along a jeep road where an evacuation may be speedily done using an akja (see Chapter 28). But skis will be very slow going both up and down hill in rough terrain, and thus for the reliability desired in rescue work, snowshoes will usually be preferred.

CHAPTER 7

RESCUE EQUIPMENT

Each rescue group member should know the operation, uses, weaknesses, and limitations of all equipment which might be used in the course of a mission because first, he may be called upon to operate the equipment, and second, he should know how one piece of equipment which he never operates interacts with another piece which he does operate.

The first part of this chapter will discuss rescue aspects of hardware familiar to any technical rock climber. Knowledge of the strengths of these items is important in rescue rigging because the loadings may be high and are relatively predictable. Every rescue group should have a dynamometer for equipment testing and observation of typical system stresses. The remainder of the chapter gives a general discussion of some important specialized mountain rescue equipment. Separate chapters will be devoted to rope, steel cable, and communications.

CLIMBING AND RIGGING HARDWARE

Carabiners. Some characteristics of carabiners which are of particular importance to mountain rescuers are strength, size, material, and safety. These features will be discussed in order.

Strength. We shall consider the following characteristics of a carabiner: a) Loading for which the gate jams, b) Breaking strength with the gate closed, c) Breaking strength with the gate open, and d) Strength for sideways loading on the gate. These are illustrated in Fig. 7-1.

a) The design of most carabiners is such that the gate is load-bearing and will not operate freely when some loading is placed on the 'biner. The gate of a typical oval carabiner jams at less than body weight, but some carabiners withstand perhaps 300 lbs (140 kg) before the gate is held shut. D-shaped carabiners such as Chouinards and Cassins (T.M.'s) have a larger gate-jamming load because more of the loading is taken on the back of the carabiner.

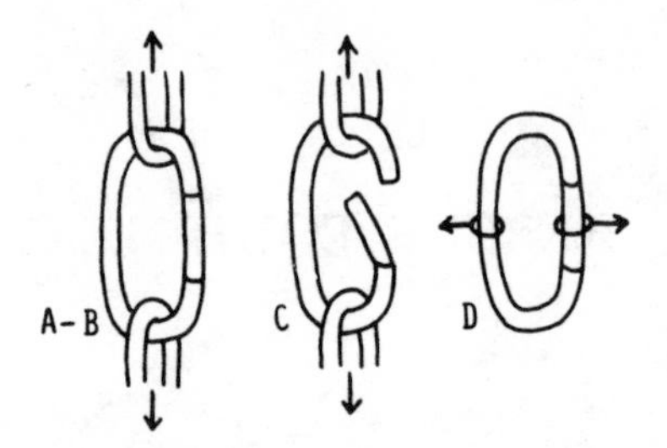

Fig. 7-1. Showing directions of applied stress on carabiners.

b) The usual figure quoted in climbing gear catalogs for the strength of a carabiner is the maximum breaking strength with the gate closed. Typical oval aluminum carabiners fail at about 2500 lbs (1100 kg), aluminum D's at 5000 lbs (2400 kg) and chrome-vanadium-steel at about 8000 lbs (3600 kg) or more, precise numbers depending on brand. The gate is the weakest part on ovals and fails at the catch or hinge.

c) Once the gate fails or if the gate is open, the carabiner strength is greatly reduced. An oval carabiner which can hold 2500 lbs (1100 kg) with the gate closed may fail at less than 1200 lbs (550 kg) with the gate open. Some D-shaped carabiners show less reduction in strength than do ovals because more of the loading is taken on the back.

d) No carabiner is designed for sideways loading on the gate, and such loading should be avoided in any system, particularly in improvised rigging or in a waist loop tie-in where the belay rope could pull sideways on the gate. Failure can occur at little over body weight.

One subtle but serious limitation on the strength of some carabiners occurs when the load is applied to the carabiner under test from two carabiners clipped side by side as shown in Fig. 7-2. Under this circumstance, the main part of the carabiner is bent open away from the gate, and the carabiner may fail at a very low stress.

Fig. 7-2. This method of stressing a carabiner results in greatly reduced strength.

Other Features. The size of a carabiner is important in rescue when the 'biner is clipped to something other than standard climbing gear. For example, the gates on most 'biners will not open wide enough for the carabiners to be clipped onto the outer rail of a Stokes litter as is often convenient. Only the old Army oval aluminum and large Stubai (T.M.) aluminum and steel carabiners have sufficiently large gate openings.

Lightweight equipment is always desirable, and most carabiners will be aluminum for this reason, but in some uses the harder and more rugged steel alloys will be desirable. Thus rescue equipment might include a few steel carabiners for ruggedness and for greater strength and reliability when large loads will be supported by only one carabiner.

Carabiners with locking gates are often a nuisance but are occasionally desirable when an open gate could lead to disaster as on a waist loop tie-in. A climber or rescuer must be careful not only to keep his belay rope attached but also that he does not inadvertently get clipped into something at the wrong time. In most systems the added safety of the locking gate can be achieved by placing two carabiners together with gates opening on opposite sides.

Other Climbing Hardware. *Brake Bars.* Standard climbers' brake bars are often used in evacuation brakes. The bars, fitted to oval carabiners, are slightly modified for rescue to speed up rope changes (see Ch. 24) by filing the lip of the bar so that the bar flips rather than snaps on and off of the carabiner. Improvisation of a brake bar brake using only carabiners is, of course, well known to climbers (see Ch. 31). All brake bar systems put side-loadings on the carabiner gates. The failure loads for such systems should be determined experimentally for each configuration. A new device, the brake plate, replaces the brake bar in rescue systems and will be discussed in Ch. 24.

Pulleys for Rope. Lightweight pulleys which can be clipped onto a carabiner are often useful in rescue hauling systems. To minimize loss of strength of the rope by bending, the sheave should be of as large a diameter as practical; 1 in. (2.5 cm) is good. The high efficiency of a ball bearing type is well worth the extra cost and weight in effort saved in any hauling evacuation. Also, pulleys without good bearings tend to bind under the heavy loads encountered in a rescue hauling system. A new type of pulley which is a sheave alone riding directly on the carabiner is unsatisfactory, due to the likelihood of the sheave slipping sideways out from under the rope leaving the rope running directly on the carabiner. Since a pulley in use may be required to hold up to double the rope load, it should be quite strong to have an adequate safety factor. The "Rescue" pulley in widespread use withstands over 4000 lbs (1800 kg) and breaks at either the eye or the shaft.

Pulleys for Cable. Pulleys for rope may be destroyed if used on cable. Special pulleys with large sheaves will be needed to pass cable connectors, as is often desirable. See the discussion in Ref. 1 of Ch. 10.

Pitons and Climbing Nuts. The discussion of this section is concerned with the intrinsic properties of pitons and climbing nuts (chocks), leaving placement, the most important factor in effective strength of an anchor point, to a later chapter. This material is presented as a review, since the reader is assumed to be knowledgeable in rock climbing, including protection in fifth class climbing.

Pitons are made from one of three materials: soft iron, high alloy steel (chromoly or chrome-nickel-iron), or aluminum, the latter being used only for large "bongs" to save weight over steel. Soft iron pitons are relatively inexpensive on initial purchase but may by used only once or twice because of severe work-hardening with use. After use the iron becomes very brittle and susceptible to breakage. In contrast the chromoly steel pitons may withstand as many as 100 or 200 drivings before becoming badly work-hardened, weakened and cracked. Thus for normal fifth class climbing, the chromoly pitons are much more economical than soft iron, but this is not usually a consideration in rescue.

It should be pointed out that a piton can be brittle but yet very strong. This is in fact the case with chromoly. The pitons should not be driven in such a way that they can be bent suddenly under shock loading. Shock loading is not usually the problem in rescue work that it is in fifth class rock climbing, such as in stopping a leader fall.

Steels do tend to become brittle at very low temperatures, but in the case of chromoly and probably for soft iron, temperature effects are not a problem in even the coldest weather (Ref. 1). The possible exception is for used and badly work hardened soft iron pitons which are very weak and should not be used anyway.

The intrinsic strength of any properly placed new piton is adequate for rescue use; the limitation is in placement. The eye or blade typically withstands in excess of 4000 lbs (1800 kg) for any good chromoly piton, and over 2000 lbs (900 kg) for soft iron and ring pitons. However, butt-welded rings may be unreliable. The blade of a piton which cannot be driven to the eye may break when loaded at the eye, and thus should be tied off with a sling around the blade. If the piton is driven hard, the weak link will be at this tie-off sling itself, breaking at the blade at perhaps only 500 lbs (230 kg).

Climbing nuts have come into use in this country only in the past few years. Compared to the piton, a nut may be much more secure, or much less, depending critically on the shape of the crack in which it is placed, the strength of the rock, whether or not the crack is expanding, and on the direction of pull. Strength limitations of completely solidly placed nuts will be discussed in the next paragraph, leaving thoughts on the placement to a later chapter.

Just as the holding power of a good chromoly piton is usually not limited by the breaking strength of the steel, the nut itself, usually aluminum or magnesium, will not fail. (Nuts of plastic or wood may fail under high loads.) But nuts threaded with a web or rope sling will fail at a relatively low pull. Typically, 1 in. webbing threaded through a nut will fail at the nut at about 2000 lbs (900 kg) and a 1/4 in. (7 mm) rope sling or 1/2 in. webbing fails at the nut at only 1200 lbs (550 kg). Failure of a properly installed steel cable threading a nut should be quite high, 2500 lbs (1100 kg) or more.

Bolts. (Fig. 7-3.) It may be necessary on occasion to place bolts for a rescue anchor. The various types of bolts available include a) self driving bolts, b) Rawl (split nail), and c) nail drive. Some physical properties of these bolts are given below. The methods of placement are discussed in a later chapter.

a) Self-driving bolts are very satisfactory for rescue because of great strength and speed and ease of placement. The bolts have their own teeth and are driven directly into the rock. As long as the teeth are sharp and clean, the hole is drilled rapidly. The bolt is set in the hole by driving it onto an expansion pin.

b) The Rawl-drive (T.M.) is fairly strong but will not hold well if its hole is slightly oversize or if the hole is not drilled deeper than the length of the bolt, and the hole is rather time-consuming to drill even with a modern percussion drill.

c) The nail drive (Star-dryvin, T.M.) is a nail driven into a lead cylinder placed in a previously drilled hole. It is much too weak for routine rescue use and is essentially impossible to test.

If self-drive bolts are used, the bolt kit should contain, in addition to several spare bolts and expansion pins, the bolt hangers, cap screws and allen wrenches for attaching the hangers, driving handles, pliers and wrench, and a blow tube of rubber or a plastic which will not crack in cold weather. If Rawl drives are used, a separate drill and stone for sharpening will be required in place of the driving handles. The entire bolt kit is best kept in a small belt pouch which may be worn by the rescuer who may have to be out on a wall or in some other precarious position when driving the bolts.

The cap screws used to attach the hanger to the bolt should be of forged alloy steel, 150,000 psi (10,000 kg/sq cm) tensile strength, from a carefully selected batch, for example, by testing to destruction or say

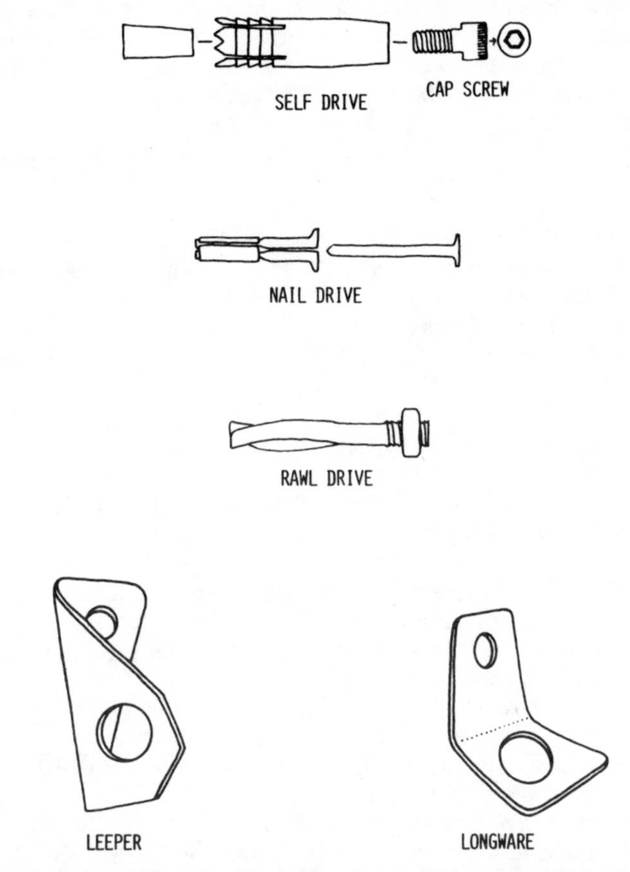

Fig. 7-3. Bolts and hangers. The hanger is attached to the self-drive bolt with a cap screw.

2000 lbs (900 kg) in shear some sizable fraction of a lot of the screws; those tested should be discarded. If any fail prematurely, the entire batch should be discarded. A convenient means of testing is to use the screw to attach two hangers back to back using a self-drive bolt as the nut, and then perform tension tests on the hangers. To be safe any screw once used should never be used again.

The best choice of hanger is a slightly flexible one such as the Longware (T.M.) type, which is a curved strip of chromoly steel. The reason for this is that a bolt may be very strong with pure shear loads, that is for a pull perpendicular to the axis of the bolt, but weak if there is an outward pull on the bolt. The stiff hanger such as a Leeper (T.M.), is excellent as long as the pull is across the bolt, but this hanger can easily lever a bolt out of its hole if an outward pull is applied. Aluminum hangers are excellent when supporting shear loads, but are weak for outward pulls, breaking at as little as 350 lb (160 kg).

SPECIALIZED RESCUE EQUIPMENT

Some of the basic and specialized mountain rescue equipment is described briefly below. Use of this equipment is discussed in later chapters. In the design of any backpack loads for mountain rescue, provision should be made for the rescuer to attach his personal pack to the rescue equipment. The rescuer who decides to let someone else carry his personal gear will sooner or later regret this decision.

Litter. The litter chosen for mountain rescue evacuations must satisfy a number of special requirements. It must be readily carried to the scene, preferably in a single backpackable load, and simple to assemble, even at night in bad weather. The design should be suitable not only for trail carrying but also for belayed scree evacuations and high angle lowering or raising. Of prime importance, it must hold the victim securely including immobilization of injured body parts, and must minimize further injury to the victim. For first aid reasons the victim will almost always need to be in the horizontal or slightly head up position, thus, it must be possible to rig the litter accordingly.

The best litter for general mountain rescue now seems to be the Stokes wire basket litter modified for mountain use. The commercially available litter comes as a one-piece unit which should be cut into two nearly equal size pieces that can then be nested and lashed onto a packframe. Details of the split litter and packing methods are shown in an appendix. Ready for backpacking, the complete litter on packframe with heavy rescue-type down-filled sleeping bag (zipper all-around) and litter pad weighs about 30 lbs (14 kg). It is appropriate to keep the litter and bag together as one backpackable unit to assure that all pieces arrive as needed at the scene.

The open wire basket and tubular frame construction of the Stokes litter is excellent for immobilization of the victim as required for many injuries. Special victim tie-in straps may be used to secure the victim in the litter easily. Tie-in straps permanently attached to the litter are preferable to the more conventional clip-on variety, which are easily lost en route and can be dislodged in use. See Ch. 22. Evacuation rigging can be readily attached to the litter rails. Furthermore, some modern orthopedic stretchers can be fitted into the Stokes.

A wheeled litter has some advantage under very special conditions of terrain and manpower. Some mountain rescue litters can be so equipped or fitted, including the Stokes. The use of the wheeled litter is discussed in Ch. 22.

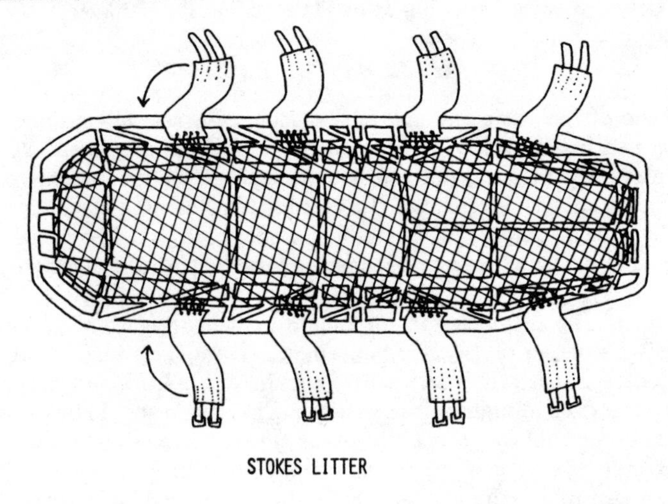

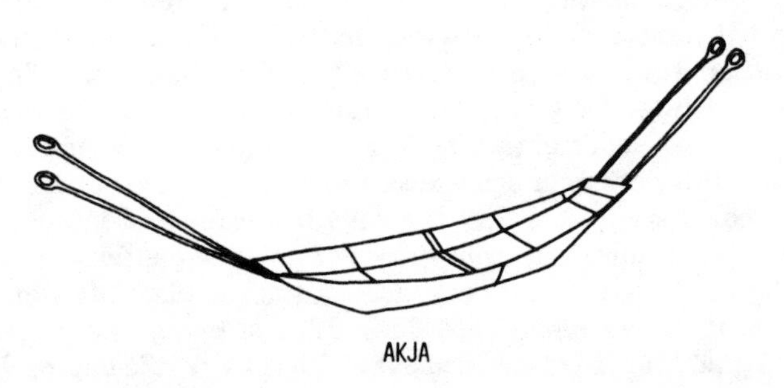

Fig. 7-4. Stokes litter with tie-in straps; Austrian akja, with handles in place.

Akja. Specialized snow evacuation equipment may be very worthwhile for a mountain rescue team. The usual toboggans used by ski patrol are not suited for backpacking, but a two-piece akja made in Austria for mountain rescue use is backpackable and works very well on snow. The akja is an aluminum boat with flat bottom and runners, and handles front and rear, designed to slide easily and track well on snow, being handled by two rescuers. It is quite specialized and works well for its purpose as discussed in Ch. 28, but it does have a few drawbacks. A tall victim will not fit in the akja, and a victim cannot be placed prone in it without a very thick pad in each half due to a cross rib at the joint. Because of its sheet metal construction, it is not readily adapted to first aid measures requiring immobilization of body parts. Furthermore, it is nearly impossible to carry over rocky areas when loaded and is essentially useless for high angle rock evacuations, but it can be belayed with difficulty for descents on steep snow. Finally, the assembly requires careful alignment of small holes for cotter pins, and this is difficult to do under adverse conditions. Its weight complete with sleeping bag and pad on packframe is 43 lbs (20 kg) without its four handles. See also Ch. 28.

A compromise litter which can be pulled through the snow is a Stokes litter which has been fitted with a sheet metal or fiberglass bottom between the main bottom rails leaving the rails exposed. Such a litter has all of the advantages of the Stokes with respect to first aid, rigging, and carrying, and does slide on snow although nowhere nearly so easily as does the akja. The Stokes litter so equipped weighs about 7 lbs (3 kg) extra.

Work continues to develop a better litter.

Tragsitz (Carry-Seat). The Austrian version (Gramminger seat) is a canvas and leather affair worn by the rescuer like a pack in which the victim sits in a piggyback position. Uses of the seat are described in Chs. 22 and 24. Similar versions may be built out of lighter and longer lasting materials. A very lightweight style made of nylon webbing is described in Ch. 31. The primary use of the tragsitz is for evacuation of an uninjured or a not very seriously injured victim. The seat is designed such that on steep faces a lowering or raising line supports the weight of the victim, who is just steadied by the rescuer.

Rock Kit. All of the basic rescue rigging gear should be carried together in a backpackable load, to assure that all necessary gear arrives and is available at the scene. A quite workable arrangement is to fit the top of a packframe (best quality frame only, e.g. Kelty, T.M.) with a packsack which has individually accessible compartments holding all necessary hardware. Some straps attached to the bottom of the frame allow the rescuer to lash on his personal summit pack. Two ropes may be stored in this location and handed to other rescuers for transport to the scene. See Fig. 7-5.

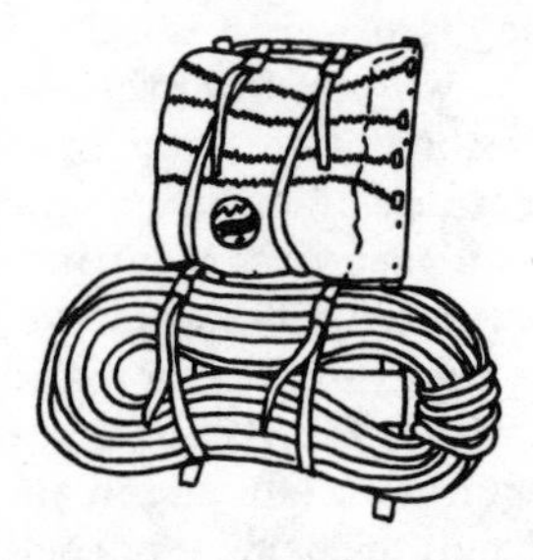

Fig. 7-5. Rock (bash) kit, with ropes attached where personal pack may be strapped.

The following is a list of contents of the kit that covers most evacuations. On snow, additional anchors will be made from the rescuers' ice axes.

2 Spiders, each with 3 slings, 1 litter bearer tie-in, 4 carabiners
2 Short prusik slings, spliced
1 Web sling
2 Brake systems, each with 5 'biners and 2 bars or 2 'biners and plate
10 Free carabiners
Assorted pitons
Bolt kit in pouch
2 Hammers
2 Pulleys
1 Etrier with carabiner
2 200 ft (60 m) ropes
1 Anchor rope
1 Deadman for snow

REFERENCES

1. *Summit,* Jan. 1966, p. 10.

CHAPTER 8

ROPE

The rope is the key item of equipment in most mountain rescue operations. Every team member should be intimately acquainted with rope properties and management knowing uses, weaknesses, and limitations since the life of several rescuers and the victim may depend on one rope. A rope used in rescue is subject to considerable abuse, much more than normally encountered in climbing, and a modern rope takes the abuse amazingly well. But the rope does have certain characteristics which can cause trouble if the user is unaware of these properties.

Some general properties including strength of rope and webbing will be given. This information is of particular value in improvisation techniques and in doing anything unusual with the rope. The first section of the chapter is quite technical in nature and should be read and understood by anyone regularly using a rope near its limits, but these details may be skimmed or skipped by the more casual reader. Only synthetic fiber ropes will be discussed here, leaving the discussion of steel cable to another chapter; vegetable fiber ropes have no place in mountain rescue.

ROPE PROPERTIES

Rope Construction. The hawser-laid rope sold as "mountaineering" rope typically consists of three twisted strands, each of which is composed of eight twisted large yarns, and each large yarn is twisted from four small yarns; finally each small yarn is made by twisting individual fibers. Each of these fibers may be at the surface of the rope at some point in its length and thus may be exposed to abrasion. There may be an additional very small yarn running more or less straight along the center of the strand, forming an "inner core" of a very small percentage of the total fibers. For convenience, we will refer to this kind of rope as "Goldline" (T.M.) even though there are other brands of equal quality.

The kernmantel construction, also known as the core and sheath, is of European make and is usually called "Perlon" in this country. The "core" is a bundle of fibers twisted to various degrees depending on brand, each strand running the full length of the rope, and the "sheath" is a lightweight braided cover, often a fancy color. This sheath does not provide much strength itself but only acts as a protective covering for the core. Thus, moderate abrasion on the sheath causes no loss of strength. On the other hand, if the sheath is torn open, the rope core may be very seriously damaged, and the sheath may conceal serious core damage.

These significant differences in construction result in major differences in performance as discussed in the following sections.

Handling Characteristics. The method of rope construction determines the knotting and handling ability of the rope. The kernmantel ropes handle beautifully and, therefore, are very popular with rock climbers. The laid ropes, particularly the "hard laid," are somewhat difficult to handle, and knots do not hold well. (Knots should always be firmly cinched down and completed with two safety overhands, and this is especially important in using a hard or stiff rope.) Soft laid ropes tend to hang up in rock cracks more readily than stiffer ropes, especially when slack. A laid rope tends to stiffen after hard use, but this seems to have no bearing on strength. The softer hawser laid ropes are nicer to handle, but they do not last as well.

Elasticity. The elasticity of nylon rope depends significantly on the type of construction. For small loadings, a kernmantel rope has less elasticity for a given rope diameter than does a laid rope, primarily because when a rope is stretched, the nylon fibers stretch themselves. Also a laid rope tends to untwist and thus elongate further, but the kernmantel rope does not tend to untwist. There is a large difference in the elasticity of the laid rope depending on whether it is allowed to twist or not.

The first moderate load on a new laid rope will permanently stretch it slightly. If a rope is loaded to over about 50 percent of its new breaking strength, it will undergo considerable inelastic deformation and may be permanently damaged. Research should be done to determine if the change in rope length is a good measure of rope use. After severe stress, the lay should be opened and the rope inspected for broken inner fibers. Of course, the inner fibers of a kernmantel rope cannot be inspected.

The elasticity of nylon may be a great virtue since high peak stresses due to shock loading are not present to nearly the degree as in an inelastic material such as steel cable. (Shock loading should always be avoided as much as possible.) On the other hand, the stretch or elasticity of the rope may be a hindrance in hauling systems, Tyrolean traverses, in setting up anchors, and in any situation involving variable loading in the rope. Elasticity is a property of the rope that the rescuer must know.

The stretch and tendency towards kinking in a laid rope depends on whether the rope is allowed to twist. For example, when the rope is passed through a brake system, it is loaded on one side of the brake and slack on the other, and there is a tendency for the rope to be untwisted as it goes into the brake and is stretched. The brake itself affects the twisting and causes extra twisting and kinking in the slack rope. These problems are much less severe in the kernmantel rope, in which the fibers are not twisted very much.

There is an additional aspect of stretch that is very significant in high angle evacuations where positioning of the litter supported by the lowering ropes is critical, or in rope changes where a knot location is important. This is the creep or additional stretch occurring over several minutes even at constant loading; that is, if a certain load is placed on the rope, there is a certain initial stretch of let us say 25 percent. During the next 5 or 10 minutes, the stretch may be increased by a few percent more. Thus, litter bearers must stop above their desired stopping point to allow for this settling. The "creep" amounts to perhaps a percent or so (1 ft per 100 ft) on a typical litter evacuation.

Cutting and Abrasion Resistance. A very significant property of a nylon rope is the ease with which it can be cut when under tension compared to when slack. A sharp edge of rock can cut a taut rope easily, thus, a rope *must* be protected when passing over a corner. This may be done by padding (preferably not nylon if the rope is running because the rope can cut and melt through the nylon pad), by "softening" the corner with a hammer, or by fixing a pulley that changes the path to avoid the rock corner altogether. Also, a rock falling onto a taut rope is more likely to do severe damage than onto a slack rope. If a falling stone hits the rope, the rope should be inspected immediately for damage.

Some tests comparing the resistance to *severe* abrasion of laid rope vs. kernmantel construction showed that the laid rope was much better (Ref. 3 and practical experience). In fact, there are reports of kernmantel ropes with the sheath intact, but with the core cut through.

Obviously strength is lost as a laid rope becomes abraded. As a rope is used, the outside fibers become fuzzy, and this fuzz may act as a sheath to protect fibers underneath from further abrasion; the fuzzy surface fibers are cut less than the others because they are not under tension. Likewise, the sheath on a kernmantel rope is not damaged much from *light* abrasion because this sheath is not load bearing. Abrasion is inevitable since in use the rope will get dragged on the ground, through mud, and across gritty rock. Thus, abrasive particles get worked into the rope and cut the fibers both inside and out. Tests on laid rope of documented history (Ref. 1) have shown that the strength loss due to abrasion is about 20 to 30 percent in about 100 days of typical climbing (not rescue) use.

In general, for light use such as typical technical rock climbing, the kernmantel ropes are quite good, but for rescue work or other severe use, only the laid ropes will survive.

Static Rope Strengths. The table below gives strengths for various ropes and webbing. All data given are the results of careful laboratory tests involving straight static, not dynamic, pull on new rope. Thus, the figures are maximums. In use the rope will never test this strong because the breaking strength is reduced by knots or bends and by abrasion. The typical reduction in strength by a knot is 40 percent. That is, the strength of a new rope in use with a knot is only 60 percent of the value given in Table 8-1. We will give in Ch. 9 a table showing relative knot efficiencies. A kink in the rope reduces the strength at least as much as a knot does. Hence, kinks are always to be avoided in stressed ropes. Also, when a rope is passed over a carabiner or pulley, it will lose some strength. Roughly speaking, a rope passed 180° around a bar of the same diameter as the rope will lose nearly half its strength, but if the bend is ten times this diameter, there is essentially no loss of strength. In practice this means that the usual 7/16 in. or 11 mm rope will lose about half its strength in passing over a carabiner, and about a third of its strength when going over a small pulley. Most significant of all is that a rope passed around a sharp edge of a rock may lose *all* of its strength by being cut.

Climbers desperately in need of extra rope to perform self-rescue should be aware that when a laid rope is unlaid into its three main strands, the strength of each strand is much less than one third of the strength of the full rope.

Energy Absorbing Ability. There is a limit to how much energy can be absorbed by a rope without its being damaged. As the rope stretches when slowly loaded or in stopping a fall, energy goes into heat and stored mechanical energy in the rope. If too much energy is put into the rope, individual fibers begin to break, each breakage taking a certain energy. A given *weight* (or volume) of rope is capable of absorbing only a limited energy, more or less independent of the rope construction or diameter. This limit for the usual nylon ropes is about 12,000 foot-pounds of energy absorbed slowly per pound of rope. This figure is reduced to about 4,000 foot-pounds per pound if the energy is absorbed quickly or dynamically, as in stopping a rapidly falling body. (1 ft-lb/lb equals about 3 joules/kg.)

Table 8-1

Breaking Strengths of New Materials
(pounds)
(kilograms)

	Goldline	Perlon	Parachute (utility) cord	Manila	Nylon web
1/8 in. dia.			550 *250*		
1/4 in. dia.	1700 *770*			600 *270*	
5/16" or 7 mm	2700 *1200*	2300 *1000*		950 *430*	
3/8" or 9 mm	3700 *1700*	3200 *1500*		1350 *610*	
7/16" or 11 mm	5500 *2500*	4800 *2200*		1850 *840*	
1/2 in. wide					1100 *500*
9/16 in. wide					1700 *770*
1 in. wide					4000 *1800*

To illustrate the latter situation, suppose an object of weight *W* pounds falls through a distance *H* feet and comes to a halt. Then an energy *HW* foot-pounds must be absorbed. If the object falls free and hits the ground, this energy goes into heating the ground and the object. If the weight is a belayed climber who is given a dynamic belay, the energy is partly absorbed by the rope, partly by the climber, and is partly converted into heat at the belayer as the rope slides around the belayer's body. But if a rigid object is tied to an anchored rope which stops the fall, the energy is absorbed by the rope alone.

Table 8-2

Weight and Energy Absorbing Ability for Mountain Goldline

Size	Wt/100 ft	Feet/lb	Foot-lbs/ft
3/8 in.	3.0 lbs	26	460 static 150 dynamic
7/16 in.	5.7	18	675 static 250 dynamic

Since 7/16 in. diameter rope weighs about .06 lb/ft (.09 kg/m), this rope can absorb about 250 foot-pounds of energy per foot of rope (1100 joules/m), with dynamic loading. (See Table 8-2.) To illustrate, a 200 pound weight falling 10 feet as shown in Fig. 8-1 develops 10 feet times 200 pounds or 2000 foot-pounds of energy to be absorbed by the 10 feet of rope, less than the 250 foot-pounds/foot limit, and the rope would not be expected to break. But on the other hand a 200 pound weight falling 10 feet as shown in Fig. 8-2 has the same 2000 foot-pounds of energy to be absorbed by only 5 feet of rope, or 400 foot-pounds/foot, greater than the limit, and the rope is likely to break. (For simplicity we have neglected the stretch in the rope due to loading.)

Tests simulating the failure of one of the two lowering ropes to a very heavily loaded litter verified the above and showed that with 25 feet of rope out and an 800 lb load in the litter, the second rope will withstand the added sudden loading. (However, the litter itself might not survive such action.)

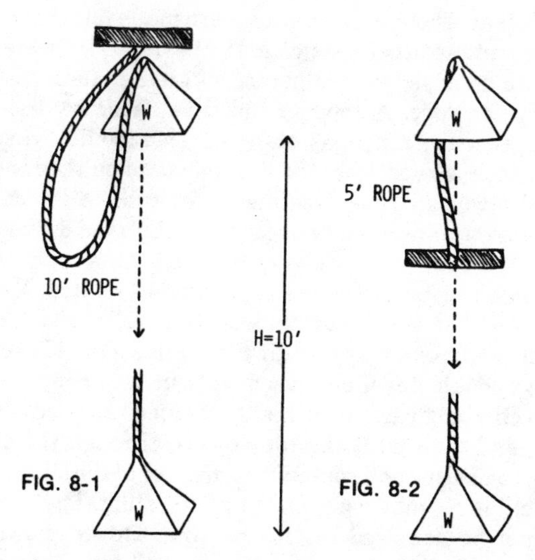

Fig. 8-1. Dropping weight 10 feet with 10 feet of rope to absorb the energy.
Fig. 8-2. Dropping weight 10 feet with only 5 feet of rope to absorb the energy.

Effects of Water, Ice, Weather and Chemical Action on Nylon Rope. The rope strength is reduced by being wet, but this is only a 10 to 15 percent strength loss. Also, if a rope is wet and subsequently frozen, it is extremely difficult to handle, and prusik knots and various types of ascenders do not hold well at all. Manila or cotton line is even less manageable when frozen than is nylon. (Recall that frozen cotton shoelaces are very hard to untie. Nylon parachute cord works better.) The weight of the rope is increased by about 30 percent in a thorough soaking. A rope should never be stored tightly coiled when wet because of possible mildew and rot even though nylon is not very susceptible to this form of damage. Nylon is chemically rather inert, but even so, a rope should never be placed where motor oil, gasoline, car battery acid, or any other such chemicals may attack it. Exposure to sun, weather or ultraviolet has been shown by various tests to do significant damage, with strength loss of 25 to 45 percent for several months of exposure. Weathering tests made on samples given a southern exposure in Boulder, Colo., for up to one year indicated that the kernmantel ropes lost essentially no strength over this period. During the first six months, Goldline showed little deterioration, but about one third of the original strength was lost during the next six months of weathering. Clearly ropes should be stored indoors and out of sunlight.

Effect of Heat. Though nylon is a superb material for rope construction, it is susceptible to being damaged by heat. Boiling water temperatures do it no damage, but temperatures greater than 300°F (200°C) may destroy the rope. A rope should thus never be dried out by a campfire because the rope may easily become too hot when it is dry, and furthermore, sparks from the fire may land on the rope, melt the fibers and destroy the rope. Heating of the rope in use can occur in dynamic belaying or in rescue work during a belayed evacuation using brake bars. The brakes can get very hot, and if the rope is allowed to come to rest on the hot metal, the rope could be melted. Nylon should never be allowed to run on nylon because friction and the resulting heating can easily melt the standing material. For this reason, used rappel slings should never be reused without very careful inspection. That is, if a climbing party on descent sets up a rappel sling, performs the rappel, and then pulls the rappel rope through the sling, there may be severe heating and consequent melting of the sling at the point where the climbing rope passes through the sling. The climbing rope itself will not be damaged by this heating. Thus, following parties should not assume that the rappel sling is sufficiently strong without careful inspection. Manila is less susceptible than nylon to damage by heat, but is much weaker in the first place and is quickly ruined by weathering.

NYLON WEBBING

Flat nylon web slings are very frequently used in climbing and rescue. The typical 1 in. (2.5 cm) width sling when new will break at a knot or where it passes over a carabiner at approximately 4,000 lbs (1800 kg). Various tests have shown that webbing deteriorates due to abrasion faster than a laid rope because of the rather large surface to volume ratio of the webbing, and that webbing may be much more seriously damaged than its general appearance would indicate. This is in contrast to laid rope, which is usually stronger than would be guessed. The rescuer should be aware of the relative inelasticity of the webbing as compared to laid rope, thus the webbing is more susceptible to destruction by shock loading. Web slings should be protected from melting which could be caused by a running belay rope by using at least one carabiner so that nylon never rubs directly on nylon, but rather on aluminum. If severe heating of the carabiner is anticipated, a second carabiner should be placed in series with the first; thus, the heat developed by the running belay rope in the first carabiner will have to be transferred into the second to reach the sling. The heating of the second carabiner will be quite negligible, and there will be no damage done to the web sling by heat. Furthermore, if the heating by the running belay rope is distributed among several carabiners, the temperature rise in any one will, of course, be smaller than if the rope ran through only the one. The deterioration of web and rope slings has been recently compared; see Ref. 2.

CHOICE OF ROPE FOR MOUNTAIN RESCUE

Material. As is clearly shown above in Table 8-1, for a given diameter nylon ropes are much stronger than manila. Manila has a few specialized uses in climbing; for example, due to its relative inelasticity it is useful for hauling, lifting, and prusiking, and it is less sensitive to destruction by heat than is nylon. Also, it is quite a bit cheaper than nylon and thus is more expendable. But since it is so very much weaker than nylon when new and may deteriorate due to rot, and since there is a chance that manila could be used by accident where the strength of nylon is essential, in rescue only nylon ropes should be used.

Construction. Since safety under all conditions is of prime importance in mountain rescue, the laid rope should be chosen over the kernmantel construction for the severe use of rescue because of the ability of the laid rope to withstand abuse and to be inspected for damage. We mention here some of the weaknesses of the perlon ropes.

Under conditions of severe abrasion, the kernmantel sheath will be ripped off before the laid rope shows signs of very severe damage. Any damage to any core fibers of the kernmantel rope will seriously weaken the rope. There are also cases reported where the core was cut through and the sheath remained intact. It is impossible to look at the fibers inside the sheath without destroying the kernmantel rope, but it is easy to open the lay to examine the fibers of a laid rope. To summarize, only laid nylon rope should be chosen for severe mountain rescue use.

Size. Since rope stress in mountain rescue may regularly approach 1000 lbs (450 kg), and a safety factor of four should be maintained, only 7/16 in. diameter belay or lowering ropes should be used; any smaller size is too weak, and larger is very heavy and difficult to handle.

For rescue a 200 ft (60 m) length is very convenient. Even though this length is too long for most climbing use, for rescue there are many times when the added length beyond the more standard 150 or 165 ft (45-50 m) length is very worthwhile because this length often avoids the need to pass a knot through a brake system. The fewer knots that appear on a face the better in rescue work because of the likelihood of a knot either jamming or knocking off rock onto the rescuers or victim.

Overall the most suitable rope for mountain rescue seems to be a 200 ft (60 m) length of 7/16 in. diameter mountain lay nylon. For special purposes other sizes may be desirable.

ROPE CARE

The New Rope. For the reasons given above only nylon materials should be purchased, no manila. Surplus store bargains that may not be nylon, or that may be damaged in some way must be avoided. One way to test material to see whether it is nylon or not is to burn some of it, and note the melting and characteristic odor of burning nylon. Even if a rope is nylon, it is not necessarily mountain lay. It could be a soft marine lay which will not last very long in mountaineering service. The most economical rope in the long run for rescue service is most likely a genuine laid mountain rope, usually unavailable in a surplus store.

The new rope should be taped before cutting to prevent unraveling, and the ends of the rope should be melted to fuse the fibers together. Furthermore, the ends should be whipped and taped, or better but less convenient, dipped in a urethane paint or equivalent. In any case, the ends should be color coded by tape or paint colors for identification of length (red for 200 ft, blue for 150 ft, yellow for less than 100 ft) and ownership. Coding the age of the rope by another color band is also a good practice.

The new rope will be stiff and hard to handle, and there likely will be severe kinking problems at first. The rope may be "broken in" by one or two full length brake bar rappels.

Some Do's and Don'ts in the Care and Storage of Ropes. *The Don'ts.* A rope should never be abused by using it for any purpose except mountaineering. It should never be used for miscellaneous purposes where loadings are difficult to estimate such as car towing, or where shock loading can occur. The rope should never be stood on and never, never, stepped on with crampons. It should not be allowed to pass across a sharp rock edge. If a rope is wet, it should not be dried out by a campfire because the rope may be overheated when dry, and sparks could hit the rope destroying it. Also, it should not be stored tightly coiled when wet, nor be exposed to gasoline or other such chemicals. Stresses should not be put on kinked or snarled rope. The rope should not be stored dirty, wet, outside, or in direct sunlight. Finally, a rope should not be borrowed from a private individual for use in rescue work unless absolutely necessary, because the past history of the rope is unknown.

The Do's. If a rope is severely jammed or hit by a falling rock, it should be inspected immediately for damage. Any rope which is cut deeply or frayed excessively should be retired immediately—a cut should be completed with a knife. If the rope becomes very dirty or muddy, it should be washed and dried before being coiled, stored, and reused. An inspection should be given casually after each use as the rope is coiled. A thorough inspection, going over every inch of the rope looking for undue fraying and cuts or other abnormalities, should be performed on all rescue ropes periodically. Any suspicious section should be examined by twisting open the lay and looking to see how deep the damage goes. A good section of a retired rope may be saved for use as an anchor rope, etc., and the worn part should be completely removed from mountaineering use. This means also not using the rope for car towing because a rope in the car of a climber may be accidentally used for a mountaineering rescue. If there is any doubt about the integrity of a rope, it should be retired.

ROPE HANDLING

Rope organization and handling involves primarily the ability to prevent "rope salads," kinks and snarls, and to avoid having the rope hang up or knock rocks loose from a rock face. A rescue is likely to involve the use of several ropes in a small area. Each rope must be piled or coiled in such a way that it will not become entangled with others. The use of each rope should be understood by all personnel handling any rope. Color-coded ropes may be of assistance here. On a steep face, if it is not actually being used at the moment, a rope may be coiled and hung from a piton. This also applies if part of the rope is in use but a large remaining part is not used. A rope to be fed into a brake should not be taken directly from a coil because individual turns are likely to become kinked and tangled even if there is a rope handler to assist the brakeman (see Ch. 24). Instead, the rope should be uncoiled and ideally laid out in a straight line, along the ground or over the face if there is no danger of the rope snagging, knocking loose rock, or interfering with the evacuation. If this cannot be done the turns should be placed in a neat heap such that the rope can be pulled from the pile and fed to the brakeman by a rope handler.

When a rope is to be thrown, the upper end must be secured, and the yell "rope" or "rock" given to warn climbers below. Rope throwing over the rock face from the turns of a normal coil usually results in a large snarl. Instead, the rope should be recoiled on the arm so that no turns overlap, or numerous zig-zags of rope should be formed on the ground closely spaced without overlap. The ground must, of course, be clear of all loose material. Then several turns can be thrown far out from the cliff face after securing the upper end, and the remainder of the rope should run freely. If both hands are free, the rope coils may be separated into two portions, one thrown by each hand about a half second apart. Lowering the free end of the rope down the face is successful only if the face is quite steep and free from projections, but this is not usually the case. If the rope is to be thrown upwards, a small bundle of rope may be grasped and tossed, as shown in Fig. 8-3. Easier than throwing the heavy rope, a hammer or other object can be tied onto a light cord (say an avalanche cord) and thrown, and the heavier rope hauled with the lighter cord.

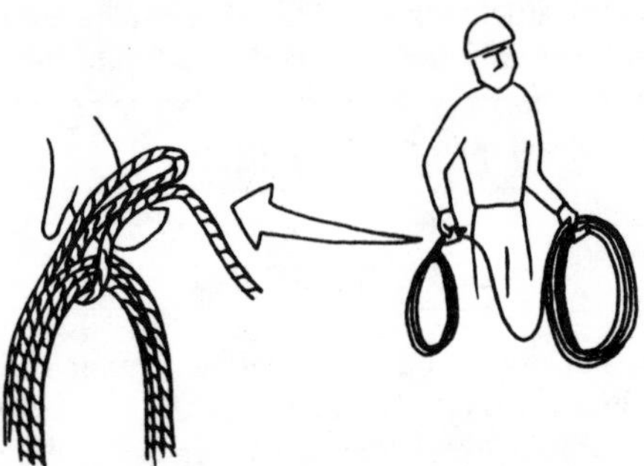

Fig. 8-3. Showing a method of throwing a rope. Several turns in a small (1.5-2 ft, .5-.6 m) coil are easily thrown.

If a rope is to be hauled up a face, across a creek, or through the woods, all knots should be removed to prevent snagging or jamming. (As every climber knows, if a rope can get snagged, it will, and at the worst possible time.) Dropping a rope completely down a face is usually bad practice; it is better coiled and carried down to prevent its being hung up making retrieval perhaps very difficult.

Rope coiling after use should be done neatly, passing the rope through the hands feeling for cuts and looking for damaged sections. The coiling is quick and easy to do simply by holding the coils in one hand and passing the rope through the other hand while swinging the hands widely apart, resulting in coils having a circumference of about 6 ft (2 m). This is a convenient size to carry over the shoulder. To prevent the starting end from being tangled in the coils, it may be left about 4 ft (1.2 m) long or may be tied loosely around the wrist of the holding hand. (This end will be used to form the bight in the securing knot, described below.) The feeling hand gives a small twist to the rope on each turn, so that coils are circular and not figure-eights. Due to the lay of the rope, there is a difference between clockwise and counterclockwise coiling, one direction will easily give nice O's, the other has a strong tendency to form 8's. (Perlon ropes *should* be coiled in 8's to keep the core from slipping inside the sheath and forming knots and kinks.) If the coiling is producing the latter, reversal of coiling direction will help. If the rope begins to kink on each turn, the entire coil may be rotated half a turn and the coiling continued on what was the back side of the pile; this procedure reverses the direction of coiling and may cause problems in feeding the rope out during the next use. Alternately, the feeling hand can force kinks away from the coil as long as possible, and then the coil can be rotated several full turns, removing the kinks. When the coiling is completed, the coil may be tied off using the whipping technique followed by an overhand or two or a square knot as in Fig. 8-4, cinched down tightly. To hold together well, this whipping should have not less than three wraps, but more than six wraps is needlessly time-consuming to put on and remove.

Fig. 8-4. Showing a method of tying off a coiled rope. The square knot should be firmly cinched down.

Other methods of coiling certainly work but are usually less efficient. For example, wrapping the rope around one's feet and knees; this is a slow way to coil the rope, and the coils tend to be of inconveniently small size. The well-known "mountaineer's coil" is complicated and generally a waste of time to coil and uncoil, although it may be worthwhile if the coiled rope *must* be dropped or hauled over a cliff.

A rope that is particularly stiff is rather difficult to coil by conventional means because the rope cannot easily absorb the necessary twist per turn of the coil. This problem is overcome with the following simple technique, but note the warning below. The first turn is made normally, say as if following a right-handed screw thread, and the second is made "upside-down" by a flip of the wrist, with the result that the rope tends to follow a left-handed screw, thus, the uncoiled rope comes out behind this turn rather than in front. The third turn is conventional, the fourth "upside-down," etc. See the arrows in Fig. 8-5. The result is, in effect, a figure-eight folded double to form an O. This coiling technique is actually easier to do than to describe, and is quite effective on a new rope. WARNING: The technique has the drawback that if the end of the rope is passed through the coils as may easily happen, and is then fed out, overhand knots will appear throughout the length of the rope. This situation *must* be avoided.

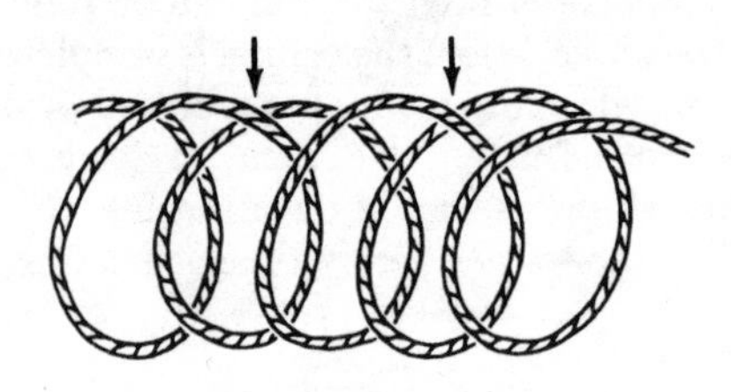

Fig. 8-5. Showing a method of coiling a very stiff rope. Note warning in text.

REFERENCES

1. *Extent and Cause of Deterioration of Nylon Rope,* L. I. Weiner and L. J. Sheenan, U.S. Army Natick Labs TR66-24-CM. Gov't Document AD 631 428.

2. British Mountaineering Council,Equipment Committee Report. See "*Summit,*" May, 1971, p. 42.

3. "Safety in Climbing Equipment," John Armitage, *Summit,* Oct., 1966, p. 30.

4. *Belaying the Leader,* R. M. Leonard et al., Sierra Club, 1956.

CHAPTER 9

KNOTS

Knots described here are ones which are frequently used or are highly recommended for use in mountaineering and in mountain rescue. Additional knots and rigging techniques are given in separate discussions. This chapter is not meant to be an exhaustive dissertation on knots, but instead, emphasizes the important knots which the climber/rescuer should know. About six basic knots and some variations are discussed. Commonly used knot-tying tricks are best learned from practical exercise and will not be explained here.

The rescuer should learn to tie knots very well, so that he can tie them correctly and quickly under the worst conditions, such as at night in a freezing, driving rain. He should also learn to recognize and check knots which he has not tied himself; thus, simplicity is a virtue in a knot.

Most knots have a tendency to loosen when tied in nylon rope, particularly in a very stiff rope. Thus, every knot should be cinched down very firmly, and two or more safety overhands should be tied tightly against the knot using the tails whenever a knot is tied at the end of the rope. These safety knots tend to work loose before the main knot does, and they should be considered as a part of the knot, but for simplicity these will be omitted from most of the sketches given. The method of tying safeties is shown below in Fig. 9-1c.

When a knot is heavily loaded, as occurs much more often and predictably in rescue than in normal climbing, the knot will tend to settle and tighten by sliding along the rope towards the free end, using up several inches of the slack. Thus, a tail of perhaps .5-1 ft (15-30 cm) should be left after tying the safety overhands to prevent the knot from sliding off the end of the rope. If a knot is not heavily stressed, it will tend to loosen and thus should be checked frequently. On the other hand, a knot which withstands a heavy load in rescue will tend to jam to an extent much greater than usually encountered in climbing, and the knot to be used should be one which can be untied readily after being strained. It is possible to untie a badly jammed knot by pounding it on a wooden plank with a hammer; pounding on a rock will quickly break the rope fibers.

END MAN OR ANCHOR KNOTS

Bowline. Fig. 9-1. The bowline is the standard knot used to tie a loop in the end of a rope. The knot is easy to tie, strong, and easy to untie after heavy loading by pushing on point A (see Fig. 9-1b). As with most knots safety backups should be used, snugged up against the knot itself. The overhand shown in Fig. 9-1c is best, and half hitches shown in Fig. 9-1d are less effective. The bowline is not designed for sideways loading, that is, stressing the loop itself without pulling on the main strand. It may slip in this incorrect use. Also the free end must not be loaded. Such a load could deform the bowline into a slip knot.

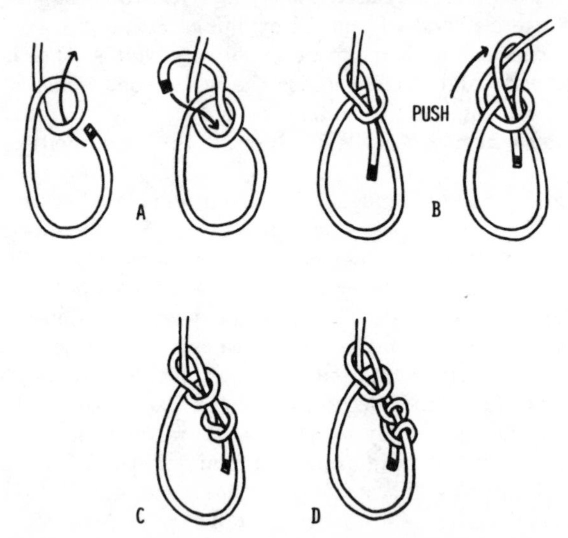

Fig. 9-1. Bowline. a) Method of tying. b) Method of releasing. c) The knot tied with overhand safety. d) The knot tied with half-hitch safeties.

Bowline on a Coil. Fig. 9-2. The bowline on a coil is usually used by a climber tying into the end of a rope when not using an independent waist loop. Although three coils are typical, any number can be used.

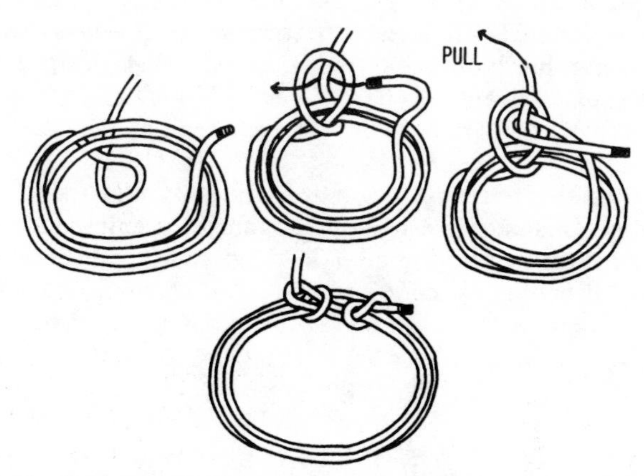

Fig. 9-2. Bowline on a coil. Showing method of tying and the completed knot with safety overhand.

Double Bowline. Fig. 9-3. The double bowline is tied exactly as is the bowline except with a doubled rope, and it gives a double loop.

Triple Bowline. Fig. 9-4. The triple bowline gives three coils and is tied as the double bowline but with the double "tail" made the same size as the two coils, thereby giving three loops. This knot makes a convenient seat (two thigh loops and a waist or chest loop) for lowering an uninjured victim.

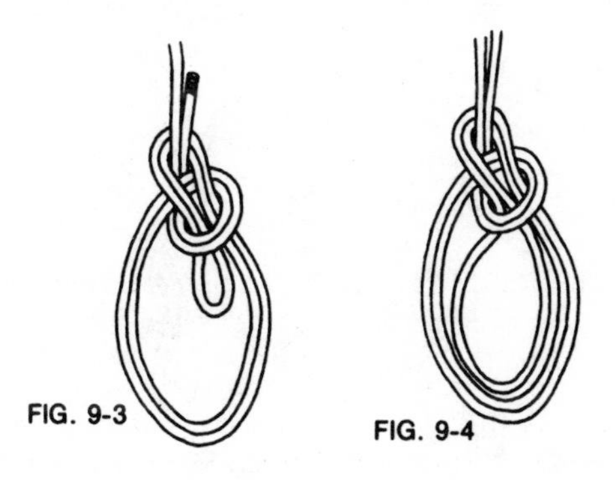

Fig. 9-3. Double bowline for end man. **Fig. 9-4.** Triple bowline for end man.

High-Strength Bowline. Fig. 9-5. Somewhat more complicated to tie than the normal bowline, the high strength bowline needs no safety overhands. It is harder to untie, and less easy to check by quick observation. The extra strength is hardly worthwhile, since a rope is more likely to break at a carabiner or rock edge than at a knot.

Simplified High-Strength Bowline. Fig. 9-6. Compared to the normal bowline, this knot is more secure against loosening and is somewhat more difficult to untie after loading, and it still needs safety overhands. It is easy to check visually.

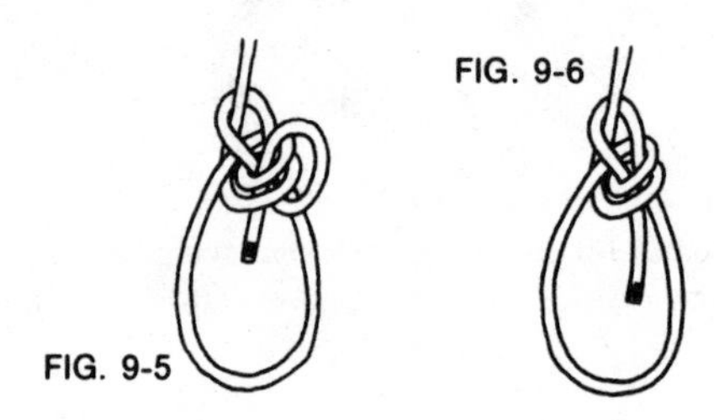

Fig. 9-5. High-strength bowline. **Fig. 9-6.** Simplified high-strength bowline.

Figure-of-Eight Loop and Overhand Loop. Fig. 9-7. These are very quickly tied when a loop is needed. The overhand is weaker and much harder to untie after loading than the Figure-of-Eight and thus is not recommended except when a loop is needed in a hurry. The Figure-of-Eight loop is seldom used as an end man knot in climbing, but is often used in rescue for an anchor loop because of its ease in tying.

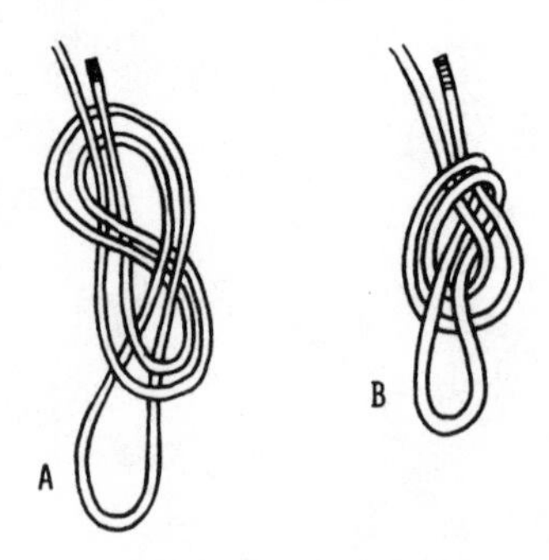

Fig. 9-7. a) Figure-of-Eight, b) Overhand, for end man or anchor.

MIDDLEMAN KNOTS (LOOPS IN THE MIDDLE OF A ROPE)

A middle man tying into the middle of a rope should use an independent waist loop which may be simply several turns of wide webbing wrapped around the waist and tied with a ring bend (below), or it may be something more complicated such as a swami belt. The climber is tied into the rope using a locking carabiner, or two nonlocking 'biners with gates opposed. A single Figure-of-Eight on a bight in the middle of the rope suffices for this purpose. On the other hand, if the middle man is not using an independent waist loop, he should use a double or triple loop, (see below) for comfort in a fall. These loops must not close when the ends of the belay rope are pulled. This danger does not arise when using an independent waist loop. If the middle man is tying into the ends of each of two ropes, he must also be careful to avoid being squeezed or cut apart if the two ropes are pulled. That is, he must not tie separate loops around his waist with the ropes. The best arrangement when tying into the ends of each of two ropes is to use an independent waist loop and clip loops tied in the ends of each rope to one (locking) carabiner with strong gate which is clipped to the waist loop.

Butterfly. Fig. 9-8. The butterfly forms a single loop and tends to jam when strained and may consequently be very difficult to untie. It does not tend to slip and is the strongest middle man knot. Figs. 9-8a and 9-8b show two methods of tying, and Fig. 9-8c shows the completed knot.

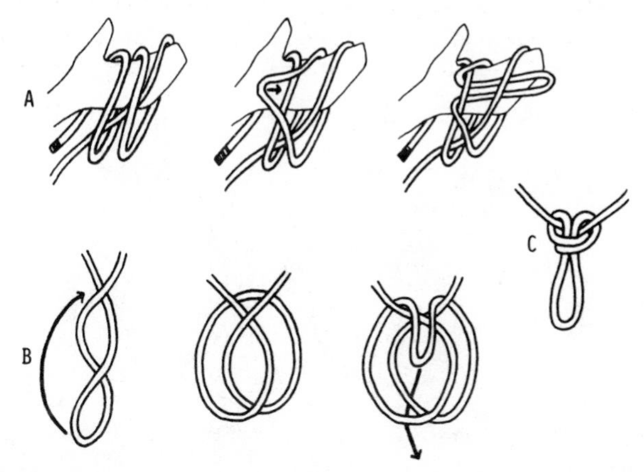

Fig. 9-8. Butterfly. a) and b) Showing two methods of tying. c) The completed knot.

Figure-of-Eight on a Bight. Fig. 9-9. The knot is the same as the Figure-of-Eight end man loop.

Most commonly used to form a single loop, this knot is easier to tie and untie than the butterfly. The Overhand on a Bight tends to jam and is weaker than the Figure-of-Eight and thus is not recommended except in a panic situation when a loop is needed very quickly.

Fig. 9-9. Figure-of-Eight on a bight.

Bowline on a Bight. Fig. 9-10. The bowline on a bight forms a double loop but has two disadvantages: 1) It is easy to make a slight error in tying, turning this knot into a slip knot. 2) If not cinched down tight, it may slip closed when the ends of the main rope are pulled.

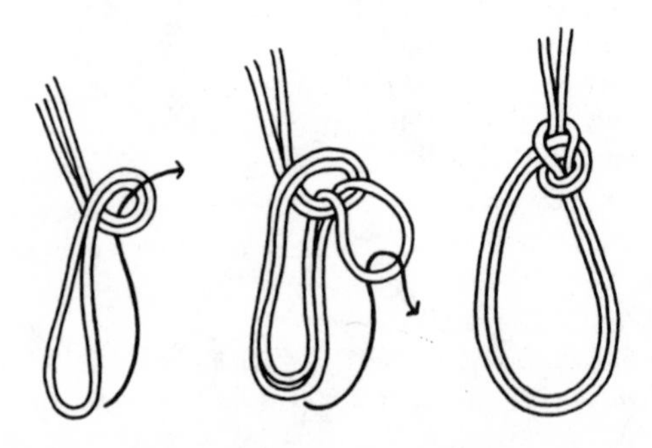

Fig. 9-10. Bowline on a bight. Showing method of tying. Note caution in text.

Double Bowline on a Bight. Fig. 9-11. The knot is tied as the double bowline in Fig. 9-3.

Fig. 9-11. Double bowline on a bight. Same as Fig. 9-3.

KNOTS TO JOIN TWO ROPES

As with end man knots, these knots should be backed up with two or more safety overhands. The well-known square knot could be used to join two ropes, but it can very easily be turned into a slip knot and thus is not recommended, except for lashing down items or other noncritical use.

Single Sheet Bend. Fig. 9-12. The sheet bend may be used to tie the ends of two ropes together whether or not the ropes are of the same size, but the rope characteristics should not be highly dissimilar. This and its variations are the only knots to be used to tie different size ropes. If this is the case, the bigger diameter rope must form the bight (U loop) as shown in Fig. 9-12, with the smaller one being wrapped around. Since the double sheet bend described below has less tendency to loosen accidentally, is easier to untie after being stressed and is stronger, the single sheet bend is not recommended; the double sheet bend should be used instead.

Double Sheet Bend. Fig. 9-13. This is the usual knot for joining two belay or lowering ropes. The knot must be cinched down very well and tied with safety overhands because it tends to work loose easily. This is the only knot in this section which can be untied easily after withstanding heavy loads. If the ropes joined are of different size, the large one must form the bight (U loop) as shown in Fig. 9-13.

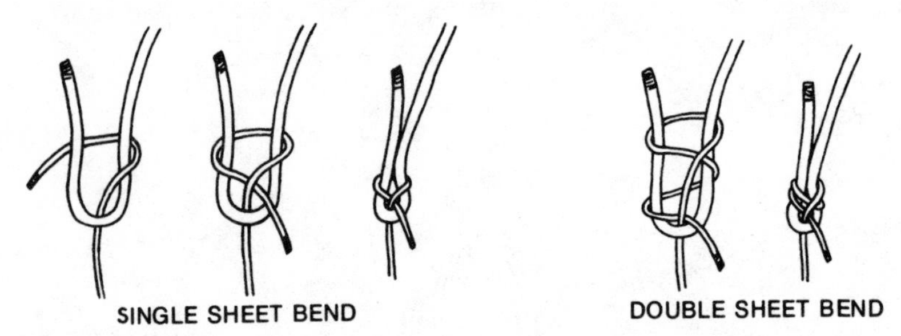

Fig. 9-12. Single sheet bend. **Fig. 9-13.** Double sheet bend. The double sheet bend is preferred.

Fisherman's Knot. Fig. 9-14. The fisherman's is commonly used for tying slings and runners of rope into loops. Because the knot tends to jam, it should not be used to join lowering ropes; only the double sheet bend should be used for this purpose.

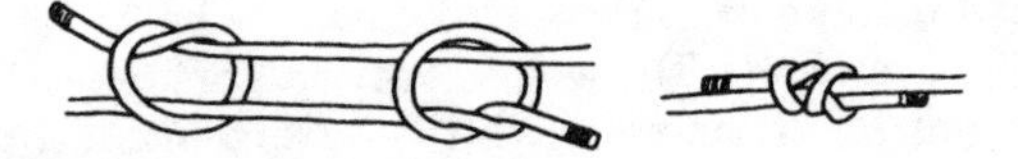

Fig. 9-14. Fisherman's knot.

Double Fisherman's Knot. Fig. 9-15. This is an exceptionally strong knot and one of the few that needs no safety overhands. The knot is tied as the Fisherman's but with an extra turn in the overhand. Each half of the knot must be tied symmetrically, that is, the extra turn should be centered and not at one end or the other. This knot is highly recommended for tying rope slings, etc., since it needs no safety overhands and it is exceptionally strong.

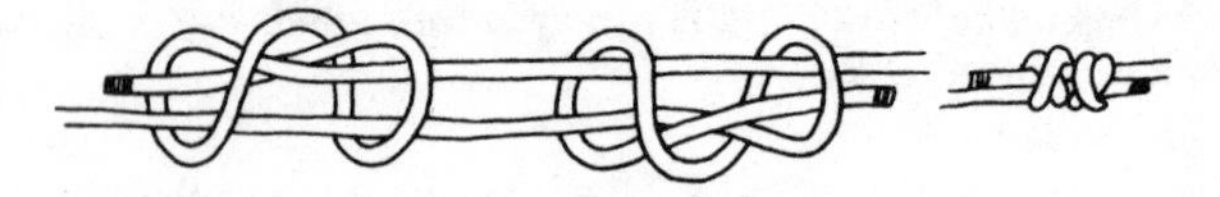

Fig. 9-15. Double fisherman's knot. Very strong.

Ring Bend (Water Knot). Fig. 9-16. The ring bend is very useful for joining ends of flat webbing as used for an independent waist loop or a sling. The knot is easily tied by first tying an overhand with one end, then following the first overhand in the reverse direction with the other end. This knot is also known as the double overhand. The ring bend is difficult to untie when stressed heavily, and hardly needs safety overhands.

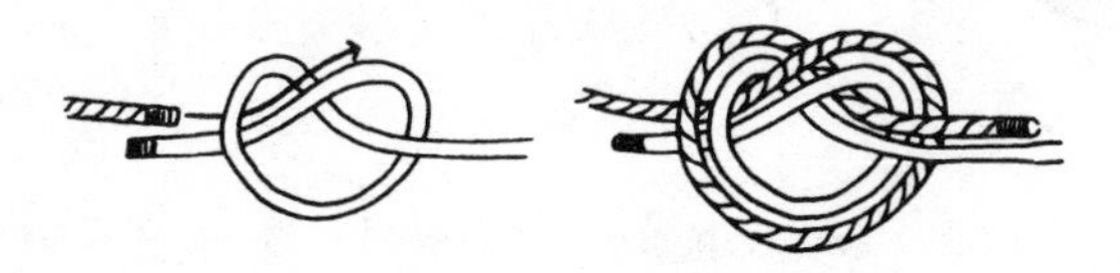

Fig. 9-16. Ring bend (Water knot). Excellent for webbing.

SPECIAL KNOTS

Only a few special knots useful in climbing and rescue will be mentioned here. Some others are given in other chapters when appropriate.

Prusik. Fig. 9-17. The prusik is tied with a small rope sling loop around a larger rope. When no tension is applied to the sling, the knot, (more properly called a "hitch"), will slide by pushing, but the knot grips when tension is applied to the sling. A three-wrap prusik holds significantly better than a two-wrap one and should be used exclusively for load holding in rescue, although the two-wrap one is quite satisfactory for ascending fixed lines when set. The knot tends to work loose when not under tension and may not hold when the sling is pulled if the turns are not snug on the larger rope. Used for ascending fixed lines, it works easier when tied with manila because the stretch of the nylon sling tends to make the knot jam closed on the ascending line, making it difficult to release. (Manila slings are not recommended in rescue because of their unreliability and inferior strength.) The prusik is easily tied with narrow flat webbing and holds loads well, but it is difficult to slide because of its small bulk.

Clove Hitch. Fig. 9-18. The clove hitch is occasionally useful as an anchor knot around a tree. It is easily adjusted. Sometimes it is put to very good use by a fallen climber dangling from his waist loop; when a rescuer lowers a separate anchored rope to the climber, the climber can tie the clove hitch around his boot and stand up, thereby relieving tension on his waist loop.

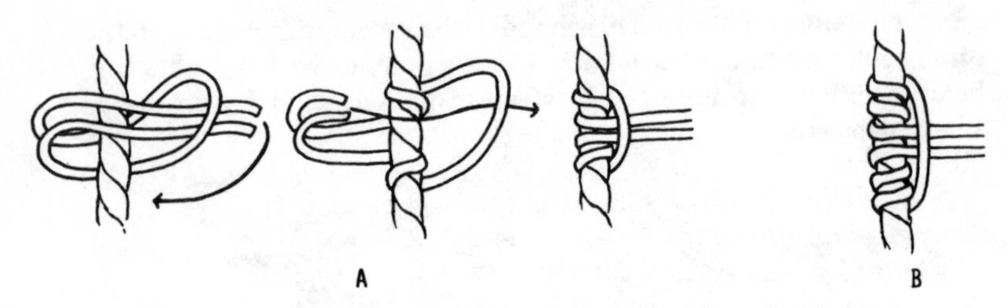

Fig. 9-17. Prusik. a) Two-wrap, showing method of tying. b) Three-wrap.

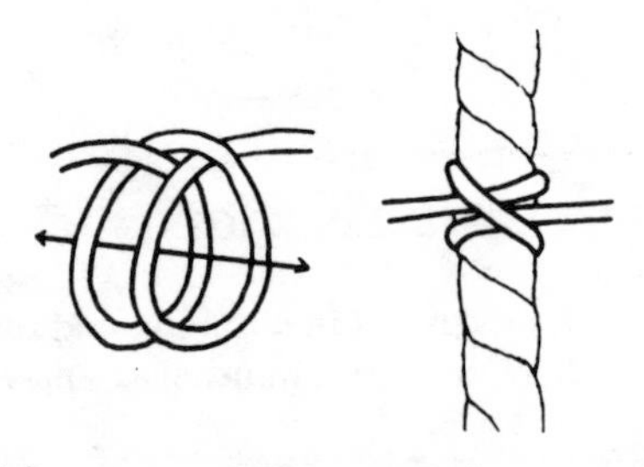

Fig. 9-18. Clove hitch.

Sheepshank. Fig. 9-19. The sheepshank is useful in rescue primarily in improvisation to temporarily shorten a rope. The knot is not at all secure when unloaded and can be easily shaken out.

Fig. 9-19. Sheepshank.

Tent Hitch. Fig. 9-20. Closely related to the prusik, the knot may be conveniently used whenever an adjustable loop is needed, such as for tightening tent guys, or as a single-ended prusik.

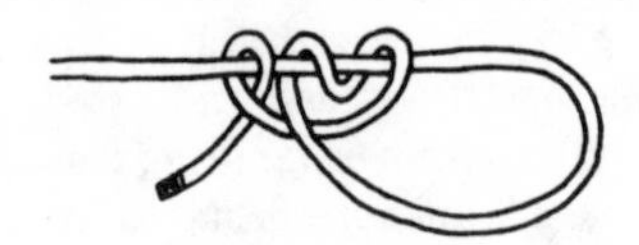

Fig. 9-20. Tent hitch.

KNOT EFFICIENCY

Knots cause a sizable reduction in the strength of a rope due to sharp bends and consequent nonuniform stress on the individual rope fibers. This reduction in strength is measured by the knot efficiency, that is, if a knot is 60 percent efficient, the rope loses 40 percent of its strength due to the knot. The table below shows the approximate efficiency for various common knots in nylon rope.

Table 9-1

Knot Efficiency

Knot	Efficiency
Bowline (a)	65 percent
Double Bowline (a)	69
Single Overhand Loop (b)	49
Fisherman's	59
Double Fisherman's	70
Ring Bend	64
Sheet Bend	49
Double Sheet Bend	63

Notes:

The efficiencies depend on material and test methods, thus the figures given are approximate.

(a) Strain between loop and standing part.

(b) Strain between standing parts.

CHAPTER 10

STEEL CABLE

Steel cable (wire rope) systems may be very useful in mountain rescue operations, particularly in hauling systems, due to the small elasticity of the cable. A brief introduction to cable rescue will be given here, and some additional operational details will be presented in later chapters. Most of this book deals with nylon rope techniques because the usual mountain rescuer is familiar with the use of rope through rock climbing. Some aspects of cable evacuations are easily understood by anyone familiar with nylon methods, but there are some significant features of the cable systems which are distinct from rope. These will be outlined in succeeding sections.

INTRODUCTION

Due to its relatively small elasticity compared to nylon rope of equal strength, steel cable is nicely adaptable to hauling and raising systems, using either a man- or mechanically-powered winch. Of course, steel cable can also be used in simple lowering systems having no lifting capability.

Power winch systems for mountain rescue have been under development for a decade, but a truly workable standard system has not yet been built due to the severe problems of strength, weight, controllability, reliability, and simplicity of not only the winch, but also all other components such as cable linkages, clamps, and pulleys. The Austrian mountain rescue hand-powered winch system was the first to be made available, but it has numerous extremely serious drawbacks in safety and operational features which will not be discussed here.

CABLE PROPERTIES

In this and the following paragraphs, we discuss some physical properties of steel cable and compare to nylon rope. The cable recommended by the Mountain Rescue Association for mountain rescue use (Ref. 1) is preformed galvanized aircraft cable, meeting Mil-specs *Mil-W-1511A*, of 7X19 construction. The 7X19 designation means that there are 7 strands, one of which is a core strand, each twisted from 19 individual wires. The ultimate test strengths for two sizes of steel cable are given and compared to similar weight nylon in Table 10-1.

Table 10-1

Material	Diameter	Weight/100 ft	Ultimate strength
Cable	5/32 in.	4.5 lbs	2800 lbs
Cable	3/16	6.5	4200
Nylon	5/16	3	2700
Nylon	3/8	4.2	3700

Steel cable is significantly less flexible than nylon rope, and thus handling is quite different. Kinks may ruin cable, and knots are not used to form loops or to join lengths. Cable bent around a radius equal to its own size loses a larger percentage of its strength, compared to nylon rope; however, various wire rope fittings are used which cause essentially no loss of strength in making joints. Pulleys must be quite large to pass such connectors.

The abrasion and cutting resistance of cable is much better than nylon, thus a rescuer need not worry so much about abrasion damage from dragging a cable across a sharp rock corner since the steel will cut into the rock instead of the rock cutting the rope. A problem can arise from this grooving if the evacuation is longer than one cable length because a connector cannot pass through the groove. The resistance to damage from a rock falling onto a line under tension is not good for either nylon rope or steel cable.

The inelastic nature of steel cable is perhaps its most important property when compared to nylon. Cable stretches about 1/2 percent when loaded to 25 percent of its ultimate breaking strength compared to perhaps 25 percent elongation for nylon rope. Advantage is taken of this in hauling and lifting or traverse systems for manual and mechanically powered systems. Because of this inelasticity, shock loading is a very major factor in safety. A few hundred pound (kg) load dropped only inches (cm) when suspended from many feet (meters) of cable is quite liable to break the cable, whereas the same situation with nylon would merely result in a small additional stretch in the rope. Similarly, if the main static line in a suspension system (see Chapter 27) is pulled taut and then loaded, the line stress may be very high. If the line is steel cable the load will not sag much, but if nylon, the line stretches, and the load sags, thus large line tensions do not build up readily. Inelasticity is the biggest feature of steel cable, both good and bad, when cable is compared to nylon rope.

As cable wears, individual wires will break. As long as there are fewer than six breaks in a 3 in. (7.5 cm) length of 3/16 in. cable with no more than three of these breaks in any one of the seven strands, the cable retains reasonable strength. But these broken ends tend to stick out, and thus cable handlers must wear heavy leather gloves for protection. A severe kink in the cable will soon cause wire breakage, and the cable must be retired.

OTHER COMPONENTS

Various other components of a cable evacuation system are likely to be unfamiliar to rock climbers. One such device is the brake block, which is the counterpart for cable of the brake bar or brake plate used in nylon rope systems. This friction brake for cable is a hardwood cylinder around which the cable is wrapped a few times. Cable clamps are used to securely grip the cable in hauling systems (see Ch. 26). Two brands of these are described in Ref. 1: Klein (T.M.) and Crescent (T.M.) The first of these has been found to be completely reliable but is somewhat difficult to hold loosely on the cable. The second (Crescent) holds well when set very firmly on the cable but may slip at as little as 50 lbs (22 kg) if merely placed on the cable and allowed to spring closed.

A shock absorber should be placed between the load (litter) and the cable to avoid high peak loadings from shock. The absorber can be as crude as perhaps 10 ft (3 m) of doubled 7/16 in. nylon rope or, better, a device specifically made for the purpose, such as described in Ref. 1. One such device is similar to absorbers made for use with a window washer's safety line, but to sustain loads of up to 1000-1200 lbs (450-550 kg).

Cable is conveniently carried in 300 to 600 ft (90 to 180 m) lengths, on reels mounted on packframes. If the reel is relatively flat and is placed with its axis perpendicular to the plane of the packframe, a 600 ft (180 m) load is easily carried. Also, when the packframe is laid on the ground, the reel may be easily operated.

Connectors which may be used to join lengths of cable with eyes are described in Ref. 1. The ideal connector is small, strong, secure, easily placed on and removed from the cable and is not yet invented. Development continues.

Pulleys for cable systems will be all metal and much larger than for nylon rope. A satisfactory pulley will pass a connector safely.

It is sometimes thought that a swivel at the litter would be useful, particularly on vertical evacuations where the litter hangs free. However, the swivel will not stop the litter from rotating, and will cause very bad kinking problems. These kinks arise because the stressed cable tends to untwist and can do so freely with the swivel; then when the cable becomes slack, it twists back and kinks. If the swivel is left out entirely, the cable does not untwist when stressed and thus has no tendency to kink when slacked.

CABLE WINCH SYSTEMS

A complete cable winch system for raising or lowering loads consists of the winch, lengths of cable, and the numerous special fittings including connectors, brake blocks, pulleys, clamps and carrying reels.

The winch itself may be either a drum type or capstan, with ratchet or brake mechanism to prevent the load from falling in the case of a power failure. The drum type has the entire cable length carried on the drum itself whereas the capstan has only a few turns of cable passing onto and off of the driven spool.

The drum type, available commercially as a hand operated portable Come-Along, may be useful for short hauls (10 to 20 ft or 3 to 6 m) but cannot be used for long continuous lifts. With appropriate rigging, a Come-Along may be used for long lifts by repeatedly pulling a short distance.

The capstan winch is much more versatile in operation and is built for either manual or engine power. To gain the necessary mechanical advantage, a speed reduction is required between the power source and the capstan itself, with chain drive giving the best efficiency.

The power source may be manual in the form of a hand crank or may be a gasoline engine. If the latter is used, there must be means of controlling the speed of moving the load. Since gasoline engines operate efficiently only in a limited speed range, the present best solution to speed control appears to be the use of a hydraulic pump driven by the engine to power a hydraulic motor, the speed of which is controlled readily over a wide range with valves.

When an engine-powered system is used, the manual operational techniques discussed in various chapters are used with some additional procedures required for safety. Because of the overall complexity and speed of the operation, a safety officer should be designated to do nothing except oversee the full operation. He must be tied into the communications system used by the winch operator to be able to order an essentially instantaneous stop of operations if a dangerous situation arises. Because of the noise of existing lightweight engines, the communications system will have to be some form of intercom with personnel wearing headsets and lip microphones or equivalent.

A major potential danger arises in engine powered systems due to the winch operator lacking the feel of the litter because he does not have his hands directly on the cable to the litter. If the litter stops on a descent for any reason, such as a connector hanging up, the winch operator may continue to feed cable out without realizing that the stop occurred. If there is some slack out and the connector suddenly becomes freed, the litter could drop and disastrously shock load the system. Thus, anytime the litter stops, the litter captain should inform the winch operator. If, for example, the litter comes to a halt for an unknown reason, the litter captain should immediately call over the radio for a stop by saying "Stop, stop, why are we stopped?" The command "Stop" should be given twice for clarity over the noise at the winch.

Litter bearers use normal techniques, but the captain should be extra careful to note possible locations for connector hangups. If a connector does get jammed, it may be freed by backing it off (reverse direction of the winch) a few feet and trying again. On very long evacuations (say over 1000 ft or 300 m) litter bearers may find adding a belay seat to their tie-in to be much more comfortable than the seat sling and worthwhile for the long times involved.

Development of better cable systems for mountain rescue is continuing. In general, cable evacuation systems are trickier to use than nylon, and the mechanically powered winches are quite complex. Only personnel intimately familiar should be in charge of cable operations.

REFERENCES

1. "Basic Equipment for Winch and Cable Systems," Mountain Rescue Association Newsletter Supplement No, 3, March 1971.

CHAPTER 11

COMMUNICATIONS

We discuss here some of the various forms of communications which are used in mountain rescue operations. Normally communications between rescue personnel out of talking distance will be by two-way radio, but on occasion radios will be unavailable or not functioning, and other means of communications will have to be used.

RADIO SERVICES

Details of two-way voice radio operation will be quite specific to the rescue unit, but usually one of three types of service will be used: 1) Commercial service, 2) Citizens Radio Service, 3) Amateur. Some general comments on these services will be given below. Occasionally military communications may be used.

Commercial Service. Rescue units often operate radios on a specific channel under a special emergency service license held by the state, by the rescue unit itself, or perhaps by the Mountain Rescue Association. The equipment used is FCC type approved and is relatively expensive, but may be operated by anyone with no requirements to pass an FCC examination.

Citizens Radio Service (CB). CB radio equipment is widely available at low cost. It may be licensed and operated by anyone, but the channels are usually busy and often abused, and transmitter power is limited. CB is a convenient route for a rescue unit to use to get on the air, but is found much less satisfactory overall than 1) above, aside from expense.

Amateur Service. Radio amateurs may operate a wide variety of equipment over a wide range of frequencies, but an operator's license may be obtained only after successfully passing an examination. Amateur equipment may be found very useful for communications from a remote base back to civilization but is much less useful for general team use in the field due to the operator licensing requirement for every user.

Mountain Rescue Service. Very satisfactory service is obtained with VHF-FM radios operating for example under the MRA license on the special emergency frequency, 155.160 Mc. Field teams carry lightweight portable units putting out several watts, and a base may be a mobile (car) radio or simply one of the portables. The radios are powered by either nickel-cadmium rechargeable batteries or by dry cells, with the latter often found more satisfactory for rescue service at irregular intervals because of less maintenance trouble. The alkaline types give service far superior to the normal industrial D cells. Battery life will be greatly diminished if the radios are stored in a hot location. If radio battery packs use standard D cells, rescuers' headlamp batteries may be used to power radios if necessary.

USING TWO-WAY VHF-FM RADIOS

Two-way VHF-FM radios are in common use in mountain rescue. This section discusses in some detail the procedures used in operating such radios on a special emergency channel. Reference is made to the Ten-code, which is commonly used in public safety radio traffic. No matter what radio service is used, operators should use proper radio procedure including call signs and codes.

Position. When using VHF-FM packsets, local quirks are sometimes noticed. Signal strength can often be improved markedly by moving the set so that the antenna is a foot (30 cm) or more from the body or holding it over the head. Simply moving the set a foot (30 cm) or so can help. In cold weather, the batteries of the small radios can be kept warm by carrying the set inside the rescuer's clothing. This is often an awkward procedure when carrying the larger five or ten watt sets, which are most conveniently carried in a rucksack. Their greater battery capacity, however, makes them somewhat less sensitive to extreme power drain in cold weather.

Antenna. A telescoping antenna, if the radio is so equipped, should be extended before transmitting. The sets also receive better with the antenna extended, but this type of antenna is very easily damaged.

The wire whip antennas often found on five to ten watt sets are excellent electronically, but mechanically they are somewhat prone to breakage where they join the connector, so a reasonable amount of care must be observed by radio users and their companions not to bend these whips too sharply. A broken antenna will still give service if it can be pushed into the wire coil in the connector. The prudent rescue organization will place a flexible copper wire attached to another connector in the battery pack for use if the wire whip is broken off and lost. Short rubber-covered flexible helix antennas are mechanically rugged but much less efficient than the straight wire whips.

Squelch. Most packsets have a squelch control knob. With this control, the radio can be kept completely silent unless a signal strong enough to be intelligible comes on. When the knob is turned fully in one direction, the set will constantly emit noise unless it is actually receiving a signal from another set within its range. As the knob is turned in the other direction (on a set not actually receiving) the static noise will suddenly disappear (noise is "squelched"), and the speaker will stay silent as the knob reaches the other limit of its motion. Radio sensitivity is somewhat reduced if the set is left at this "full squelch" position. On the other hand, leaving the set buzzing away unsquelched is not only distracting, but also places a ruinous drain on battery power. The proper setting is to have the knob turned so that the set is just barely silent, that is, at squelch threshold.

The squelch level also serves as a very rough indicator of battery strength. As the batteries are drained, more and more "squelch" will be needed. As the last gasp is approached the set may be "unsquelchable." Fresh batteries should clear up the problem.

Microphones. Packset microphones are located in the body of some small sets, or in a separate microphone or speaker/mike in others, and are actuated with a transmit button (key) on the set or microphone. It is usually best to speak from close range (1-2 in., 2.5-5 cm) across the microphone rather than directly into it. On some sets the operator has to talk fairly loudly, something which should be kept in mind if other stations are having problems receiving. Yelling directly into the microphone, however, will just distort the signal.

The most frequent error in using the transmit key is depressing it while still deciding what to say. Transmission, which occurs whenever the key is depressed regardless of speech, drains batteries far faster than the receive or the listen modes and blocks all other radios receiving the signal. Panicky individuals have been known to forget to release the transmit key, with the result that no return messages of assistance could be sent, increasing the panic. It is also possible to key the transmitter inadvertently (for instance, with a piton hammer shoved into the rucksack after the radio is put in) which airs all conversations, prevents receiving any message, and can disrupt communication between other sets. Another error is short-keying—starting to talk before the button is depressed. On older radios utilizing "instant heat" tubes, a half second delay is needed to allow the tube filaments to warm up.

Set Reliability. Immediately before taking a packset into the field, the following tests should be made: Turn the set on and to the correct channel (important), adjust the squelch for noise and adjust the volume, assuring that part of the set, at least, is working. Reset the squelch at threshold. Then key the microphone for an instant. If a sharp "click" is produced in the speaker, the set will probably transmit. Then before going more than a short distance up the trail, make a test transmission to a nearby station, checking both transmit and receive operation. The radio still may fail later under more demanding circumstances.

If a set seems suddenly to malfunction in the field for no obvious reason, not too much can or should be done by the ordinary user. Batteries can be removed and replaced again to see if a contact was bad, and fresh batteries can be tried if they are available. A cold radio *might* respond for a short while if it or its batteries are rewarmed. Occasionally ice may make the transmit key stick on. If the situation cannot be remedied, the set should be turned off. The rescuer with a useless radio should recall that successful searches and rescues were indeed carried out before the age of two-way radios.

Reliability is the main reason for spending about $900 each for radios. Mountain rescuers do depend heavily on the radios and expect these sets to work perfectly even when given necessarily rough treatment. Cheaper radios are available for the commercial service, but these are more liable to break down often. Quality is available, but only at its high price.

Radio Procedure. The procedures used by rescuers in communicating over two-way radios are a product of FCC requirements, police radio practice, and common sense. The jargon of radio procedure is designed to keep transmissions short (saves batteries and lets others use the air), to be easily understood, and to be unambiguous. Use of standard procedures especially facilitates communication between different rescue organizations, or with the law enforcement agencies generally involved in search or rescue situations. The standard reference on procedure is the *Public Safety Communications Standard Operating Procedure Manual* of the Associated Public-Safety Communications Officers (APCO).

Radio Codes. Most two-way radio communications systems use some form of code to improve reliability of transmissions in the presence of interference. In voice communications this is done by coding the common phrases in a set way allowing the radio operators to take advantage of context to interpret unclear statements. There are many ways to say essentially the same thing. For example, "please repeat," "say again," "what did you say?" all have about the same meaning. The code "ten-nine" (see below) carries the meaning of these phrases and may be more easily understood in the presence of interference than the other phrases because of the fixed way of expressing the given meaning and the ease of understanding spoken numbers in the presence of noise.

Ten-Code. The 1969 Colorado State Patrol Ten-Code, given in Table 11-1 and typical of ten-codes in use throughout the country, is designed to provide speed and reliability in communication. Since it is a *code,* it can on rare occasions be used to conceal information from relatives or others if they are within hearing distance of a radio. Since most rescuers know only the more common codes, use of obscure numbers in mountain rescue can be confusing.

Urgent situations are not the appropriate time for using perhaps unusual 10 codes. One will have to judge if the other operator will understand the code thrown at him in an emergency, and dispense with the code if need be. After all, "No" is quicker to say than "10-74." Conversely, if a code is not recognized, one should be quick to say "I don't understand 10-75; what do you mean?"

The code signals can be either a question or a statement depending on the operator's inflection. The speed of the system is destroyed by redundant usage: "what is your 10-20?" should be simply "10-20?" or "Your signals were unreadable, you will have to 10-9" should be "10-1, 10-9." The code is at its best in short transmissions. A long string of ten-codes is likely to be not understood at first.

MRA Code. A useful simple code adopted by the Mountain Rescue Association is the following:

Code 1: Victim found, no assistance needed
Code 2: Victim found, assistance needed
Code 3: Unforeseen emergency, much help needed
Code 4: Victim found dead
Code 2-1: Return to base.

Table 11-1

Colorado State Patrol Communications Division

Official 10-Signal Code

10-0 Caution
10-1 Unable to copy—change location
10-2 Signal good
10-3 Stop transmitting
10-4 Acknowledgment (OK)
10-5 Relay
10-6 Busy—unless urgent
10-7 Out of service
10-8 In service
10-9 Repeat
10-10 Fight in progress
10-11 Dog case
10-12 Stand by (stop)
10-13 Weather-road report
10-14 Prowler report
10-15 Civil disturbance
10-16 Domestic problem
10-17 Meet complainant
10-18 Quickly
10-19 Return to
10-20 Location
10-21 Call by telephone
10-22 Disregard
10-23 Arrived at the scene
10-24 Assignment completed
10-25 Report in person (meet)
10-26 Detaining subject, expedite
10-27 (Drivers) license information
10-28 Vehicle registration information
10-29 Check for wanted
10-30 Unnecessary use of radio
10-31 Crime in progress
10-32 Man with gun
10-33 EMERGENCY
10-34 Riot
10-35 Major crime alert
10-36 Correct time
10-37 (Investigate) suspicious vehicle
10-38 Stopping suspicious vehicle
10-39 Urgent—use light, siren
10-40 Silent run—no light, siren
10-41 Beginning tour of duty
10-42 Ending tour of duty
10-43 Information
10-44 Permission to leave for
10-45 Animal carcass at
10-46 Assist motorist
10-47 Emergency road repair
10-48 Traffic standard repair at
10-49 Traffic light out at
10-50 Accident (F;PI;PD)
10-51 Wrecker needed
10-52 Ambulance needed
10-53 Road blocked at
10-54 Livestock on highway
10-55 Intoxicated driver
10-56 Intoxicated pedestrian
10-57 Hit and run (F;PI;PD)
10-58 Direct traffic
10-59 Convoy or escort
10-60 Squad in vicinity
10-61 Personnel in area
10-62 Reply to message
10-63 Prepare to make written copy
10-64 Message for local delivery
10-65 Net message assignment

Table 11-1 (continued)

10-66 Message cancellation
10-67 Clear for net message
10-68 Dispatch information
10-69 Message received
10-70 Fire alarm
10-71 Advise nature of fire
10-72 Report progress of fire
10-73 Smoke report
10-74 Negative
10-75 In contact with
10-76 En route
10-77 ETA (estimated time of arrival)
10-78 Need assistance
10-79 Notify coroner
10-80 Chase in progress
10-81 Breathalizer report
10-82 Reserve lodging
10-83 Work school crossing at
10-84 If meeting advise ETA
10-85 Delayed due to
10-86 Officer/operator on duty
10-87 Pickup/distribute checks
10-88 Present telephone number of
10-89 Bomb threat
10-90 Bank alarm at
10-91 Pickup prisoner/subject
10-92 Improperly parked vehicle
10-93 Blockade
10-94 Drag racing
10-95 Prisoner/subject in custody
10-96 Mental subject
10-97 Check (test) signal
10-98 Prison/jail break
10-99 Wanted/stolen indicated

Reprinted by permission

The Transmission Series. Each communication is initiated by the calling station first listening to be sure that the channel is clear and then giving the unit designator of the station it wishes to speak to, followed by its own unit designator: "1923, 1922" means 1922 wishes to speak to 1923. 1923 indicates he is listening either by giving his own unit designator "1923" or by saying "Go ahead." Unit designators are derived through various schemes according to the licensee. Most mountain rescue units using a special emergency channel have a number assigned to each packset, mobile, or base which is used. On the other hand, various governmental agencies may assign a number to each man rather than to a particular radio. If an operator is in doubt as to what number to use to call some team in the field, he could just say the man's name ("Klaus Ironhands, 1922") or some other designation ("Team on Peck Glacier, 1922"). Both of these procedures should be used if there is trouble raising a given set. The person carrying the radio may not be familiar with procedures, or may simply be half asleep. The team will answer with its designator. After the address and response, the stations simply talk back and forth much as on a telephone. The word "over" is *not* needed in VHF-FM transmissions due to the audible click over each radio when a transmit key is released. The phrase should not be used, even though radio amateurs often use it on their bands, and it is used in some telephone-radio patch systems where a middleman has to switch the telephone end of the conversation from send to receive and vice versa.

The answer to every query should be acknowledged. The acknowledgment can be a brief "10-4." For example:

"10-20?"

"Greenman Springs."

"10-4."

If the acknowledgment is not given, the person responding to the question will wonder if the message was received and will then inquire about it. On occasion, when response by voice is awkward, two clicks with the transmit key will provide the desired acknowledgment.

Overformalizing transmissions and adding superfluous words can make it hard to get communication started, especially in the operational phase of a rescue:

From a litter being lowered: "1923, from 1922."

The brakeman replies: "This is 1923, go ahead, 1922."

"1923, this is 1922. Stop quick."

An unannounced transmission "Stop the litter" would have been appropriate and sufficient.

After each exchange of transmissions, the stations are to be identified by the assigned call signal (the license). An individual unit may use the word "clear" to indicate that the transmission is ended and no response is expected: " . . . 1922 clear, KL3122." Usually the station acting as a base will do this; otherwise it will be the unit initiating the conversation. If the units engaged in traffic are operating under different licenses, then each unit will give its call signal: "KL3122." "KBC-877." An alternate method of identification which may be used when radio traffic is heavy is for the base (a base station or mobile or packset assigned the job) to give the call sign every 30 minutes, rather than identify after each conversation. This method is the one used by law enforcement dispatchers, who will end each exchange of transmissions with the time. Users of mobiles and packsets licensed by agencies with dispatchers do not give call signs; the dispatcher takes care of this.

Message Length. A lengthy message should be broken into pieces no longer than about 30 seconds to let the receiving station finish writing down or digesting what was said, to ask for a repeat, or to let some other station with an urgent message break into the transmission. The break should be done by finishing a sentence and adding "Break." The receiver usually says "10-4" when he is ready for the continuation. A station wishing to break into a windy conversation can try to do so by keying immediately after one station has stopped sending, and saying "Break, 1922" or "10-3" and taking over. This does not always work, however.

Special Transmission Problems. Occasionally, sets will transmit but not receive due to some electronic problem in the set (some small, low power sets are affected by cold in this way, especially if the battery power is down.) If the radio suddenly dies and will not get through to other stations even after checking the obvious (set on? correct channel?) and playing with batteries, etc., it may be appropriate to transmit "in the blind" anyway. It may well be that someone will hear the transmission, although alternate means of communication should also be pursued if necessary.

A more frequent problem arises when the more powerful base is understood by the field set, but the weaker transmission from the field is unintelligible at base, even with the packset carefully positioned for optimum performance as discussed above. At the worst, the base can transmit its information or instructions "in the blind." More frequently, however, some response can be elicited from the field by asking the field operator to key his transmitter twice (or whatever) for yes, and once for no. This will often produce a discernable click over the base radio when voice is too garbled to understand. If the message is from base to field, a simple acknowledgment is easy enough to arrange. If the message is from the field, the base operator will have to play a sort of "20 questions," aided by his experience and intuition into what the field station might be trying to say.

"Is your message urgent?"

"(click, click)"

"Have you found the victim?"

"(click, click)"

"Alive?"

"(click, click)"

"Do you need first aid?"

"(click)"

"I understand that you have found the victim alive and that you do not need first aid. Is this correct?"

"(click, click)" and so on. Considerable redundancy is absolutely necessary in these nearly one-sided conversations to avoid misunderstanding, whereas it is to be avoided in normal conversations.

General. As another refinement, field stations can make a point of giving their location when they respond to a call: "1923, 1920." "1923, Boulder Falls." Similarly, a station going out of service should always inform the base of this. Any operator whose set has been suspiciously quiet for some time during a mission (especially if some standard conversation generators like evacuations, helicopter operations, or multiple line searches are going on) should check his set to see if it has been inadvertently turned off or has been keyed continuously or is malfunctioning.

Since VHF radios operate best on a line-of-sight basis, a relay up on a ridge or at the end of a valley must sometimes be used to enable stations in separate, deep mountain valleys to communicate. The relayer must strive to repeat *verbatim* the message of each station, and avoid adding his own interpretations unless he has some important, hard data the others lack. Any messages passed through a relayer should be kept short and simple. This is particularly true if the relay station is not part of the rescue operation but is, say, the state patrol.

Although transmissions should generally not be made unless there is some real reason to do so, field teams may from time to time feel the need for some radio traffic just to see if the radios are still working. A signal check (10-97) or location report (10-20) is well suited to this purpose. This should not be overdone on urgent rescues, but has its place in extended search operations.

AUDIBLE AND LIGHT FLASHING SIGNALS

Loudhailers are often found useful in search and rescue. Those with a listen feature are especially good to hear calls from victim or rescuers, but difficulty is encountered when used in an area of high noise such as near a rushing stream, traffic, or on a windy day. Also, there is some difficulty locating the source of calls when echoes are present. Lightweight bullhorns are good on searches not only for controlling a line but also for calling to a victim, and they are useful on steep scree evacuations for giving warning calls about loose rock, etc.

The MRA codes given earlier should be known by all rescue unit members. Internationally known distress signals are SOS (. . . - - - . . .) and the simpler triplet (- - -) with response (- -). These codes may be sent by yells, auto horns or sirens, flashing headlamps, pengun noise makers, etc., or by simple voice over the radio, especially when confidential information is to be transmitted, for example, "Code 4." It should be kept in mind that sounds do not carry at all well in wooded terrain.

A common occurrence in mountain rescue is for the victim to be spotted in a relatively inaccessible place (for example, on a rock wall), and for the rescuers to be able to talk to him but to be unable to understand the return comments, even with listening equipment. In such a situation, the victim may be able to signal in some way, for example, by yells which are audible or visible but not understandable, waving a parka, flashing lights, etc. For reliable communications, the rescuers redundantly ask the victims for responses to slowly spoken simple statements. A "conversation" might be:

Rescuer: "If you need assistance, wave (give a yell. . .)"
Victim: (waves)
Rescuer: "If you do not need assistance, wave."
Victim: (no response).

Such questioning does not require a "yes" or "no" but either a response or none, and questions are repeated in the negative to assure that the victim understood the question by giving the opposite response.

The Very pistol or the less efficient but more compact pengun flares can be quite useful, *if* the observing party is watching at the time. For team-to-team or team-to-base communications, the flares are not effective because of the problem of attracting the attention of the observer, but for ground-to-air signalling these are good. *Flares must not be fired into terrain where there is fire danger.* Since the flares are available in various colors, additional coding can be agreed upon.

A signalling mirror may be effective to attract the attention of the observer or to send simple messages. The mirror is silvered on both sides and has a hole in the center. When used as shown in Fig. 11-1, the mirror is held at arm's length to reflect the sun in approximately the right direction. Good aiming accuracy is easily achieved by sighting the target through the hole in the mirror while simultaneously adjusting the mirror so that the sunlight passing through the hole and falling on the chest of the message sender is seen by him reflected in the mirror and centered on the hole.

Another attention-getting technique is the use of smoke. Green leaves thrown on a hot fire will smoke rather nicely. Smoke grenades last only minutes and should be used only when there is a very good chance of the observer seeing the smoke, for example, on the approach of an aircraft, not when the plane is overhead.

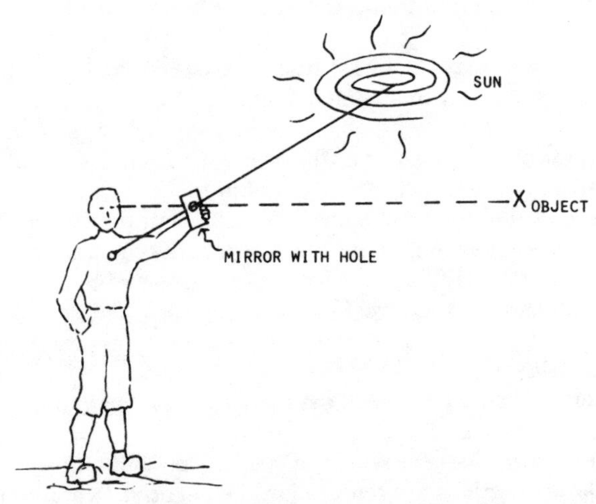

Fig. 11-1. Showing simple method of aiming signalling mirror.

GROUND-TO-AIR SIGNALS

There are a number of internationally recognized ground-to-air signals, shown in Tables 11-2 and 11-3. The signals of the first table are used by survivors of downed aircraft and are included here only for completeness and so that a ground search team will be familiar with these and will not make another signal similar and cause confusion. All pilots should be familiar with these, and also with the aircraft responses, in Fig. 11-2. The ground personnel should make the signals about 10 ft (3 m) high or more by any convenient means, such as stamping in snow or with branches, bright cloth, etc., on a background as contrasting as possible. Some means should be used to gain the attention of the aircraft personnel, and this should be done before the plane is overhead. Smoke or flares are good (used with care to not create a forest fire), and signalling mirrors may be effective.

Table 11-2

Ground-to-Air Signals For Use By Survivors

Symbol	Meaning
I	Require doctor, serious injury
II	Require medical supplies
X	Unable to proceed
F	Require food and water
□	Require map and compass
¦	Require radio
K	Indicate direction to proceed
↗	Am proceeding in this direction
L⅂	Aircraft seriously damaged
△	Probably safe to land here
L	Require fuel
LL	All well
N	No
Y	Yes
JL	Not understood

Table 11-3

Ground-to-Air Signals For Use By Ground Search Parties

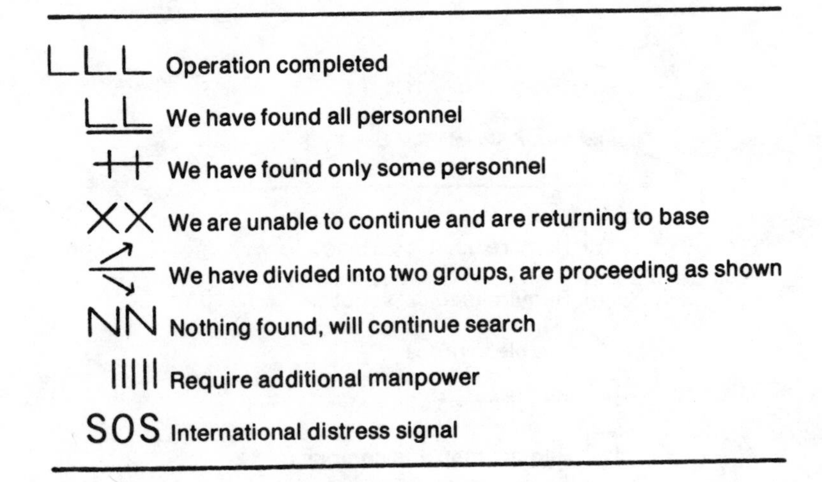

Signal	Meaning
LLL	Operation completed
LL	We have found all personnel
++	We have found only some personnel
XX	We are unable to continue and are returning to base
⇄	We have divided into two groups, are proceeding as shown
NN	Nothing found, will continue search
IIIII	Require additional manpower
SOS	International distress signal

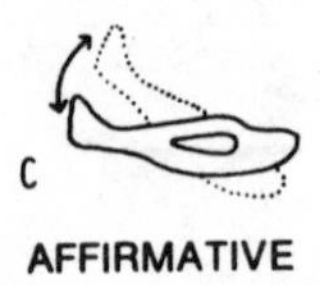

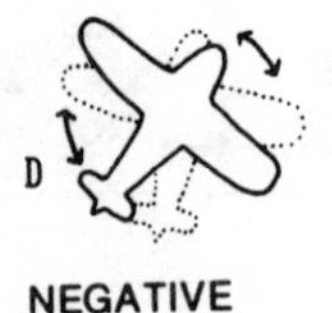

Fig. 11-2. Showing aircraft responses to ground-to-air signals.

PART II

The chapters in this part deal with a variety of individual skills needed during many mountain rescue missions including the very important topic of search.

Ground search, the "bread and butter" of mountain rescue, has a smaller percentage of space in this book than its importance would imply. The basic techniques are readily learned by the individual (but perhaps not so readily applied), with the major problems of search falling to the leaders. The chapter on observation techniques includes some practical aspects of eye physiology that could be put to good use during searches if only searchers would think about such things. Some searching is best done by personnel other than mountain rescue troops on foot, and hence the chapters on aircraft, dogs, and snowmobiles as used in mountain search and rescue are presented.

Various individual skills useful in rescue and known to mountaineers are reviewed here with emphasis on techniques applicable to rescue. We have found that too many mountain rescuers lack familiarity with maps, thus included here is a chapter on those aspects of map reading which will find considerable use in mountain rescue. Techniques of ascending fixed lines and of river crossings are given and should be among the well-learned basic skills of the mountain rescuer. Finally there is a brief review on conditions leading to avalanche and on avalanche probing.

CHAPTER 12

MAP, COMPASS, AND GRID

A mountain rescuer will often need map and compass skills beyond those of the recreational mountain visitor. In addition to being able to read a map and navigate to given locations, he must be able to search an assigned area; or failing to complete that search, to describe exactly what area was searched. He must be able to give his location at almost any time and preferably in more than one way. If he is in a leadership position, his knowledge should extend to the map, compass and grid methods of those other organizations with which his own unit works.

This chapter reviews some basic topographic map reading skills and discusses topics of particular value to mountain rescuers. Many references are listed at the end of the chapter. The examples given throughout the chapter make use of the 7.5 minute series U.S. Geological Survey topographic map "Longs Peak, Colorado," 1961 edition. A black line reproduction of a portion of this map is included with this book.

PUBLISHED MAPS

USGS Maps. Most mountain rescue units prefer the U.S. Geological Survey 7.5 minute series of topographic maps. They are printed at a scale of 1:24,000 (approximately 2.6 inches to a mile) and usually at 40 foot contour intervals.

These maps are printed in multiple colors, with each color reserved for certain uses. For example, blue indicates water, including lakes, streams, and glaciers. Man-made or cultural features, political boundaries, and names are in black; brown lines are used for topography or relief, mainly contour lines. Red is used for important roads and public land survey lines; pink or light red indicates urban areas in which only the most important man-made features are shown. Green shows various forms of vegetation. Finally, on some new maps, purple shows revisions determined from aerial photographs but not field checked.

The so-called "advance" maps are printed in single color (black or dark blue) and are preliminary versions. These may be available years before the final map and are welcome when an area has no better coverage. Our sample map looks like an "advance" print.

For some areas, 15 minute series maps may be available instead of, or in addition to, the 7.5 minute maps.

The particular edition of a final map is indicated by notation in the margin at the lower edge. This information should be inspected carefully in comparing maps.

Example. The date "1961" in the lower right under the quadrangle name "Longs Peak" gives the edition, while the date "1967" in small type at the bottom edge of the map on the right indicates the date of printing.

Other Maps and Aerial Photographs. USGS maps covering the United States at a scale of 1:250,000 are also available but lack the detail of the 7.5 minute maps. These or Sectional Aeronautical Charts (1:500,000) are useful for large area searches and observers aboard aircraft.

Other maps which are of use from time to time on search and rescue operations include those from the Army Map Service, U.S. Forest Service, and state highway departments.

Occasionally a rescuer uses aerial photographs when recent maps are unavailable. Photos may be particularly helpful on a search of a newly subdivided mountain area if a maze of new roads are not shown on the topographic map which may be many years old. When commercial photographs are not available from either Governmental or local sources, a light plane may be sent up, and crude but useful pictures taken with a Polaroid camera.

NORTH

The rescuer may encounter three "North" directions: true, magnetic, and grid.

True North means meridian north or geographic north, that is, in the direction of the north pole.

Magnetic North is the direction in which the north-seeking end of a compass needle points in the absence of local perturbation in the magnetic field. The difference in direction between magnetic and true north is known as "declination" and is stated in degrees east or west of true north. In the contiguous U.S., the declination varies from about 23° east in northwest Washington to 22° west in northeast Maine. These figures are slowly decreasing, at the rate of about 2 minutes per year throughout much of western U.S.

Grid North. In true rectangular grid systems (see UTM grid, below), north-south grid lines do not converge to the poles of the Earth; therefore the directions of these lines may differ from true north by more than a degree. However, the side lines (neat lines) of the USGS maps are true north-south lines.

Example. The arrow labeled with a star and shown at the bottom of the map shows true north. The direction of magnetic north is shown by the arrow labeled MN, and we see that the magnetic declination was 14° east of true north in 1961. The direction of the UTM grid north is 22' or slightly less than .4° west of true north for the area covered by this map.

AIDS TO MAP READING

Compasses. The basic compass is of course a magnetized needle set on a bearing allowing the needle to line up in a magnetic field. Cheap compasses have poor quality bearings which soon wear out from vibration and rattling and then have so much friction as to be useless. Somewhat better compasses have a needle lock which prevents the rapid wear of the bearing. But these compasses with no needle damping are inconvenient to use in the field because of the time required for the needle to come to rest. Perhaps the best compass for the mountain rescuer is one of the many liquid filled types, graduated 0° to 360°, which may include such extra features as declination setting, luminous points, sighting aids, or clinometer. Additional precision and features of the very expensive compasses are usually of no particular value in mountain rescue.

Some general precautions in using all compasses are worth mentioning. The presence of anything magnetic or the flow of current near the compass may cause incorrect readings. Such items as an ice ax, pitons, knife, etc., are obvious, but a light meter, overhead power lines, radio microphone, headlamp in use, and iron ore deposits may be overlooked. Wearers of steel-rimmed glasses should not use a compass which must be held near the eye for sighting. Further details in the use of a compass are left to the references and to the manufacturer's instructions.

Watch Compass. A watch can be used as a crude compass with the sun. With the watch held in a horizontal plane and with the hour hand pointed in the direction of the sun, a north-south line is given approximately by the radius vector half way between the hour hand and 12 o'clock (1 o'clock during daylight saving times).

Altimeters. As a supplement to map and compass and to help with the vertical dimension, a pocket altimeter is very useful, particularly with poor visibility. Knowledge of elevation is often a valuable aid to determining location and may be very important in itself. The user should not forget to set his altimeter at base camp, and he should remember to check or reset it regularly at known elevations, particularly if used for many hours or during a storm. Meteorological altimeter variations of over 200 feet (70 meters) a day may be expected, and long term variations of well over 500 feet (150 meters) are common. Pocket altimeters calibrated in 20 foot or 10 meter intervals are much more useful and worth the additional expense over the cruder ones.

LOCATION

Most search and rescue missions involve communicating a location by radio. Precision of location to within say 100 yards (meters) or within about 1/8 inch (.3 cm) on a 1:24,000 map will be commonly desired in communications between a team leader in the field and the mission leader at base. But specifying the position to the half mile or mile (a kilometer or so) may suffice to direct personnel outside the rescue unit itself, for instance, helicopter pilots. Various means of specifying and determining locations may be used for these different purposes.

Determining Location. We discuss very briefly two methods that a person in the field might use to locate himself or a terrain feature on a map, leaving more extensive problems of map reading to the various references.

Resection. A team leader reporting his location will first have to decide where he is on the map. If he has not been following his course in detail on the map as he moved, he may use a simple technique, known as "resection," with map and compass when two visible distant points are shown and found on the map. A compass sighting is made to each of the distant points, and the sightings are reproduced on the map by drawing lines. Two such sightings should "resect" at the observer's position on the map. A third sighting serves as a check, and altimeter readings give further verification. This technique is used in a crude fashion by most team leaders as they move, simply "eyeballing" features to keep track of position.

Intersection or Triangulation. A technique closely related to the above is used to locate on a map a distant or inaccessible point when two observer positions are known on the map. The direction to the distant point is determined for each observer position by compass sighting, and a corresponding line for each is drawn on one map. The observation points are preferably such that the sightings are nearly at right angles to each other. The lines on the map should intersect at the location of the distant point on the map.

Grids and Coordinates. Various grid and coordinate systems have been developed to define areas or points. We discuss briefly those which will be of prime interest to mountain rescuers.

Geographic Coordinates (Latitude and Longitude). Geographic coordinates use the degree as the basic unit of measurement, with subdivision into minutes and seconds. (Other angular measures used in map reading include the "mil" and the "grad." In the full circle there are 6400 mils and 400 grads). The origin of this system is just off the west coast of Africa where the Greenwich meridian (0° longitude) intersects the equator (0° latitude). Latitude is measured north or south of the equator up to 90° at the poles, and longitude is measured west or east of the Greenwich meridian up to 180° in the Pacific Ocean. The contiguous states, Hawaii, and most of Alaska are in latitude north and longitude west. Therefore, "north" and "west" may be dropped when giving geographic coordinates in the United States. In the United States latitude and longitude cannot be confused with each other, but by convention the latitude is usually given first. At 40° latitude (central U.S.) a minute of latitude is approximately equal to 6100 feet on the earth's surface, and a minute of longitude is about 4700 feet. A rule of thumb is that a minute is equal to a mile. Therefore if a position is to be given by geographic coordinates to an accuracy of the nearest mile, it should be given to the nearest minute of arc. This is difficult to do with charts or maps of a scale of 1:500,000 or smaller but is easy with the 1:24,000 scale.

USGS topographic maps use latitude and longitude lines for the basis of the map printing. The 7.5 minute maps have black ticks printed every 2.5 minutes of both latitude and longitude, both on the border and internally. With a little practice, geographic coordinates can be estimated by eye to the nearest .5 minute of arc (approximately .5 mile or 1 kilometer).

All rescue personnel should know this grid system; for of all the systems, geographic coordinates are most often printed on charts and maps and are most universally known.

Example. The lower right corner of the map is at 40° 15' (north) latitude and 105° 30' (west) longitude. The latitude 40° 17' 30" is indicated by a black tick labeled 17' 30" at each edge of the map approximately 8 inches (20 cm) up from the bottom. Four black crosses may be found in the body of the map indicating each 2.5' (that is, 2' 30") of latitude and longitude. For example, such a mark can be found approximately 1 inch (2 cm) south of Wind River Pass.

Military (Metric) Grid System. The Military Grid Reference System (MGRS) was developed for use with the Universal Transverse Mercator (UTM) grid. The basic unit of measure is the meter. The grid coordinates may be determined on recent USGS topographic maps from blue ticks extending out from the map along the border indicating one kilometer intervals. These ticks are labeled with numbers indicating distances (in meters) from a reference. The north-south distance is measured from the equator in the northern hemisphere, and east-west, from a UTM grid zone edge (see Refs. 2 and 3). Since the MGRS is not printed on many maps used by civilian search and rescue personnel, it is currently not a preferred grid or coordinate system.

Example. Near the bottom right corner of the map we find notation near a tick extending out from the body of the map which indicates 457,000 meters east of the UTM grid zone edge, and similarly for another tick just up from the lower right corner, 4,456,000 meters north of the equator. Most of the metric grid ticks are labeled with the 000 omitted. An example of the use of this system is given later.

Public Land System. The Public Land System (PLS), used to divide public lands for sale, is of occasional interest in mountain rescue. Public land surveys in a given area are based on two primary lines: a true north-south line called the "Principal Meridian," and a true east-west line, the "Baseline." "Range lines" are north-south lines spaced about six miles apart separating Ranges which are numbered from the Principal Meridian to the east R.1E, R.2E, and to the west R.1W, etc. Similarly strips of land about six miles wide running east-west are called "Tiers" (or the very confusing terminology "Townships") and are labeled T.1N, T.2N if north of the baseline, and T.1S, T.2S if to the south. The area of about six by six miles in common between an intersecting range and tier is called a "Township" (not the same as the "Township" in the previous sentence). These townships are divided into 36 "Sections," each about one mile square and numbered 1 to 36 starting in the northeast corner of the township and working back and forth. The section numbers on the 7.5 minute topographic maps are near the center of each section. Sections may be further subdivided in halves, quarters, etc., and fences, roads and property lines are often found along these divisions. Further discussion of the PLS terminology may be found in Ref. 6.

Section, Tier, and Range boundaries are shown in red, dashed when unreliable and black on old maps. The sections are often not exactly one mile squares and may sometimes be rather distorted but are usually close enough that mileage can be estimated on the map using the section lines.

Occasionally a location can be confirmed by a small card tacked to a tree by a forester and marked in the PLS to show the location of the card.

This PLS should never be used in communication with a helicopter pilot or anyone else who is unlikely to have a suitably marked map or who may not understand the system.

Example. Near the bottom right hand corner of the map the lines separating R.72W from R.73W and T.3N from T.4N are so labeled. Section 36 near the lower right hand corner is in the Township designated T.4N, R.73W. Note that it is slightly distorted from a square.

Civil Air Patrol Grid (Standarized Sectional Aeronautical Chart Grid and Identification System). In air search operations the CAP uses a grid system based upon individual Sectional Aeronautical Charts (1:500,000). Grid lines are drawn on each chart at 15 minute intervals of both latitude and longitude, and the resulting quadrangles are numbered consecutively from left to right and top to bottom. Each quadrangle or grid is further divided into 7.5 minute quarters which are designated "A" northwest, "B" northeast, "C" southwest, and "D" southeast. For example, the area of the Longs Peak map would be defined in the CAP system as Cheyenne 526 D, where "Cheyenne" is the name of the chart on which Longs Peak appears. The system is useless unless a chart is available with grids prenumbered.

State Plane Coordinates. This land surveying system uses the foot as its basic unit of measurement. Some of the marginal information on the USGS topographic maps is in this system (e.g. "1970000 feet" at the lower left) but it is of no value to the mountain rescuer.

Reporting Location. We discuss below some techniques of describing a location to another person. It is always a good practice to give confirming or redundant data, such as one's elevation or an alternate means of specifying the location. The examples given below show several ways to report the location of a pond shown in Section 3 at the bottom of the map. Most of these methods use the grids or coordinates described above.

Landmark Method. Location is given by a direction and distance from some readily identifiable and prominent feature. The system is independent of the particular maps used if the reference feature is on both maps. High accuracy may be obtained by transferring distance on the map with a stick or piece of paper to the scale which is always present on the maps used in search and rescue. The usual way of specifying both distance and direction is not with a compass azimuth and radial distance but rather by distance north or south and then distance east or west to the reference.

Example. The pond could be described as "The upstream pond on the Roaring Fork, about 1.1 miles west of Highway 7 and .9 miles south of Longs Peak Ranger Station, at about 9420 feet elevation."

Mapmark Method. Location using the mapmark method is given by reference to any markings on the map at or near the rescuer's position, such as topographic features, political boundaries, letters in words labeling features, ticks, etc. This method requires that the rescuer and the recipient of the information have *identical* maps, that is, the same edition and printing of the same series map.

Example. The particular pond could be described as being "about 1/4 inch north of the 4 in 9400 in Section 3 at the bottom of the map, at about 9420 feet elevation, 3/8 inch below the Park boundary."

Geographic Coordinates. A position could be specified with any desired precision using geographic coordinates, but accurate division of the 2.5 minute intervals into finer subdivisions on the 7.5 minute maps is a rather inconvenient field operation. With some difficulty the geographic coordinates of the pond can be determined to be 40° 15' 34" N by 105° 33' 22" W. An effective system is to combine the landmark method with geographic coordinates by specifying a reference in terms of convenient geographic coordinates, and then giving the desired location as distance from this reference. Good accuracy can be achieved even if the two maps used are of completely different series and scale.

Example. "The pond is 3500 feet north of 40° 15' and 4000 feet west of 105° 32' 30", at about 9420 feet elevation."

MGRS. A 1000 meter square is designated by a four-digit number, the first two digits specifying the distance west or east of the grid reference, the last two digits giving the north-south coordinates (mnemonic phrase for which comes first: "Read right up"). The two-digit numbers refer to the UTM or metric grid tick numbers, with the 000 omitted, and the small superscript digits also ignored. Similarly a 100 meter square would be designated with a six-digit number, adding a third digit to each of the coordinate digits, specifying distances from the grid references to the nearest 100 meters. Designation to the 10 meter square could be given with an eight-digit number, but such precision is hardly worthwhile. The edge of a piece of paper can be used to transfer distance from the map location to the ticks and to the kilometer scale at the bottom of the map, accurately obtaining the decimal fractions within a one kilometer square.

Example. The pond in question is in the 1000 meter square 5256. The 52 specifies the (unlabeled) tick appearing at the second L in "Allens." Likewise the 56 specifies a tick which represents a distance 4,456,000 meters north of the equator. More accurately the pond is at 527565. The 7 indicates that the pond is seven-tenths of the way west to east from the 52 km tick to the 53 km tick, and the last 5 signifies that the pond is five-tenths of the way south to north from the 56 km tick to the 57 km one. The reader easily should be able to verify that the summit of Longs Peak is near 476560.

Public Land System. This system is designed to define areas, but it can be used to describe location; the system is very awkward to use with great precision.

Example. The pond location could be described as "On the east side of the northwest quarter of the northwest quarter of Section 3."

SOURCES OF MAPS

USGS maps: 7.5 minute, 15 minute, 1:250,000:
Denver Distribution Section
U.S. Geological Survey
Denver Federal Center Bldg. 41
Denver Colo 80225

Ask for index maps and order forms for the states of interest.

"Advance" maps and Aerial Photographs:
Topographic Division
U.S. Geological Survey
Denver Federal Center Bldg. 25
Denver Colo 80225

Ask for Advance Material Index (Status Map) for the states of interest.

U.S. Forest Service Maps:
Contact a District Office for the National Forest of interest, or if this is unknown, write to
Division of Information and Education
U.S. Forest Service
Washington D.C. 20250

Ask for the address of the appropriate Regional Office.

Sectional Aeronautical Charts:
Contact a local aircraft supplier or write to
Distribution Division (C-44)
National Ocean Survey
Washington D.C. 20235

REFERENCES

1. *Be Expert with Map and Compass*, B. Kjellstrom.
2. *Map Reading*, Army Field Manual, FM 21-26, January 1969.
3. *Grids and Grid References*, Army Technical Manual, TM 5-241-1, June 1967.
4. *Manual of Ski Mountaineering*, chapter on compass and map, D. Brower, ed.
5. *Mountaineering: The Freedom of the Hills*, Chapter 5, Navigation in the Hills.
6. *Elements of Surveying*, Army Technical Manual TM 5-232, June, 1971.

CHAPTER 13

SEARCH

The overall problem of mountain search may be considered at various levels. One of these is the general organization of the search operation including jurisdiction and authority, means of obtaining needed resources, the interaction of various groups with different capabilities, and the details of operating a search headquarters including communications, press, etc. Another is search strategy, that is, the overall search plan of how the various and many resources are put to best use. A third includes search tactics, or the details and techniques of actually looking for a person in the field. It is the last of these that most directly concerns the individual mountain rescuer on a search team, and search tactics will be a major part of this chapter. But some discussion of search strategy and organization will be given to provide a basis and motivation for the tactics applying to ground search. The overall problem of search is too vast to be covered thoroughly in a book such as this; experience will show the individual that there is always more to be learned, and that a search operation does not follow a set format neatly described in a book. The chapter concludes with a survey of individual and team responsibilities.

SEARCH TACTICS

The following search methods will be discussed in this section: a) Survey, b) Scratch, c) Saturation, d) Tracking. The second and third of these will likely be the ones with which the individual mountain rescuer will first become acquainted in the field, and the techniques and terminology should be learned. Which of these techniques is to be used in a given situation is a matter of search strategy, discussed in the next section.

Survey Methods. Initial searching will often be by a very rough but very rapid method covering huge areas quickly. Often productive is a search of any roads in or around the search area. Any sensible victim would be likely to stay on a road once coming upon it, thus the roads should be regularly patrolled.

Aircraft are frequently used to survey large open areas such as above timberline. Although it may be difficult for a spotter in an airplane to see a small fixed object such as a person, he may see tracks or signals in snow or a recent avalanche and determine likely spots for later ground search. A person who is long overdue or in trouble very well may be able to signal the aircraft upon hearing it by setting out or waving brightly colored clothing or the like, thus repeated flights should be made to allow the party time to signal. Helicopters are often used to attract attention and to search out areas such as cliffs and cliff bottoms or scree gullies. More details on the use and limitations of aircraft in search are given in Ch. 15.

A large area may be viewed from a prominent point by a searcher with binoculars. Again it is difficult to spot a person this way, but a tent or other such object may be seen, as might a smoke signal or fire (even a match) lit by the lost party.

Sometimes beacons of various sorts are used to attract attention of a missing party. For example, airborne loudhailers may be used, or at night, a searchlight could be aimed skyward to give the victim a readily visible goal. Lanterns with notes could be placed at intervals along a road bounding the search area or within the area, but unless secured, such lanterns would tend to disappear.

Scratch Searching. A scratch ("hasty") search is a rapid search by a small team travelling lightly, searching routes or locations where the missing party might logically be expected. (The scratch team may also be able to survey search from its advanced position.)

For example, if the person was known to be hiking up a given peak when last seen, a scratch team would be sent to the summit along the obvious ascent route, searching for visible or audible signs along the way, to check the summit register for the party's name. Another scratch team might simultaneously be sent up a logical descent route, and the first team would come down some other probable descent route. Likely escape routes along the way would be checked also.

The missing party might have been known to be climbing a route with some hazards such as cliffs, gullies with loose rock or likely avalanche, etc. The bases of the cliffs and gullies would be checked by scratch teams for recent activity.

In the case of bad weather or nightfall, a lost person would be expected to seek shelter. Any known buildings in the area would be checked as would natural shelters along the logical route. If a lightning storm had hit the area, locations of obvious lightning danger and shelter should be searched, when the danger has passed.

A person lost in the mountains can usually be expected to go downhill and would thus wander towards a valley bottom. A likely place to find a missing person is along a stream, perhaps following a game trail. Thus a small scratch team might be sent up along a stream from an obvious point of departure such as where the stream crosses under a road. The team would not make a thorough search of the entire area on each side of the stream but would follow obvious trails along the stream and would check out any prominent feature that might provide shelter for the victim along the way. The stream itself should also be searched.

Once a person lost in the mountains comes upon a road or prominent trail, he would be expected to follow it downhill. Scratch searching also includes simply sending a team along all such paths in the search area. Teams may be sent out to take several obvious or logical routes from the last seen point including roads, trails, game trails or merely routes that seem reasonable.

There are various features which may attract a lost person. These include prominent points from which a view may be obtained or signals may be sent, lakes by which there may be civilization, and any man-made structure such as a radio antenna, power lines, mine shacks, etc. Each of these features might be the object of a scratch search.

The philosophy of the scratch search is to check out quickly the areas thought to have a relatively high probability of success. For speed the scratch team will travel lightly, carrying only the minimum of rescue gear including a radio, small first aid kit, some extra warm clothing for the victim or for a bivouac, and technical gear if appropriate. If the scratch searching fails, then the slower but more thorough methods described below would probably be used.

SATURATION METHODS

When the rapid "logical" searches as described above fail, thorough systematic methods will have to be used. These saturation methods involve a search of *all* of the terrain in a given area. Thoroughness is the key here, and this means checking every possible place for any form of clue. Objects such as trees, hollow logs, boulders, caves, scrub, thick undergrowth, and buildings will be checked over, under, beside, inside and behind. Clues which may be of extreme importance include candy wrappers, cigarette butts, bits of clothing caught on branches, footprints, notes, signs of recent campfire or bedding down, etc. Any such clue should be reported, located on a map, labeled and evaluated before disturbing. Saturation searches *should* find all such items within the search area, but in fact, can never be sure of achieving 100 percent coverage. Team leaders should make an estimate of the effectiveness of the search based on terrain, time of day, capability and alertness of the searchers, weather, and so forth. If a job was poorly done or not completed, this must be reported honestly to the search leaders so that the area may be searched again if deemed appropriate. Areas may have to be rechecked again anyway because a victim could be moving.

Saturation searching is slow and tedious. A good rule for rugged terrain is that it takes one man-hour to search an acre or 640 man-hours (say, 80 man-days) to search one square mile (250 man-hours or 30 man-days per square km) of heavily timbered or rugged terrain, with thorough coverage. This figure is based on a speed of 1 mph (1.6 km/hr) fifty percent of the time, and 16 ft (5 m) spacing between searchers. For easy open terrain and not very thorough searching, the speed of coverage may go up by as much as a factor of fifty.

Line Search. The usual method of saturation searching an area is known as a "line search," so named because the searchers simply form a line, individuals being close enough together that they can see and search all of the ground between themselves and their neighbors in the line. The line is then swept through the search area. To start the search, the team leader will place people in the line at appropriate intervals, and they will remain in position until given the command by the team leader "Move the line." At this time the line begins to move forward at a very slow walking pace. Even though the line normally moves perpendicular to its length, individual searchers may walk in a zig-zag path to examine thoroughly all the ground. Every searcher should turn around and look back frequently since a victim or clue may be behind a large tree, boulder, or other terrain feature.

If a searcher finds something important, he will call out "Stop the line." Any team member may stop the line, but only the team leader has the authority to start the movement. If any command cannot be heard throughout the line, the command is relayed along the line from individual to individual. The team leader may call "Are you ready on the left?" The response is "We are ready on the left." The simpler query

"Ready on the left?" should not be relayed towards the left because the questioning intonation may be dropped before the left end of the line responds. Then someone in the middle of the line is liable to start the message back to the leader "Ready on the left" as a statement, and the team leader would then start the line moving before it is really ready.

The team leader will have indicated "Guide right" or "Guide left." Guide right means that the person at the right end of the line is controlling the direction of motion and speed of the line. Each person in the line is then responsible for keeping his distance essentially constant from the person on his right. As the nature of the terrain changes, the spacing between the searchers may change, but always "Guiding right."

The search area is best defined by obvious terrain features such as a road, fence, stream bed or ridge. It is much more effective in mountain search to use such topographic features than to search by grid lines, but in gentle terrain, the area may be defined by a starting point and a compass direction, for example. Thus, the defined areas may be irregularly shaped rather than neat rectangles, and the guiding end of the line may not move in a straight path.

If "Guiding right" and if the right end has to swing towards the left, the right end will have to move quite rapidly forwards, and in fact, the left end may remain stopped for a while as the right end moves. Similarly if the line swings to the right, the left end may have to move with the guiding right end stopped. Gross changes in direction are best accomplished by stopping the line and regrouping.

It is desirable, but not essential, that the line be kept straight. It is *mandatory* that the line be unbroken. If the line is accidentally broken, it should be stopped immediately. The team leader may then have members "count down" to determine the location of the break. If guiding right, the break is the fault of the person at the right end of the left hand segment of the line, since this searcher failed to maintain his proper distance from the man on his right. Each searcher should try to stay on a straight line between the man on his right and on his left. If he gets ahead of either, he must slow down or stop until they catch up. If a man is slowed by a patch of especially difficult terrain, he should stop the line rather than try to catch up after it has moved on. Sometimes in dense timber it is difficult to be sure that the line is indeed straight. The team leader may stop the line as it moves into a clearing or opening such as a road or power line cut to check and correct its progress. A line is very likely to change directions or break when it crosses a ridge on a diagonal. Individuals should be careful to hold their course, perhaps noting the direction of the sun, moon, or prominent landmark, and the team leader must check the direction of travel carefully.

Very long lines (half mile or a km or more) can be run but are unwieldy. Messages relayed in such long lines are very likely to become distorted by the well-known "gossip effect" and are best transmitted by radio. These long lines are very difficult to manage unless several competent assistant leaders are in the line with radios.

Flagging. An important part of search is the knowledge of what land has and has not been searched. On an extensive line search with no obvious natural boundaries for each end of the line to follow, the path of the line will be marked by the end searchers using some type of flagging such as brightly colored surveyor's tape tied to tree branches or placed in some prominent location as often as is needed to make the boundary of the search area very obvious from either direction. An alternate technique is to run a string along the entire area boundary. In this way, a second team could cover precisely the adjacent territory, and the ground covered is well defined. The various teams will use different colored tape to identify who has been where, since it is easy for anyone to become disoriented in say, very dense timber.

For good visibility, the flagging should have a long tail, 1 ft (30 cm) or more. For ease of removal later, the flagging should be tied, preferably on dead twigs, with a slip knot rather than an overhand. If one team is running the line back and forth, the flagging at the end of each sweep should be placed double or triple indicating the end of that sweep, and all of the flagging should be removed from the interior boundaries as the team sweeps along a boundary previously searched to the other side. The tape is most easily removed by the same man who placed it. If a second team searches an area adjacent to an area previously flagged by a first team, the new team can either add its color or remove the first team's flagging from the common boundary.

The end men tying the flagging will be too busy to do much searching. Also, the team leader is likely to be occupied full time keeping track of the line direction and location on the map, radio traffic and general line control. He may be at the guiding end of the line, or he may take a position (perhaps roving) in the middle of the line to maintain better observation and control of the line, especially in the case of a team of inexperienced searchers.

Frequently the line search will not be intended to cover every bit of the ground but will be run in what may be termed a "loose line" in order to gain speed. Here a combination of line and scratch techniques are used. The individual searchers generally hold the line formation but will rapidly search only the most likely locations in their swath.

Such a line may search as much as 50 acres per man-hour (that is, only 5 man-hours per square km), but with very low probability of finding small clues.

Tracking Methods. Dogs can be very useful in searching for a missing person. A dog may be able to follow an actual track left by the person, or it might attempt to make a "find" by air scenting, as described in Ch. 16.

If a victim left footprints in soft snow, he may be tracked with some reliability even if long series of the tracks have been subsequently filled in by fresh or blown dry snow. Slight depressions of the filled-in tracks are best seen by looking along the surface of the snow, searcher's eyes as close to the snow level as possible, wearing amber or Polaroid lenses for emphasis of variation in surface conditions. Such depressions are easily followed at night by holding a flashlight close to the ground. The depressions are seen as shadows.

Tracks fully filled in can be analyzed in detail. The technique, simple but tedious, is to carefully dig out the track. A lightweight aluminum shovel works well and is easily carried on winter searches. The snow which fills in the track will be relatively soft in consistency, and the precise shape of the track can be determined. Footprints more than ankle deep will leave a very obvious toe hole, indicating the direction of travel. These are easily distinguished from animal tracks. Furthermore, by carefully digging away snow around the print and then using a soft brush to dust out the snow on the print itself, details such as the actual sole pattern may be exposed in cold weather. On the other hand, today's woods are likely to be full of other people's footprints, especially after a few days of searching. Also, complainants' descriptions of shoe sizes and sole patterns are notoriously unreliable. Thus, a clear print may not turn out to be a good clue.

SEARCH STRATEGY

Information Gathering. A typical organized search would start by locating the vehicle driven by the missing person or determining the starting point, destination, objective, or last seen point; otherwise, the possible area to be covered would be much too vast to begin a ground search. It may be feasible to spot a vehicle in remote territory by air.

A thorough questioning of the complainant and other witnesses privately one at a time is of prime importance. Information to be gleaned over a period of hours or more includes conversations which the witnesses held with the missing person concerning routes, possible alternate plans, state of mind, etc. Of course, a physical description of the lost party would be obtained, with information about equipment carried, experience, knowledge of the particular area and the area in general, physical condition of the victim at the time, special medical problems, habits, etc. It is important that the complainant and witnesses remain available for questioning by the mission leader throughout the search, not only to clear up questions concerning possible clues which are found, but also so that the witnesses can provide later-recalled information. Often a friend of the victim can or will tell information unknown or withheld by a relative.

A novice search leader is likely to find useful a questionnaire covering the points mentioned in this chapter and more. The prospective interviewer is well advised to make up his own questionnaire, ahead of time.

Initial Searching. Depending on the circumstances, the initial searching would be by a survey method, scratch teams or small scale saturation search plus a careful and continuous check of probable exits back to civilization. If a route is known, any search strategy will have scratch teams check out the route and alternate routes which could have been forced upon the missing party by weather, injury, darkness, lack of navigational ability, etc. A small saturation search in the immediate area of the last seen point or several scratch teams sent out in logical directions from this point might be appropriate.

Urgency. A decision must be made concerning the urgency of the search. If it is a group rather than a single person overdue, urgency is usually greatly reduced. Various factors to be considered include length of time overdue, weather, difficulty of the terrain, time of day, age and health of the missing person, experience, reliability, past history of such incidents, equipment carried, and so forth.

There is always the fear that an overdue individual is injured, and hence the situation is urgent. This compares to the simply late or lost person, which is not an urgent situation unless there are additional circumstances such as bad weather, medical problems, or the person is either quite young or quite old. A search strategy would be to quickly check out areas of high danger where the victim might have become injured, and not finding him, consider the situation less urgent in the absence of other circumstances.

Night Searches. A person often is reported missing at night. Because night searching is generally rather unreliable or inefficient, a search would be started immediately only if the situation is deemed urgent. One significant exception to the inefficiency of the night searching is the case of a fire or other pyrotechnics which might be lit by the victim. A survey search method has a high probability of finding a fire at night.

Search Perimeter. A reasonable perimeter to the search area should be determined. Such perimeter might include streams, major trails, road, etc., and this perimeter would be searched more or less continuously in the expectation that the missing party would find his way to this border which would then be followed back to civilization. However, the experienced search strategist will not rule out the possibility of the missing party's crossing an obvious boundary. Such is often the case with children, that is, crossing an "uncrossable" stream or a sizable road. In fact, a search team specifically out looking for an easy way across the "uncrossable" stream is often successful.

The distance travelled by a victim can easily be a matter of miles (kilometers) in a relatively short time. If there are no topographic features defining reasonable perimeters, the probable search area should be set large enough. However, the time required to do a thorough search can be staggering. For example, suppose a victim were within a 4 mile (say 6 km) radius, that is, inside an area of about 50 square miles (120 square km). The time for a thorough saturation search of such area is about 32,000 man-hours or 4,000 man-days.

If a victim is thought to be at some distance from the nearest roadhead, circumstances may make it appropriate to move some rescue gear such as a spare litter to a location nearer the prime search area, providing quicker availability of this equipment at the scene when the victim is found.

Search Routes and Areas. Decisions as to priorities of areas to be searched are based on a little reasoning and a lot of intuition. Normally, a missing person would be expected to travel downhill and downstream, but there are many cases where the lost person has gone uphill, especially to gain what might appear to be a vantage point or up what looks from the bottom like a short steep section. Descents are seldom down the steepest path when alternate gentler routes exist. Small children often go uphill, sometimes rapidly and for several miles. Anyone suffering from shock, fear, or hypothermia may wander aimlessly or not move at all.

Scratch search methods may be the only practical way to cover large areas because of manpower limitations. Repeated scratch searches through only the more probable areas may make sense, especially if the victim is thought to be moving, or during the winter if bad weather is impending.

If a search team finds promising tracks, it would, of course, attempt to follow them, calling upon tracking specialists if necessary. When the tracks can no longer be followed, a thorough line search would then be run in rectangles of increasing size about the last seen tracks attempting to pick up the tracks again.

An exceptionally difficult search situation arises when the lost person is senile or becomes mentally affected by being lost, panics, and then hides from the searchers. While not a common occurrence, this does actually happen and will require considerable cleverness on the part of the strategist and alertness of the searchers.

In-Town Search. The importance of checking and rechecking alternate possible destinations for a missing party should not be forgotten in any search strategy. A note should be left at the victim's ultimate destination (car and home). There may have been a change of plans by the missing person unknown to the complainant, the car may not have started, or the too-common case of a boondoggle, arising from a disappearance because of a domestic quarrel or family friction (which will not be discussed or volunteered freely by the relatives in an interview) or deliberate disappearance for another reason (shackup, etc.). Careful detective work pays off in such circumstances. It is most difficult for searchers when the relatives of the victim lie rather than expose intimate family matters. Questioning a friend rather than a relative may prove fruitful. A well-planned search strategy will take these possibilities into account and will also be able to cope with vague clues and red herrings such as unconfirmed sightings of the victim in far away places.

Personnel Assignments. The initial search assignments should be made up in advance of the arrival of the first ground troops if possible; otherwise, these searchers will be standing around recognizing that they are wasting time. Throughout the search, the strategy should always be planned several hours in advance, allowing time to obtain additional resources, etc., yet ready to follow up immediately on new clues. Contingency plans should be ready in case of foul weather or the like. Flexibility is needed to give assignments to well-meaning but relatively unskilled or incompetent volunteers, for such tasks as searching again an easy or nonhazardous area already searched with insufficient thoroughness or into which the victim may have subsequently moved. Individuals sent into the field should be in good physical condition and possess some general knowledge of the outdoors and some common sense; otherwise, they may be a negative asset to the operation as a whole. Volunteers with four-wheel drive vehicles and CB radios must be assigned tasks appropriate to their capabilities, such as transport of foot teams to or from their search areas, regular road patrols, and checking of unoccupied buildings accessible by road.

Extended Searches. When a search is unsuccessful after several days, the question of terminating the search arises. The search leaders will have to cope with rumors of a boondoggle or fatality. In either case searchers will lose enthusiasm and morale, and then efficiency will drop to very low levels. The boondoggle problem should already have been handled by careful detective work, with questions not only to family but also to friends. Times of survival have been known to be amazingly long, as witness ten days for a child dressed in shorts and shirt and out in occasionally subfreezing weather.

After days of searching, it is appropriate to rethink the entire search strategy. Distances travelled by even an injured victim in several days could be large. Areas once searched should be searched again. A person not equipped with adequate warm clothing will change his normal habits of being awake during the day and asleep at night to the opposite, taking advantage of daylight warmth for sleeping, and travelling at night to keep warm.

Calling off a search is always a difficult decision. This is usually done only after a joint discussion by the various leaders and officials involved.

SEARCH ORGANIZATION

A large search operation involving many different organizations including volunteers, police at local and state levels, military, forest service, etc., must necessarily be highly structured in order to have anything but chaos. Jurisdiction varies with the location and is occasionally complex because the search may spread into several normally separate jurisdictional areas such as two counties, a National Forest or Park, etc. We assume that the overall search leadership is established in one person, the Mission Coordinator, who may work closely with one or two assistants. He will set up a field headquarters into which will come only the leaders of the various organizations involved. Communications will be established to each of the units in the field by radio and to the outside world via telephone, amateur radio, press releases, and so forth. Coordination of the ground teams will be done in the headquarters, and accurate and thorough records *must* be made from the very beginning of the operation. A chronological log will be kept, listing clues and which team searched where, when, and how thoroughly, along with a map recording the searched areas. Requests for outside resources (food, transportation, special equipment, dogs, weather reports, etc.) will be made by the Mission Coordinator or his staff through the appropriate agencies.

No Mission Coordinator can adequately perform his job from the field with the possible exception of an early overview of the terrain. He will be occupied full time assimilating clues, coordinating and evaluating the numerous organizations wishing to be helpful and in working out search strategy. He may give a briefing directly to ground troops or just to the team leaders, but debriefing will be held only with the team leaders for efficiency. A highly significant aspect of coordinating a search is maintaining high morale among the volunteers; good food and comfortable shelter is important.

Further discussion of the overall organization of a large search operation is too lengthy for inclusion in this book.

INDIVIDUAL AND TEAM CONDUCT

The "Do's" of Search. Keep alert. Use your eyes, sometimes your nose, and always your head. Look behind you (this is very important). Make lots of noise and also some silence in which to listen for the victim. This is a particularly good technique at night when the victim is thought to be simply lost and uninjured or at least conscious. Call out the name of the lost person. You should have learned the name and description of the missing person including type and color of clothing, prior to leaving base camp, even though this information should not be trusted fully. Be properly clothed and equipped. When talking to another searcher at night, be careful not to shine your headlamp into his dark adapted eyes. On a line search learn the names of the searchers to each side and don't change your outer layer of clothing without their noticing. Bright colored, high visibility clothing is always appropriate in the mountains and is particularly important in line searches.

Searchers should always use common sense, checking the obvious. This means for example, looking in buildings which would make good shelter, inquiring of hikers encountered along the way, or even checking with anyone seen walking along a road near the search area, since such a person may be the missing one.

The safety of the searchers is more important than the search itself. If the individuals or teams are put in danger because of lack of personal skills for the terrain at hand or due to objective hazards or weather, that part of the search must be at least temporarily abandoned.

It is very important for individual searchers to maintain a proper attitude towards the search. Line searching is hard work, rather boring and tedious, and usually does not turn up anything. If an individual cannot discipline himself to be an effective searcher in spite of bad weather, fatigue, and discouragement, he should sign out of the search and not discourage those who can.

When in the base camp area, individuals should stay out of the mission headquarters. Loose talk about the mission must be avoided in base camp, since a casual remark may be overheard by the press or may be the origin of a distracting rumor.

Only unit leaders or the mission coordinator may give information to the press. The best response to a question about the mission from any stranger is "I don't know. Ask the leader over there." Complaints about the conduct of the mission should be made in private to the team leader, or saved for the critique meeting.

Team Responsibilities. A team leader should always brief his team as to their assignment. If this is a line search, he should give a very short summary of the techniques and terminology to be used. The time spent on such a lecture will be saved many times over in avoiding confusion later.

A map and compass should be taken along and used carefully by the team leader or other designated person so that the terrain covered and the locations of any clues found can be accurately reported to the mission leader. An altimeter is frequently of value. The assigned area should be completely covered and any deviations reported to the mission leader.

If a possible crime situation is encountered, the absolute minimum number of personnel should approach the scene, and the entire area secured until arrival of authorities. All evidence must be left in place and marked by flagging. The only reason for moving anything is to assist an injured victim. Likewise in the case of a fatality, the area should be secured (see Ch. 21).

Care must be used in the choice of words spoken over the radio, because press and relatives may be listening to every word, and prearranged code words may be required. All messages should sound routine.

CHAPTER 14

SIGHTING AND OBSERVATION TECHNIQUES

Some techniques used by effective lookouts or observers will be discussed. There is first a paragraph on eye physiology, presented as a basis for understanding the observation procedures; this section may be skipped by the reader interested only in applying scanning techniques. The second section is on general scanning and eye fatigue problems. Some special consideration of observation from aircraft will be given next leaving the larger problem of effective use of aircraft in search to the next chapter. A discussion of night vision will be given. Finally, there is a brief description of some characteristics and uses of binoculars.

BASIC EYE PHYSIOLOGY

The eye contains two types of sensors or receptors: rods and cones. The cones function in brightly illuminated surroundings and perceive color and much detail. Under such conditions the pupils are constricted, and visual acuity is optimum. The rods, on the other hand, are far more sensitive than the cones and give rise to twilight and night vision with the pupils wide open, but the rods do not distinguish colors or see fine details. Both rods and cones respond to a range of colors, but the rods are very insensitive to red light. (The rods respond to various colors but give a sensation only of black, gray or white.) The rods and cones are distributed nonuniformly across the retina, with only cones at the center (the fovea), while in the periphery, the rods dominate. Thus the best visual acuity in good illumination is obtained for that part of the image focused on the fovea, and the eye is most sensitive in conditions of weak illumination to images focused off center, that is on the periphery of the retina. Further implications of this will be discussed below.

GENERAL TECHNIQUES

A scanning routine should be used for best efficiency in searching large areas as from an airplane, above timberline or across a valley. For example, the eyes should move, then pause for about a half a second, and move about 3° etc., keeping up a regular pattern most appropriate for the circumstances. The routine is somewhat similar to proofreading, scanning say left to right, top to bottom. The eye should not move much at a time, to have every portion of the scanned terrain come at some time to the center of the retina where visual acuity is best (assuming daylight hours).

Avoidance of eye fatigue is quite important. Under ideal conditions an observer in an airplane can maintain good efficiency for perhaps two hours, with poor flight conditions reducing this time. Motivation is also very important for visual searching, particularly after fatigue begins to set in. Eye fatigue occurs early when binoculars or a spotting scope is used.

Mountain searching may involve scanning snow fields with little contrast or detail, or in partial whiteout. Under these conditions, the observer's eyes have a natural tendency to focus short of the surface being scanned after a time. To avoid this form of eye fatigue the observer may focus occasionally on some well-defined object. Amber lenses help emphasize the shadows.

OBSERVATION FROM AIRCRAFT

When searching is to be performed from aircraft, the rescuer/observer should be sure that the windows are clean prior to takeoff, and he should sit for a good forward view and next to a side window, which might be opened for better visibility.

There are some significant limitations to searching from aircraft. Those dealing with the operation of the aircraft itself such as speed, maneuverability, weather, etc., will not be discussed here. If the object sought is small, such as a person, this object must contrast with the surroundings to be spotted. A moving object is relatively easy to spot, but mountain rescuers are likely to be seeking something stationary. It is nearly impossible to spot small objects on the ground in a sunlit forest because the treetops are brightly lit, reflecting much light, while the relatively dark ground cannot be scanned. This effect is similar to attempting to see the road while driving a car at night in fog or with a dirty windshield in the presence of oncoming car lights.

NIGHT VISION

Dark Adaptation and More Eye Physiology. We recall from preceding paragraphs that the eye sensors, cones and rods, differ in function. Cones provide high visual acuity but are not very sensitive. The highly sensitive rods are very much desensitized by exposure to bright light (by bleaching of a substance in the rods known as "visual purple" or "rhodopsin"), and a period of time is required for the rods to regain their inherent sensitivity when the exposure to bright light ends. This is the well-known phenomenon of "dark adaptation," which occurs in two steps. The first stage takes place in the first five minutes of darkness and is due primarily to the cones. The second step, taking about twenty minutes, is the debleaching of the rods giving rise to the very high ultimate sensitivity of the eye. The inverse of dark adaptation is "light adaptation," which is the desensitization process (in part bleaching of the visual purple), which occurs much more quickly than dark adaptation, within a few minutes.

There are procedures influencing dark adaptation that are of importance to night observers. The most effective way to dark adapt is obviously to avoid light. Sunglasses should be worn during the day, otherwise the eyes may be strained, and night vision will be poor. When it is important to maintain eyes dark adapted and yet light is needed, a red filter can be used on the light, because the rods remain sensitive in moderate intensity red light. (Recall that the rods are not sensitive to red light.) It is for this reason that red room lights or red cockpit lights in aircraft may be used to see and yet have the eyes dark adapted.

Anoxia (lack of oxygen) reduces the sensitivity of the eyes for night vision. This is of interest to mountain rescuers simply because of the lack of air at high elevations, but little can be done about it. The effect is very noticeable at 15,000 feet (6 km). It has been shown that hyperventilation somewhat compensates for the lack of oxygen, but this is not a recommended technique. The phenomenon of tunnel vision, occurring at high elevation, is an extreme case, where the rods, present in large number around the periphery of the retina, are almost completely desensitized due to the lack of oxygen. A minor amount of this tunnel effect, poor peripheral vision, can be noticed by mountaineers at high elevation, in having to look at their feet more often while walking along a trail.

Night Observation Procedures. Keeping in mind the above paragraphs, we now discuss techniques for night observation. First, unless special care is taken, such as wearing red goggles or being in red light, 15 to 30 minutes will be required for the eyes to fully dark adapt. In trail walking, flashlights should not be used unless absolutely necessary, and then only briefly. One flashlight may be sufficient for several people, thus there is the side benefit of saving batteries. Also, the dimmest bulb available gives adequate light for almost any situation and is better for quick readaptation. If red lenses are used on flashlights when light must be used, night vision will not be lost. Nearby team members should be warned before a flashlight is turned on, or even when a cigarette is lit, so that others can close their eyes. Users of flashlights, especially headlamps, should be careful never to shine their lights in anyone's eyes.

It should be kept in mind that at night colors do not show up; for example, red turns to black. Also, details cannot be seen, thus observers should look for shapes, shadows, contrast and movement. Since the fovea is very insensitive at night, all looking should be towards a side. Once an object is seen, it should not be looked at steadily, but the eyes should be kept in motion to keep the rods that are actually detecting the image at their peak of sensitivity. The tendency to stare directly at a sighted object must be overcome since the sensitivity of the fovea is poor.

These effects can be demonstrated easily in a dark room using a watch with a luminous dial. If the observer dark adapts his eyes and then looks sideways at the dial, he will see it easily, but if he stares directly at it, it will seem to disappear.

In general, the chance of visually finding anything on a night search is small, with two exceptions: first, if the victim uses pyrotechnics, fires, lights, etc., in which case the chances of spotting him are excellent, and second, if a tight line search is made. A line search through even open woods may be ineffective if the trees have light-colored bark such as birch or aspen. Since the tree trunks reflect much light, it is difficult to see far—this again is like trying to see through fog while driving at night, the fog reflecting much light. A searcher may see more by turning off his light and taking advantage of his neighbors' lights or the moon.

Eye fatigue is as important at night as during the day. Every few minutes the observer should close his eyes for a few seconds to allow them to rest. This is particularly important for searchers who have been up all day and are tired at night.

BINOCULARS

Binoculars can be very useful in scanning. The wider their field of view, the more effective they are likely to be. Binoculars chosen for mountain search use in the field should be of high quality for many reasons. One of these is that they will be given very rough treatment, and misaligned binoculars cause rapid eye fatigue. General optical quality, including good resolution, will help ward off early eye fatigue. Binoculars with individually focused eyepieces, usually made for marine use, are sealed better against dust and water than are most center focus types (there are exceptions), but are less convenient to focus.

Lightweight binoculars and those with power no greater than about 7 or 8 are easiest to hold and thus can be used for longer times without fatigue. The binoculars should be steadied as much as possible by supporting the arms firmly. This can be done, for example, by sitting on the ground with the arms against the knees, or, if standing, by holding the arms tightly against the chest or by using a natural support such as a tree. Simply steadying the binoculars by placing the thumbs on the cheekbones is nearly as effective; this is a particularly useful trick for observers wearing eyeglasses when the binoculars cannot be steadied against the eyebrows. To avoid early eye fatigue, binoculars should not be used steadily aboard aircraft because of vibration and motion; they are useless aboard helicopters.

A high powered spotting scope is sometimes of great use, but should be supported very securely, and an observer should stare through one for a limited time, say less than an hour.

Binoculars may be used to great advantage at night. One measure of the effectiveness for night use is the "exit pupil," which is the diameter of the bundle of light rays exiting towards the eye from the eyepiece of the binoculars. This number is simply found by dividing the objective lens diameter by the power, e.g., for 7X35, 35/7 or 5 mm exit pupil, and for 7X50, about 7 mm. Since the pupil of the eye is about 7 mm diameter when fully dilated, the eye is not being fully used if the exit pupil of the binoculars is less than 7 mm. Thus 7X50 binoculars are a good choice for night use. Note that for daytime use a small exit pupil is satisfactory since the eye pupil will be only about 2 mm in diameter; however, the large exit pupil is advantageous because of the ease of centering the eye behind the eyepiece. Note also that the larger the objective diameter, the more light is gathered. Another measure of night usefulness is the "twilight factor" which is the square root of the product of the objective diameter and power. Thus the effective binocular brightness at night depends on both the exit pupil and power, and also on the overall optical quality of design and manufacture.

In use at night, the binoculars should be held aimed straight forward, and the eyes turned off center, to avoid using the insensitive center of the retina. This technique requires practice, but is quite effective.

CHAPTER 15

AIRCRAFT IN SEARCH AND RESCUE

Aircraft are often useful in mountain search and rescue operations. Fixed wing planes are usually most effective for rapid search of large areas for prominent objects such as downed aircraft, brightly colored tents above timberline or for ground-to-air signals in any open terrain. Helicopters also may be used for such searching and are frequently employed in attempting to spot a small object such as a person in a forested area, but such searching is seldom successful and is always quite expensive. Often helicopters, and occasionally fixed wing aircraft, will be able to move personnel or equipment to the scene of a mountain rescue, by landing or airdrop. Messages may be dropped or called out over airborne loudhailer equipment. The most common use of helicopters in mountain rescue is for evacuation of the injured; such evacuations will be discussed in a later chapter.

LIMITATIONS AND CAPABILITIES

Aircraft may be very useful in mountain search, but ground rescuers, particularly the leaders, should be aware of various limitations and should not expect or request pilots to fly under some conditions of altitude, weather, and terrain. All aircraft are limited in their working altitude (service ceiling) and may not be able to maintain a reasonable margin of safety flying in high mountains. This limitation is particularly pertinent to the light planes which are most useful in mountain search due to their slow speed and maneuverability. Visibility is essential for mountain flying even for aircraft with instrument flight capability. Turbulence may be a serious problem to a pilot, and mornings are usually the best time for flights because there is less of the turbulence associated with afternoon heating by the sun. Cumulus clouds indicate turbulence and strong updrafts and downdrafts. Also, there are often downdrafts over the middle of a valley, and such currents may be quite dangerous at high elevations because of reduced engine power. Upcurrents often exist over ridges. Terrain features are obviously of concern to the pilot. A fixed wing airplane should not be flown low in a blind canyon leaving no "out," and a pilot will usually fly near one side of a valley to allow U turns to be made easily if necessary. Power lines and aerial tramway cables are very hazardous because they are not readily seen, and pilots appreciate a warning of their presence.

If at all possible the observer aboard the aircraft should be an experienced mountain rescuer, familiar with communications to ground personnel, the nature of mountain search, and probable locations of mountaineering accidents. The search for downed aircraft is usually best left to Civil Air Patrol personnel, trained in appropriate techniques.

There are severe limitations to the use of fixed wing aircraft in mountain landings and takeoffs because of the obvious need for a runway. Skilled pilots with suitably equipped aircraft may land on river gravel bars, lakes, frozen lakes, or snow fields as terrain permits. All personnel flown into the mountains must be prepared to hike out since flying conditions can quickly deteriorate. In fact a light aircraft may be able to safely land at high elevation but not take off with a heavy load aboard.

Light fixed wing aircraft may be specially modified to fly at low speeds with good maneuverability. With such an aircraft, searching and airdrops may be most effective. Any cargo to be airdropped, either with or without parachute, must be very securely packed for shock resistance and marked with long brightly colored streamers for ease in recovery by ground personnel.

Contrary to popular belief, helicopters do not normally land on a dime but require or desire a sizable landing zone, particularly at high elevation. The various limitations and uses of helicopters are discussed more fully in another chapter.

GROUND-TO-AIR COMMUNICATIONS

Radio. Ideally, ground teams will have direct radio communications with aircraft involved in a rescue. Since aircraft and ground rescuers normally use different radio frequencies, it will be necessary for one or the other to use "foreign" equipment. The easiest (but not the best) solution is usually for the aircraft to carry a portable radio from the ground unit; however, this is not the ideal solution for several reasons. First if there is no passenger on board, the pilot will have to operate unfamiliar equipment while flying and will not be able to pay full attention to the radio. Even if there is someone on board to operate the radio, communications will not be good due to noise which affects both transmission and reception. Some of these problems can be overcome by using a headphone and lip microphone in place of the normal speaker and mike. The best complete alternative system is for the ground unit to have aircraft radios adapted to mobile use.

Visual and Audible Signalling. Visual signals will be needed occasionally to supplement radio communications. The standard ground to air symbols and aircraft responses are given in Chapter 11. Air to ground messages may be transmitted by airborne loudhailer equipment. Such spoken messages may be very helpful to a victim in a search operation or to ground search teams for added instructions in the absence of radio. The ground-to-air response may be made with the standard visual signals. A written message may be dropped from the aircraft by placing the message in a small can to which are attached some long colorful streamers (surveyor's flagging) to aid recovery. Another technique is to secure the message inside the tube in a roll of toilet paper which is unrolled when thrown from the aircraft. If the message is not recovered, the toilet paper soon dissolves and does not clutter up the landscape.

AIRCRAFT AVAILABILITY

There are various sources of aircraft for search and rescue. The Civil Air Patrol is usually willing and able to assist with fixed wing ships, and their pilots are trained in search and rescue techniques. The military, various governmental agencies including the Forest Service and state and local agencies, public utilities, and radio stations may have suitable aircraft and pilots available at no charge.

DOWNED AIRCRAFT BEACONS

The Emergency Locator Transmitter (ELT, also known as the DART for Downed Aircraft Rescue Transmitter) will soon be in widespread use on aircraft due to Federal legislation requiring such devices. The ELT, set off by sufficient g-loadings as encountered by a crashing aircraft, should greatly aid in locating downed aircraft in the mountains by appropriate use of receiving or Direction Finding (DF) equipment on the emergency channels 121.5 Mc. (civilian) or 243.0 Mc.

(military). If visibility is good, search aircraft should be able to spot the downed plane quickly. In bad weather or at night it is presently unknown how accurately search operations can pinpoint the ELT in the mountains. It is known that the technique of observing the ELT signal strength when flying a grid pattern is not accurate, uncertainty being as much as 10 mi (16 km) thus possibly locating the downed plane in the wrong mountain valley. Ultimately, DF-equipped search aircraft may be able to locate the ELT with sufficient accuracy that ground personnel could be immediately dispatched to the scene even though no visual sighting was made. On the other hand, from experience gained thus far it now seems appropriate for mountain rescue units to have portable DF equipment (backpackable or mobile) too, in order to better locate the accident scene.

CHAPTER 16

DOGS IN MOUNTAIN SEARCH

A dog trained to use his nose for searching has two distinct capabilities. One of these, referred to as "tracking," means, simply, the ability to follow a ground scent, which is the specific path followed by a person. The other capability is called "search" or "air scenting." Most successes at present come from using the dog in its ability to air-scent rather than track.

Search operations can be categorized from the point of view of the dog handler: 1) The lost person is thought to have entered, for example, a forest area but has left no clues as to exactly where he might have entered. A dog looking for a track would most likely be unsuccessful. A search dog might well be able to indicate the proper direction in which to search. Dogs would be used in a preliminary rapid search, seeking the direct air scent from the victim. 2) The lost person is in a limited area but has been in that area for one to three days or more. A dog used for his tracking ability would most likely find many tracks but would have little chance of success in locating the last track made by the victim. A search dog could well locate the victim by air scenting for him. 3) The lost person is known to have taken a certain route but, because of hazardous conditions along that route or the distance from the start of the route to the place where the victim is thought to be, the search is begun from another direction. A search dog would be used to air scent the victim. 4) The lost person is known to have taken a definite course in his departure from a certain area, but so many persons helping in the search have crossed and recrossed the track that a tracking dog would have no opportunity to pick it out. The search dog, using his ability to detect the air scent from the victim, would be of great assistance.

This last situation brings up an essential point. In the past it was felt, were tracking dogs used, no other search teams could enter the area because it would be "fouled" by conflicting scents. This is not the case with the search dog. Using a search dog does not require that an area be kept uncontaminated. In fact, because of the necessity to begin immediate action in searching for a lost person, any search should not be held up waiting for the dogs to arrive and begin working. A search dog is trained to discriminate scent and should not be adversely affected by other persons in the area. Given scent articles (the lost person's socks, gloves, night clothes or even a scent from his automobile seat) the search dog will know exactly what scent he is seeking.

Advantages and Limitations of Dog Teams. Naturalists have recognized that there are days on which, for some unknown reasons, scenting conditions are very poor. It is also known that wind can adversely affect the dogs or, on the other hand, can be of tremendous assistance. There are limitations depending on atmospheric conditions and terrain as to the distance a scent can travel. It is expecting the impossible to plunk a dog team down a mile or two from the victim and expect them "to find." As is the case with an expert line search team, if the dogs are not positioned in the right area, they will not find the victim. Dogs can, however, easily and quickly determine that it is the "wrong" area, except for the case of bodies. Some dogs respond to the scent of live victims only, others will find a person dead or alive. A dog cannot climb rock and will have extreme difficulty in plowing his way through deep soft snow, though it should be mentioned that dogs have been successfully used on snow fields and in searching crevasses by being belayed on ropes. A dog cannot be worked six to eight hours without sufficient rest periods. Both human and canine noses suffer from nose fatigue, which is a desensitizing of the olfactory sensors allowing people to work in glue factories or fertilizer plants without suffering daily from the stench.

Equally important as understanding the limitations of dogs is realizing their advantages, some of which can never be found in a human search team. Of prime importance is the speed and saving of manpower, especially in situations that provide the greatest difficulty for line searchers. These would be areas of large boulders, heavy pine, thick scrub, areas where a human team must spend much time in thorough exploration of every nook and cranny. These same conditions are easy for a dog. Dogs are also invaluable in cases where the victim is running and hiding from his searchers. This type of situation presents itself in the mountains under all too common psychological circumstances even in the complete absence of crime. In many practice situations of this type, victims have been unable to evade the dogs. Dogs can be used to assist in determining the area where the prime search force should be concentrated. A dog handler knows immediately if his dog has located the proper scent or if there is nothing in the area. Dogs can be used to check out an area and pretty well assure the searchers that the victim is not there, thereby giving the operations leader the chance to concentrate his efforts in more likely spots. Dogs can be used to relieve many teams of unnecessary drudgery and can be valuable in saving time.

Search Operations with Dog Teams. Although a dog team can work independent of other agencies, some assistance to the team can be extremely helpful: First, could an adequate description of the situation, weather and terrain be given to the dog team leader? Many of these factors, unimportant to the line search team, are of extreme importance when using dogs. For example, dogs do best when the ground is moist, with a breeze blowing, on a cool day. They do poorest on a very hot day, dry and calm, or in heavy rain. Some cannot make much headway in snow, and short-haired dogs cannot be used in very cold weather. They should be kept off steep and loose scree since they tend to start rocks rolling. The dog team leader should know the terrain features and weather conditions, including wind direction, before the search begins, so that he can decide how the dogs should be used to best advantage.

Second, assistance can come if the base operations leader has decided ahead of time how he would like to use the dogs. Would he like them to completely search an area (even if it shows negative signs from the first) or would he like the dogs to perform a superficial search, abandoning unlikely areas in the hope of better prospects? Would he like them to keep in constant radio contact, even if nothing has turned up, or would he prefer radio silence unless a positive sign has been found? Does he have any designated areas that he feels are important for the dogs to check?

Third, and this is possible only when there is the manpower and willingness, are there people available to accompany the team? A dog handler may easily miss landmarks necessary to locate his position on a map. Because the handler must watch the dog, noting carefully all signs that indicate either a positive or a negative reaction, locating himself on a map may be difficult. Is there a radio man available to accompany the team? It would be unfortunate to have the team make their "find" with no means of communicating the information to base camp. If it is a dangerous area, can someone accompany the dog team for protection?

Fourth, are there scent articles (clothing from the lost person) available for the team's use, or can they be obtained? Most dog team handlers have plastic bags in which to carry these scent articles and insist that the articles not be handled by other searchers but picked up with tongs or a stick and dropped in the dog team's bags.

Fifth, if there are a few miles between the area in which the dog team's cars must be parked and the search area, can jeep or other transportation be provided to take the dogs closer to the search area? Dogs will work better when fresh, and a four or five mile hike to the beginning of the search area will lessen the dog's efficiency. Furthermore, the dogs will experience nose fatigue and need a rest every now and then.

This chapter is adapted from a paper by Mrs. Helen F. Phillips, a member of the Colorado Canine Search Group, Denver, Colorado.

CHAPTER 17

SNOWMOBILES

Snowmobiles can be a great aid to winter mountain rescue, but their successful use is not easy. Much depends on the operator: his skill in handling the machine, his detailed knowledge of the terrain and of mountaineering and mountain rescue operations. The particular machine is less important than the operator, but the vehicle chosen should be suitable for the terrain and special tasks at hand. Snowmobiles in rescue can be a large liability unless properly used, and this use requires considerable knowledge and skill. The paragraphs below will describe some vehicle types, special equipment, major uses, advantages and limitations of snowmobiles in rescue, and some operational techniques.

Throughout the chapter, the term "snowmobile" refers to the nonenclosed machines which make contact with the snow by a moving rubber track usually driven by a two-cycle engine and steered by a ski system.

The large enclosed over-snow machines are usually available only near their home base since over-the-road trailers are usually not available for them. While much less maneuverable than the snowmobiles, these vehicles will carry perhaps ten persons with equipment at up to 20 mph (32km/h) on suitable terrain. Sometimes utility companies, the Forest Service, the Soil Conservation Service, and operators of mountaintop radio equipment will have vehicles with trailers which could be useful in rescue, but these machines will not be discussed further in this chapter.

Machine Types and Capabilities. There are three types of snowmobiles which are of interest in rescue. First is the big (500 lb, 220 kg) machine with double track and reverse gear, and excellent capability on deep powder. The packed track width is about 30 inches (.75 m). Next is the medium weight (300-450 lbs, 140-200 kg) high power vehicle with a single wide (18-20 in., 45-50 cm) track. The surface pressure is high, thus it is best for pulling sleds in rather open terrain which is not too steep and without deep powder. Third is the small light-weight (240 lbs, 110 kg) machine excellent for quick reconnaissance by one man in difficult terrain including deep powder and high angle hillsides. Only this last machine can be easily unstuck by a single person.

Any machine used in rescue should be highly reliable, with modern tread design, adequate disc brakes, and a good clutch. Much of the reliability depends on the operator, not only in routine maintenance but also in spare parts carried and in actual techniques of operation, for example, in deicing the track to prevent drive belt burnout.

Some snowmobiles have enough power to operate at speeds in excess of 60 mph (100 km/h). These are of little value in rescue. More important is a low gear ratio and heavy duty clutch for pulling loads and ascending steep hills. Gas mileage varies from 10 mpg (4 km/l) for the large machines to 25 mpg (10 km/l) for small ones, depending on use. A good operator should be able to run for six to eight hours with the gas normally carried.

Equipment for Rescue Operations. To give the most satisfactory service in the conditions encountered in mountain rescue, the standard snowmobiles should be modified slightly. Special attention should be given to the engine air intake to assure engine breathing capability under the worst condition, dense blowing snow. Lubrication must be adequate for the coldest weather encountered. In search and rescue, auxiliary lighting may be very useful, and a special generator could be installed, particularly on the bigger machines where some additional weight is not very important. Modifications to the seats may be appropriate, to allow storage of necessary rescue gear or an extra passenger. Finally the over-snow machine should be towed by a four-wheel drive vehicle on a trailer with the same track as the towing vehicle, to make easier driving to the base of rescue operations which may be on an unplowed road.

Quite important in rescue work is the use of a sled. The ideal sled is not available commercially, but we describe here some important characteristics of a rescue sled. It should be readily handled by either machine or man (the latter will be needed occasionally) and hence should be light (perhaps 30 lbs, 14 kg) but must be very durable. The Austrian akja or snow boat does not approach being rugged enough. The sled should be towed with a drawbar, not with rope because of lack of control, and the drawbar should have three degrees of freedom, allowing up-down, sideways, and rotational movement. A sled on skis will track much better than a smooth bottomed one, and for the smoothest ride on rough terrain, a four-ski (two front, two rear with independent mounting) system will be used to prevent slapping. The sled should be designed to handle cargo, securely hold a litter, or transport rescue personnel.

If a sled is unavailable, a snow boat towed by rope could be used to pull equipment along a fairly level trail, preferably slightly uphill. For control, a person on skis should hold a tail rope to the sled to prevent it from sideslipping downhill or running into the rear of the snowmobile. This will require a strong and knowledgeable skier, perhaps using downhill skis for snowplow control.

Uses and Limitations in Rescue. As stated earlier, successful use of the snowmobile depends largely on the operator. Here we assume that the operator is skilled, and we discuss some general uses and limitations. There are three main uses in rescue. First, fast reconnaissance and search might be done by one man with a small machine. More details will be given below. Second, a trail can be packed so that personnel on foot can follow easily. Third, equipment or personnel can be hauled. Trail packing can be very helpful if done carefully, since personnel on snowshoes or skis have a much easier time moving along a packed trail than through deep powder. However, the initial trail must be put in along a good route. The snowmobile may be used for moving heavy rescue equipment, thereby conserving energy of the foot troops (but individuals should not allow their personal packs to leave their persons, particularly in winter), or for giving rides either on the snowmobile or on a sled.

Of course, the terrain, choice of machine, and the skill of the operator in handling the snowmobile all provide limitations on use. Another obvious limitation is the snow cover and condition of the snow itself. Fresh deep powder may be a problem, depending on the machine, and wet, fresh snow is always difficult due to clogging of the tracks.

Skijoring. A snowmobile can be used to tow three or four skiers, but the skiers must be quite strong and skilled. The speed limitation is with the skiers who may tire quickly. Speeds up to 15 mph (24 km/h) may be achieved under good conditions. The tow rope used should be long enough that the skiers can be about 10-15 ft (3-5 m) apart. Two tow ropes are useful. There are several means by which the skier can grip the rope. One way is to simply tie a loop about 1 foot (.3 m) long with a Figure-of-Eight knot; this loop is held with one hand, the poles held with the other (the poles are not used). Another method is to tie a longer loop (about 6 ft, 2 m) and pass the doubled loop 180° behind the buttocks with the skier *not* standing in the loop. In this way the skier can lean against the pull, and he will not be caught in the rope should he fall. Perhaps the best method is to wrap the rope in a half hitch around the ski poles near the handles and to hold the poles together between arm and side, leaning against the baskets. This technique is less tiring than holding the rope, and the hands may be wiggled to prevent frostbite. If the going is somewhat difficult, as through woods, where falls may occur, the rope should be gripped directly without knots. With any method, the skier must never be tied to the rope, because of the danger of being dragged in a fall.

There must be considerable cooperation between the skiers and the vehicle operator. The speed should be maintained as uniformly as possible, and any changes made slowly. Turns should be gentle. If a sharp turn is necessary, the vehicle slows, and the skiers walk around the turn. In starting motion, the vehicle gathers speed gradually, and the skiers start moving under their own power and slowly put tension on the rope to avoid being jerked. On downhill runs, when the skiers tend to move faster than the snowmobile, they can either snowplow, move into unpacked snow out of the tracks of the vehicle, or let go of the rope entirely and ski down the slope.

The Operator. The operator of an over-snow machine in rescue must know the capabilities and limitations of his machine. He should have his equipment maintained and ready for use at any time. He should also have an intimate knowledge of the terrain so that he can choose the most suitable vehicle for the purpose at hand, and do the best job of route finding in packing a trail. He should have the judgment and good sense to know when and where *not* to use the snowmobile. The operator will need several years of extensive experience in techniques of operation, including unsticking, sidehilling, sled pulling, and in-field servicing. The emphasis must be on a variety of experience, since many years of running on packed roads is of little value.

Not only should the operator know his machine, but also he should be a strong mountaineer with experience in various aspects of mountaineeering: snowshoeing or skiing since he may have a machine failure, avalanche hazards (important), first aid since he may be the first to an accident scene, and mountain search and rescue techniques. A man who knows only snowmobile operation may prove to be a major liability in a search and rescue operation.

The experienced operator will be aware of the need for very warm clothing. Frostbite of the face is a serious problem, since the chill temperature on a moving machine may be very low indeed (see Chapter 1). The knees need special protection because the operator is likely to be kneeling for extended periods. His boots must be extremely warm for protection during times of relative inactivity, and also usable on skis or snowshoes which may be needed in event of machine failure or rescue away from the vehicle.

Operational Techniques. Efficient use of a snowmobile will depend on the operator's knowing the terrain and conditions very well. Operators likely to be involved in search or rescue in a given area might find it valuable to make a snowmobile terrain application map of the area showing in detail the likely snow conditions, routes and which types of machines are and are not capable of going where. Such a map requires considerable effort to make but would contain information highly valuable in a search and rescue mission. An operator would then really know the best route locations for packing trails and reconnaissance, and would be able to accurately inform the mission leader the extent of the snowmobile assistance likely or if the machine would be a liability under existing circumstances.

On occasion, difficult terrain will be encountered. It is up to the operator to decide whether to fight to get through or not. For example, if there is a high angle or sidehill barrier beyond which the machine could be used both extensively and effectively, it might be worthwhile to set up snow anchors for a hauling system or pendulum to get the machine past the barrier. In the case of bad snow conditions, it will be kept in mind by experienced operators that not only do snowshoers make good progress in a track packed by a snowmobile, but also snowshoers can pack a route through bad snow for the machine.

The operator on a reconnaissance should do a careful job of search, but this is difficult because operating the machine may require full attention of the operator. A search for a missing person or for snowshoe tracks may be useless unless the operator is completely at home on his vehicle and in the mountains. Since the machine is noisy, it does attract attention, but shouts of a person in distress will not be heard unless the operator stops, not idles, the engine perhaps every 500 feet (150 m).

The use of sleds is important. Much equipment may be towed, saving foot troops a great deal of work. In loading a sled, heavy items should be placed at the bottom so that the sled is not top-heavy, and slightly towards the rear so that the sled rides well over the snow. Gear such as shovels which may be needed enroute would be placed on top. The entire load must be lashed in very securely. Because of limitations on vehicle brakes, a machine towing a heavy load may be driven over a lengthy zig-zag path rather than down a steep hill. If a victim is in a litter which is towed on a sled, he must be protected not only from wind, but also from flying snow, and he should be given as smooth a ride as possible, relying on operator skill.

General Comments. There are areas in which motorized vehicles are not permitted, such as Wilderness Areas or off the roads in National Parks. Rules may be lifted for search and rescue operations, upon request to the area authority.

Even though the snowmobiles may be found very useful in search and rescue, they should not be counted on too heavily in any mission because of the possibility of their bogging or breaking down. Anytime a machine used for convenient transport of foot troops stops because of difficulties, the rescuers should immediately start moving on foot, not waiting on the undependable machinery. Likewise, foot troops should be hiking rather than waiting around at base camp for a ride. If the snowmobiles are being used in performing a search, backup plans using personnel on foot should always be made.

CHAPTER 18

AVALANCHE CONDITIONS AND RESCUE

The danger of avalanche should never be underestimated since even a small sluff can bury a man. Mountain rescue teams are not likely to be standing by close enough to an avalanche scene to be called in for initial probing or search as might occur near a ski area, but members should be acquainted with the techniques because a team may be in avalanche danger and directly involved (as has happened). When a rescue situation arises in an area of high avalanche danger, thought should be given to the possibility of jeopardizing the rescuers for the possibility of saving one person. Before describing techniques of avalanche rescue, we will briefly describe some elementary snow physics and conditions of terrain and weather that are likely to lead to avalanche.

The subject of avalanche rescue is a part of the more general problem of mountain rescue, but is highly specialized and is the subject of many papers and books. The survey given below will introduce the reader to the references given at the end of the chapter.

SNOW PHYSICS

Snow comes in various forms, even though the English language has only the one word, *snow*. Snow flakes, needles, and pellets (*graupel*) are common. Falling snow is very different in a structural sense from settled snow. Freshly fallen dry snow is very porous, but the snow consolidates and the pores shrink as the snow ages. When snow is compacted and solid enough that it will no longer pass air, it is called ice. Even though the temperature of the snow may always be well below the melting point, 0°C, it still goes through major metamorphism. The initial settling usually takes a few days when the temperature of the snow is well below freezing, and transformation continues to take place for years after this, assuming that the snow does not melt, as above snow line or on a permanent snow field or glacier. The density of new snow is typically 0.1 g/cc, that is, ten percent of the density of water, and rises to about 0.5 g/cc after a winter of settling. As snow becomes more compacted, it may be called *firn*, which eventually becomes the harder glacier ice.

This metamorphism at temperatures below the melting point may be due to simple pressure, as supplied by the weight of snow on snow, or may occur from wind. As snow crystals are pushed together, they tend to bond to one another, forming structurally strong snow. If the snow is wind driven, it is called *wind slab*.

In the case of dry snow, a type of low temperature metamorphism, known to metallurgists as *sintering*, applies. This is a process during which the molecules move slowly, perhaps by actual diffusion of solid through solid, or by sublimation, that is, by vaporization from the solid without melting, from the warmer regions of the snow (usually found near the ground at elevations below snow line) and then are redeposited at colder layers (nearer the surface). When the snow is transported from a lower layer and redeposited nearer the surface, the lower layer becomes less dense and weaker and is known as *depth hoar*. The redeposited crystals near the surface are *hoar crystals*.

The above discussion assumed that the snow was dry, that is, that its temperature was always below freezing, so that no liquid water could be present. However, spring snow is wet, that is, the snow is mixed with water, and its temperature must be at 0°C throughout. With the snow at constant temperature, the sintering mechanism, which depends on temperature differences, does not apply. Wet snow undergoes transformation by melting and solidifying or by water percolating through the snow.

The processes described above may make the snow either weaker or stronger. When the snow is made denser, by sintering, pressure, or melting and solidifying, it is made stronger. The snow particles become interlocked with one another, bonding firmly. Snow flakes in the form of six-pointed stars tend to interlock much more firmly than snow pellets or needles. On the other hand the presence of depth hoar indicates very weak snow, and water in the snow may mean that the snow or ice crystals are well lubricated and can slide on each other.

AVALANCHE DANGER

Avalanches are frequently classified into two categories: loose snow, and slab. Loose snow is weak snow, such as freshly fallen snow that has not had time to consolidate and strengthen or be consolidated by wind, or snow that is wet and well lubricated with the snow crystals not stuck firmly together. Slab is strong snow, well consolidated or firmly set up by the wind as it falls. We will see below the conditions for serious danger from each of these types.

Terrain. When snow is deposited on a slope, in addition to the transformational forces described above, there is also the tendency for gravity to cause the snow to flow as a viscous fluid downhill. If falling snow tends to stick to its base as it falls, gravity applies strong forces which may cause the snow to slide. If the slope is rather gentle, less than about 25°, then there is usually not much danger of the snow sliding. Also, if the slope is steep enough, steeper than say 60°, then the snow sluffs off as it falls and does not accumulate. It is the intermediate range, 25° to 60°, that causes the most avalanche danger. Avalanches are just rare, not impossible, on the gentler or steeper slopes.

The nature of the ground cover is certainly important in holding the snow. Rocks, underbrush, or trees form good natural anchors, while smooth and grassy slopes make fine slide paths. If old snow completely covers the natural anchors, then avalanche danger depends on the nature of the bonding of the fresh snow to the underlying layers. If the base layers are very loose, new layers cannot be strongly held in place, and the danger of either loose snow or slab avalanche is high. Also, if the base surface has a hard icy crust, new snow does not tend to bond well at all. The bonding is particularly weak if water percolates down through the new snow to this crust because the water will lubricate the crust surface. If depth hoar has formed just above this crust, thereby weakening the snow, the bonding is very weak.

The slope profile and aspect are also significant. Since snow is quite weak in tension, it is most likely to break or fracture on convex slopes. North-facing slopes are the most dangerous in midwinter, because the surface temperature of the snow is coldest, and conditions are most conducive to the formation of depth hoar. South-facing slopes are dangerous in the spring, when the sun melts the snow, making it wet and thus perhaps so well lubricated that it can slide readily on the suncrusts previously formed.

Weather. The weather over a period of many weeks is important in determining the nature of the base and the formation of dangerous depth hoar. If cold temperatures prevail, snow is slow to settle, and the temperature at the surface is likely to be much below that at underlying layers, thus depth hoar is most readily formed. Warm weather means more rapid settling.

Weather conditions during a storm are also important. Snow accumulating at more than about 0.5-1 inch per hour (2 cm/hour) does not have time to settle much as it falls, and avalanche danger is high. The type of snow is significant, with flakes being able to bond better and quicker than needles or pellets. A rising temperature during the snowfall is bad since the first snow to fall is likely to be very loose, forming a weak underlying layer for the succeeding snow.

Wind is critical in avalanche danger. The formation of dangerous wind slabs is obvious. These are extremely dangerous because of the unannounced and catastrophic way in which an entire mountainside of wind slab may suddenly slide. The danger is highest on a leeward slope because there the snow accumulates to greatest depth. On the windward side snow cover tends to be rather slight and thus less dangerous. Cornices, formed on ridge tops at the leeward side, may break off and set loose an avalanche or turn into one themselves.

The overall avalanche danger at any one time is a complex interplay between the details of the terrain and the weather, not only recently but also throughout the entire season's conditions.

A person in avalanche country usually does not have any way to know the detailed nature of the snow that has fallen during the season, but there are some clear signals of avalanche danger. Hollow sounding snow indicates a weak base and great danger. Any cracks which form while a person is standing on the snow also indicate that the snow is stressed in a way that could easily avalanche. A ski pole or ice ax inserted into the snow may indicate weak layers underneath.

Route Selection. If it is necessary for a team to be in potential avalanche danger, some safety procedures should be followed. The obvious slide paths should be avoided as much as possible. These are the steep gullies and open hillsides, and bare paths down a fall line in timber. The bottom of a V valley is the runout path for a slide from either side. The top windward side of a ridge is safe, but the leeward side may be corniced and thus dangerous. A party climbing or descending an avalanche slab should go straight up or down rather than zig-zag, because the zig-zags tend to cut the snow loose and set the slab sliding.

When necessary to cross an avalanche path, only one person should move at a time, and be watched, or belayed if less than a rope length across, by the others on safe ground. Everyone should be wearing avalanche cord (50-100 ft or 15-30 m of lightweight red nylon cord) tied to the waist and strung out behind. The cord tends to be carried to the surface in a slide and is readily found by the observers. Caution should be taken as each party member moves since slopes sometimes slide as the fourth or fifth person crosses. Safety straps and wrist loops on skis and poles or ice axes should be removed, pack waist bands undone, and clothing should be secured—parkas zipped up, mittens worn, etc. In a loose snow or powder avalanche, snow tends to get packed in every possible place including inside clothing and in the lungs.

In the event that one member of a party is caught by an avalanche, he should yell, attempt to discard the equipment and swim, keeping his head up, staying on top of the slide. If buried he should try to get his hands in front of his face and make an air space as the slide comes to a stop. He should make one violent effort to get free at this moment but then be as calm as possible, to conserve precious air around his face. Members of the party not caught should watch the victim, carefully noting the Last Seen Point and probable descent route from there.

AVALANCHE RESCUE TECHNIQUES

Speed. Speed is *important.* In an avalanche, particularly in wet snow and slab, when the snow stops sliding, it sets like concrete almost instantly. A victim will suffocate in a few minutes, hence it is critical that the victim clear a space around his face for breathing. Even if the snow is loose, sooner or later an ice mask will form around the breathing space at the face, and suffocation will take place. As a general rule, the chances of survival are good (50 percent) if rescue takes less than an hour, but poor (less than 20 percent) if the victim is buried for more than two hours.

Hasty Search. Other members of the party not buried should note carefully and mark the Last Seen Point. The victim is surely not above this point and is likely to be down the fall line from there. These survivors should immediately make a hasty search for clues along the fall line in the avalanche debris, marking the clues found. The survivors should move in a diagonal line rather than being abreast of each other, with those behind looking into the footsteps of searchers in front and each searcher looking back; this is a streamlined version of what was called the "scuff line." The hasty search should be extra thorough at trees, small rock outcroppings, bends in the fall line, etc. A person is likely to be caught in snow eddies at such places. If any of the victim's gear such as an ice ax, ski pole or clothing stopped on the surface, the victim is likely to be found just uphill from the gear, since surface snow slides faster than snow deeper down towards the ground.

If hasty searching finds nothing, a decision will have to be made to send for help immediately or to search for awhile with the party at hand. Assistance should be sought immediately if rescuers can return within about an hour. The party members going for help should clearly mark the route for the return of the rescuers. Those remaining will start probing in the most likely places as described above. A probe may be improvised from a tree branch, ski pole with the basket removed or reversed without the wrist loop, a ski, willow wands, or ice ax. Any resistance to probing should be checked by digging with a shovel, ski tail, cookpot, etc.

Probe Lines. If the above procedures fail, then a systematic probe line will be run by the rescuers who come equipped with probe poles (often just a 10 ft or 3 m length of standard 1/2 inch steel electrical conduit), shovels, marking tape, lanterns, etc. If there is any danger at all of further avalanche, a lookout will be posted to give warning, and all rescuers should wear avalanche cord and have an escape route in mind. The probers stand in a straight line, elbow to elbow with hands on hips, facing uphill in a straight line, starting at the bottom of the avalanche on the fall line below the Last Seen Point. On command from the probe team leader, who does no probing himself, each prober inserts his probe between his feet. On command the probers move forward 2 ft (.6 m) and probe again. The probers always remain in a straight line. To assist the leader in keeping the line straight, a guide cord can be tied between the outermost probes. Following this procedure, the entire slope is rapidly probed in rectangles approximately 2 by 2.5 ft (.6 by .8 m). As the probing goes on, the leader looks along the tops of the probes to see if all probes go equally deep into the snow. If a probe meets resistance with gentle probing, the prober leaves the probe in place and is handed another by a member of the shovel crew which follows the probe line. The shovel crew digs around the probe left by the prober while the probe line moves on without delay. If the snow debris is fairly soft, the shovel crew, when not digging, should zig-zag behind the probe line looking for clues in the footprints of the probers. The probed areas should be clearly marked with surveyor's tape or equivalent. The result of one study (Ref. 2) indicates that the above probe pattern will result in a 76 percent chance of finding the victim on a given pass. If the victim is not found during the first pass, the entire area is probed repeatedly until success is achieved or hope of finding the victim alive is abandoned.

Hope for life may be given up in perhaps three hours, the time depending on the snow and other conditions. Then the rescue leader will change the probing pattern from the rapid *coarse* probing described above to the slower and more tedious *fine* probing. In this pattern, the probers again stand shoulder to shoulder, on about 2.5 ft (.75 m) centers, with their feet about 10 inches (25 cm) from the neighbors on either side. On command each prober inserts his probe in front of his left foot, then between the feet, and finally in front of the right foot. The probe line then moves ahead one ft (30 cm) on command. In this way the slope is probed completely in 10 by 12 inch (25 by 30 cm) rectangles until the victim is found.

Careful studies indicate that a victim is more likely to be found alive by repeated rapid coarse probings than by the much slower fine probe line, even though the fine probe is almost sure to find the victim on its first pass.

Other Considerations. Typically a victim will be found in a prone position within 2 ft (.6 m) of the surface. His head should be dug out first, and first aid administered as needed.

A highly successful technique of avalanche search is the use of specially trained dogs, if an area is fortunate enough to have such dogs available. Even an untrained dog may be useful if it has a good nose. The dog may be able to sniff out a victim very quickly if the snow is not too dense and if the victim is not too deeply buried. Experience in Europe has proven the technique.

Many more details of avalanche conditions and rescue are given in the references cited below.

REFERENCES

1. U.S.D.A. Handbook 194, "Snow Avalanches."
2. U.S.D.A. Snow Safety Guide No. 1, "Modern Avalanche Rescue."
3. *Manual of Ski Mountaineering*, D. Brower.
4. *Mountaineering: The Freedom of the Hills*, ed. H. Manning.
5. *The ABC's of Avalanche Safety*, E. LaChapelle, Highlander Publishing Co., Denver, Colorado (1961).
6. *The Avalanche Enigma*, Colin Fraser, Rand McNally, New York (1966).

CHAPTER 19

ASCENDING FIXED LINES

Frequently in mountain rescue it is necessary for personnel to climb terrain, with or without loads, sufficiently difficult or exposed that a rope should be used. Two general techniques will be described: 1) use of a fixed line primarily for safety, and 2) ascent using the fixed rope for aid. We assume that the rope has been placed by an advance party. In both techniques the climber is attached to the fixed line with a sling that has been tied on the line with a knot that will slide easily when the sling is slack and will hold tight when the sling is pulled. For convenience, mechanical devices may be used in place of the knot. Test strengths of the knots and devices are given in an appendix.

It is an interesting observation that if a fixed line is available for a short moderate pitch (say 10-20 ft or 3-6 m), the line will be used by the most experienced people, ignored by others. Also, on descents of such a pitch, the experienced climber will use a "Hasty" or "Hotseat" rappel, whereas the novice may use the much more time-consuming brake bar rappel.

KNOTS AND ASCENDING DEVICES

Knots. The most common knot used for the purpose described here is the prusik, tied from a rope sling loop as shown in Fig. 19-1. Another knot recently developed is the Penberthy, shown in Fig. 19-2. The prusik is usually more convenient to use since it may be tied with any sling loop normally carried by the climber, whereas the Penberthy requires an untied length which the climber may not otherwise have. The rope for either knot may be kernmantel (perlon) or laid (Goldline or Columbian) construction. A web sling does not work nearly so well for this purpose. Manila slings are easier to use than nylon because they stretch less when loaded and thus bind less when released. However, they are not recommended in rescue work because they are much weaker than nylon and could be used accidentally when the strength of nylon is needed. Each knot must be tied carefully and cinched down tightly to the main rope to hold when the sling is pulled. The knots may be moved by pushing from the end. In principle the knots move easily when the sling is slack, but in practice they tend to jam due to stretch when loaded. The prusik is most easily loosened by unwrapping slightly at point *M* in Fig. 19-1. Neither knot holds well on an icy rope, and both are particularly hard to move when the rope is wet. Both may be used nicely as ratchets, as discussed in the chapter on hauling systems.

The Bachmann (carabiner) knot shown in Fig. 19-3 is more convenient to use than those knots above because it is easier to slide. It nicely holds body weight on Goldline, but tests of maximum load holding ability have shown considerable variation, from body weight when the sling shown in the figure is flat webbing, to 2700 lbs (1200 kg) with perlon sling.

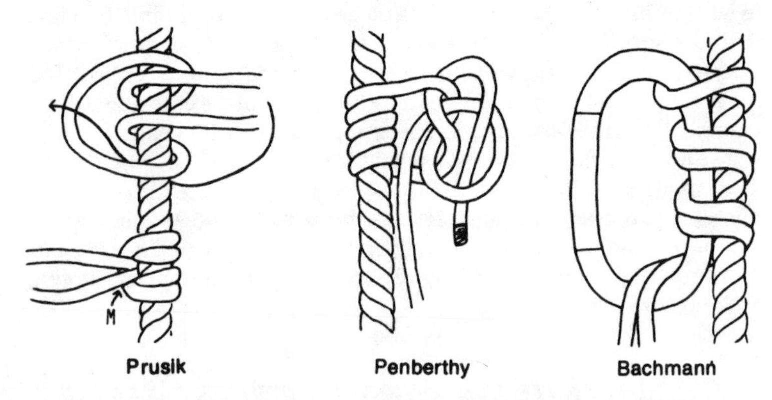

Fig. 19-1. The two-wrap prusik knot. Released by unwrapping at *M.* **Fig. 19-2.** The Penberthy knot. Tied with a straight length of sling rope. **Fig. 19-3.** The Bachmann knot. Holding ability depends strongly on the ropes used.

Mechanical Ascending Devices. *Hieblers* (T.M.) These hold by placing an S bend in the rope, as shown in Fig. 19-4, when the sling is pulled. Inexpensive, they do hold on an icy rope (a significant feature), but they are relatively inefficient to use in climbing a fixed line because of a loss of about 3 in. (8 cm) each move, due to the rope straightening when slacked and then bending when loaded. Hieblers are easily attached to the line, and sometimes too easily removed; they have been known to come off the line accidentally when traversing on a taut line.

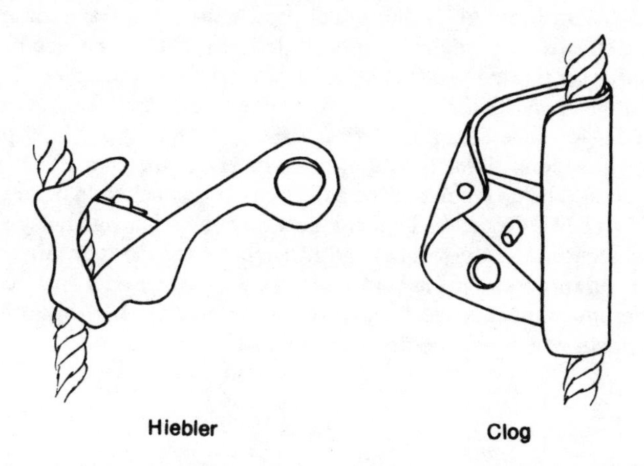

Fig. 19-4. The Salewa Hiebler ascender. **Fig. 19-5.** The Clog ascender.

Clogs (T.M.) These must have the carabiner removed from the hole shown in Fig. 19-5 to be placed on or removed from the line. This is a safety virtue but is a practical defect in actual use. Because the author has known Clogs to have slipped due to a jaw jamming open against the side wall, they are not recommended for any use whatsoever.

Jumars (T.M.) Shown in Fig. 19-6, they grip by squeezing the rope with a toothed jaw or cam. This rocker should be replaced when worn. They are efficient, easy to use and versatile, but have been known to come off during a traverse of a taut rope and do not hold well on an icy rope. They may hold on iced up lines if used like a Hiebler by clipping into the top eye rather than onto the bottom of the device. Their major drawback is expense, and they are not strong enough for use in high loading situations.

Since Jumars are quite popular, we give here further discussion of their possible drawbacks when loaded at the top and on traverses. When the Jumar is used by clipping a carabiner to the top eye, it is possible that the carabiner can pass down over the Jumar frame and actually open the jaw, thereby preventing the jaw from gripping the rope. A short sling of webbing or rope hitched to the top eye in place of the carabiner will prevent this. When a Jumar is used traversing on a taut (not slack) rope, that is when the Jumar is pulled at an angle to a taut rope instead of parallel to it, the rope may actually tend to slightly open the jaw and prevent the teeth from gripping. Attachment to the top of the Jumar seems to overcome this problem, as does clipping a carabiner at the bottom of the Jumar around the main rope holding the Jumar nearly parallel to the rope. There are also reports that a Jumar has come off a diagonal rope (*American Alpine Journal* Vol. 14 No. 1, p. 62, 1964), but that this was due to the safety catch not being in place ("Summit," Oct. 1968 p. 32 and Apr. 1969 p. 26). Under these conditions, the Jumar can be easily torqued off the rope. There should be no trouble if the safety catch is checked to be in place.

Gibbs (T.M.) Fig. 19-7. This is a new device which has not yet had the chance to stand the test of time and experience in mountain rescue use. Initial impressions are that it is strong, secure, and safe when put together, but that it is overly complicated to apply to the rope and has small parts which will be damaged or lost.

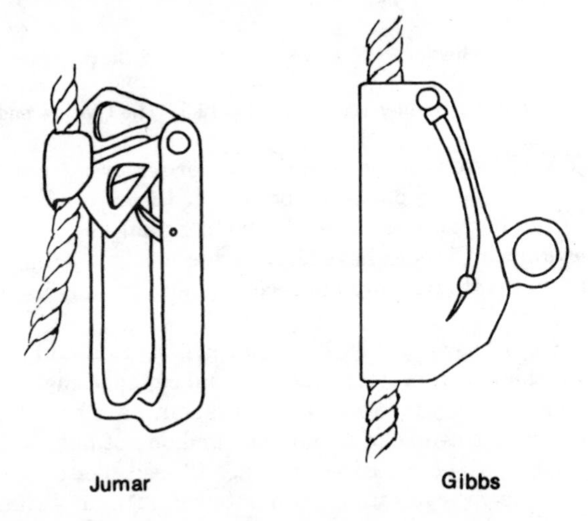

Fig. 19-6. The Jumar ascender. **Fig. 19-7.** The Gibbs ascender.

ASCENDING A FIXED SAFETY LINE

We assume here that the climbing is easy using only rock handholds (fourth or easy fifth class), thus the rope is for safety only. The climber wears an independent waist loop onto which is clipped a sling going to the ascending device or knot. We will assume in this section that a prusik knot is used, but the principles apply for any knot or device. We give a special discussion in the use of Jumars later.

The sling used to tie the prusik and clip to the climber is about an arm's length (2 ft or .6 m) long, and the climber keeps the knot ahead of himself as much as is possible and convenient, remembering that if he gets above the knot, he cannot pull it up the rope using only the sling. Normally he will not take the time to cinch the knot down snug at each move, and there is the possibility that the knot could slip should the climber fall. Thus, the bottom end of the rope (if not at the ground) should be tied to an anchor point or tied with a large and bulky knot. This will prevent the climber from falling off the end of the rope. Anchoring the end of the rope makes moving the knot easier when ascending the first few feet (meters) of the rope, since the knot may be pulled up with one hand and the other hand need not hold the rope down. Higher up the weight of the rope is sufficient.

If the climbing is very easy, several climbers may use the same fixed line simultaneously. But all should be aware that if one climber falls or grabs the rope for a handhold, the stretch in the rope may be sufficient to pull climbers above off of their stances. If the going is more difficult, so that the climbers are very likely to want to use the rope occasionally for a handhold, only one climber at a time should be on the rope between anchor points.

When the ascent is longer than one rope length, either two ropes will be tied together, or, better because of rope stretch, a second anchor should be installed, with each rope tied separately. In either case, the climber will need to move his safety off one rope onto another. If the ropes are anchored to a common point, the ascending knot will need to be untied and retied. When it is felt necessary to maintain the safety on the rope at all times, the climber should carry a second sling with which he clips himself into the anchor while he transfers the prusik past the anchor, or alternatively, he can use the second sling to tie on the prusik above the anchor, and then remove the lower knot.

If the climbing is relatively difficult so that only one climber is on the rope at a time, additional anchors along the rope may be used so that climbers may move up closer together. A Figure Eight or Butterfly knot clipped to a piton will work satisfactorily. Too many anchored points will not be of value, however, because of the time required to move the safety knot past each anchor point.

A Jumar may be used in place of the prusik knot and is much superior because it slides upwards much easier, does not loosen on the fixed line as does a prusik, and is much faster to put on and remove from the line. Since the Jumar does slide very easily, it may be used in a manner eliminating the need for handling it, except at knots or anchor points. The technique is to simply attach the top of the Jumar directly to the climber's waist loop. The Jumar then slides upwards with the climber, but note the warning above about clipping a carabiner to the top of a Jumar.

ASCENDING A FIXED AID LINE

We now assume that the climber is ascending a nearly vertical wall using only the rope and not the rock for holds. We also assume that he is using a pair of Jumars, but the techniques apply equally well to knots or other ascending devices.

Ascents While Not Wearing a Pack. The technique described here and shown in Fig. 19-8 amounts to little more than climbing a ladder. A sling from one Jumar goes to one foot. A small adjustable loop can be snugged down onto the foot to hold the sling on the boot. Another sling goes from the other Jumar to the other foot. Finally, a safety sling goes from the upper Jumar to the climber's waist loop or chest loop. If knots rather than Jumars are used, this safety sling may be attached either to the main rope or to the upper sling with a prusik. The first of these choices requires moving three knots along the main rope. The safety sling is necessary to take the climber's weight in case he becomes too tired to hold himself vertically. The length of the slings are chosen unequal, the one from the upper Jumar reaching down to about the knees when the Jumar is at an arm's reach up, the other one about 2 ft (.6 m) shorter. The result is that the steps taken by each foot are about the same height. The climber keeps his weight on his feet, his body vertical. If he leans back, his arms will take some weight and will rapidly become tired. The arms will become tired much more quickly if holding weight when bent at the elbow than when extended straight. This method requires considerable arm strength when used to negotiate overhangs.

Ascents While Packing a Load. The technique above is not suitable for use when wearing a pack because the pack tends to pull the body backwards, and the arms will have to hold the trunk towards the vertical and thus become tired rapidly. The technique described here provides less climbing speed than the one above, but is much less tiring to use when wearing a pack, and is highly recommended. The sling from the lower Jumar goes to the foot of the strongest leg and another short (2 ft, .6 m) sling from the climber's comfortable seat sling goes to the upper Jumar, as shown in Fig. 19-9. For best efficiency, the length of the upper sling is chosen such that the attached Jumar is conveniently at the upper extent of the climber's reach with his weight supported by the Jumar. The lower sling is adjusted for a convenient step up onto that sling when the lower Jumar is moved to the upper one.

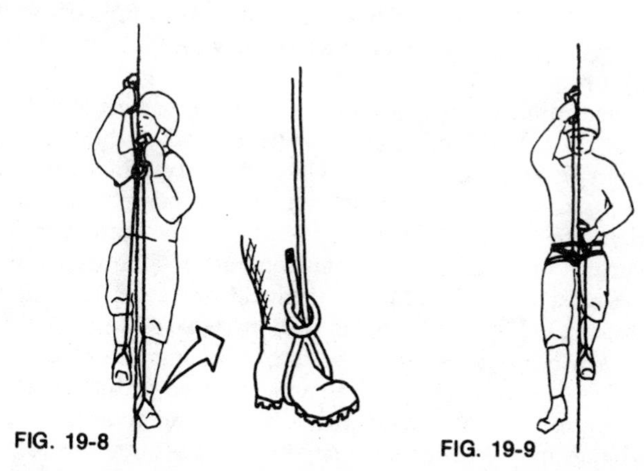

Fig. 19-8. Showing the two-foot (with chest sling) method of ascending a fixed line. **Fig. 19-9.** Showing the one-foot and seat (with chest sling) method of ascending a fixed line.

The procedure is simple. The climber is seated with his weight supported by the upper Jumar. This is the resting position. He raises the lower Jumar to the upper one. He then stands up on this lower sling and simultaneously slides up the first (upper) Jumar as far as possible. As he does this, he may wish to use his other hand for balance on the rope, since the lower Jumar is too low on the rope for use in balance. Just as the climber stands vertically and the upper sling is raised taut, he can sit easily in the resting position and bring up the other Jumar. In this way his arms do not have to hold his body vertical continually.

General Comments. Of the two methods described, the first (two foot) is faster but should always be used with a chest sling safety, and the second (foot and seat) is less tiring on the arms and thus is suitable for ascending with loads. The techniques may be combined for the best features of each with a little extra complication. The simplest modification is to use basically the first method with an extra sling from the upper Jumar to the seat sling of the climber, thereby providing a resting capability when needed. Somewhat more complex is the use of a belay seat from the upper Jumar as a safety sling around the back and under the armpits, and this seat may be used as a comfortable resting seat when desired.

No matter what system is used, for best safety the two Jumars should be tied together by some means, either directly with slings or with a safety sling from the lower Jumar to the climber's seat sling. In this way failure of the upper ascender will not leave the climber hanging upside-down from a foot.

If several climbers are to ascend the line, it is sometimes convenient to anchor the bottom end of the rope firmly just as the first man gets his weight fully on the rope and has thus stretched the rope; the climber may ascend several feet (meters) of rope without leaving the ground due to stretch. Anchoring the rope at the bottom makes pulling up prusik knots an easy one-hand operation. Also, climbers following the first will not have to "climb the stretch." On the other hand, if the rope is held away from the wall anywhere in its length where it would touch if not tied at the bottom, climbing this section is made more difficult. It is much easier to ascend a line with the feet against the wall than to climb a rope which is taut and slanting.

Overhangs may be difficult to negotiate if the climber's feet cannot touch the rock. Jumars may be passed by the lip of the overhang by jerking out and simultaneously sliding up, or by removing the upper Jumar from the rope and then replacing it above the lip, but ascending knots will require more of a struggle. The reason for the difficulty is that the climber's weight is holding the rope against the rock and he cannot push out with his feet. Once the knots or ascenders are over the lip, the going becomes much easier. If the lip of the overhang is not horizontal, it may be possible to slide the rope to the side where the lip is highest. Then the knot is moved up to the lip. When the rope is moved back towards the low part of the lip, the knot is forced over the lip. If this trick does not work, it may be possible to get a shoulder between the rope and the rock, and get the knot above the lip. In any case, there will be a struggle, and the climber is well advised to wear gloves.

If the rope is to be pulled up after the last climber ascends, of course the last climber must untie the anchor at the bottom and remove any knots so that the rope may be pulled up without snagging. With no knot in the end of the rope, the climber is missing a safety precaution since his ascender could possibly slide off the end of the rope in the event of failure of the ascenders (assuming that the bottom end of the rope is not on flat ground). To maintain the safety of the knotted end, the climber may use the following procedure. When ready to start, he ties a Figure-of-Eight knot in the slack and clips this knot to his waist loop with a carabiner. Then as he ascends, a loop of rope hangs below him. After ascending say 30 ft (10 m), he ties another Figure-of-Eight in the slack, clips this to his waist loop and unclips and unties the first knot, dropping the excess slack. In this way he could not fall far if the ascenders fail, and he has no large loops of rope hanging below to get snagged.

ASCENDING WIRE ROPE

The only practical way to ascend a steel cable is to use the Hiebler ascender. Jumars do work, using either top or bottom attachment point, but the teeth wear out very quickly. A rope prusik loop will not hold, but a small web sling may be used. The latter is difficult to move once set and wears out in as little as 20 ft (6 m) of ascending but can be used to hold small loads.

CHAPTER 20

RIVER CROSSINGS

As in general mountaineering, the mountain rescuer may occasionally have to cross a swiftly flowing stream, knee to thigh deep or deeper. Such a crossing is not to be treated lightly since the force of the flowing water may be very great, and should be taken very seriously if the water is more than knee deep. This force may be sufficient to move large stones rapidly downstream. The rescuer will probably not have a chance to wait until the time of day for optimum crossing. Early morning hours are often best, both for lowest water when glacial runoff is likely to be at a minimum and for the most daylight to dry out wet clothing, or the best time may be a long while after a rain allowing time for the excess runoff to pass.

INDIVIDUAL CROSSING

Considerable effort should be made to find a dry path across on fallen timber or log jams or by jumping from boulder to boulder. It should be kept in mind that wet logs and boulders may be very slimy and slippery, and the ice ax can be used for an additional point of contact. If the best route appears to be by boulder hopping, the climber should carefully pick a route involving no long jumps which are difficult while wearing a heavy pack. He should then memorize the route so that once he starts crossing he need not stop in a precarious position part way across.

If it is necessary to wade, a distant view from a high vantage point may help to find the best ford. The widest, and thus shallowest and least swiftly flowing, flattest crossing point should be found. The crossing is easiest on a smooth firm gravel bottom. To be avoided are a bottom covered with large rocks which provide poor footing and cause turbulence, sand which may be quicksand, and snags. The best ford is often found above rapids. Also, if the river runs in channels, it may be easier to pick a route through several small channels than through the one main course. Sharp bends in the river are to be avoided since the water is likely to be deep with strong current along the outside of the bend.

The crossing should be made wearing boots (*not* tennis shoes and *not* barefoot) for foot protection and warmth, but the socks may be removed and these dry socks carried to be put back on after crossing. Loose baggy pants should be rolled up to avoid resistance to the current, but the legs need protection from very cold glacial runoff; wool longjohns are good. The pack should have the lightest items (clothing and down things in waterproof bags) at the top for additional bouyancy in case of a slip. All items should be inside or very securely lashed on. The pack should be worn with loose shoulder straps and the waist strap *free* so that the pack can be removed if footing is lost, at which time the pack may act like an anchor.

If an individual is crossing alone in swift current, he can keep his balance best by using an ice ax or a sturdy tree branch as a third point of support for contact to the stream bottom upstream from his feet. He will lean heavily on the ax facing upstream and move only one foot or the ax at a time. For best stability the feet are shuffled along and not lifted from the river bottom, and they are kept widely spaced. Also, the feet should be placed on the upstream side of underwater obstacles encountered. However, crossing should be downstream from partly submerged timber to avoid being swept under and caught.

An important part of stream crossing, even a precarious dry one, might be termed "mental balance." One should never think in terms of going under and should not look at the surface of the water, but should look at a landmark on the far bank. Speed of crossing is important because of the severe chilling potential of the water. Cold which is tolerable at first may produce pain and panic a few minutes later.

TEAM CROSSINGS

Much more secure than the one-man crossing is the two-man or team crossing. If two men cross, the taller and stronger member will use his ice ax as a third point of contact and will be the upstream man, facing upstream and breaking the force of the flow for his partner who also faces upstream and hangs onto the hips or belt of the upstream man. Then there are a total of five points of contact with the stream bottom, two pairs of boots and the ax. It is also helpful for a smaller man using his own ax as a third point and doing an individual crossing to have someone just upstream breaking the current somewhat. This form of assistance may be put to use when one member of a party gets into difficulty or "freezes" in midstream.

When conditions are fierce, the two-man or larger team is much safer than for one to try it alone. A stable configuration for the large team crossing is a line, with each man's arms linked with his neighbor's arms at the elbows, and his own hands locked in front. A more stable arrangement is for each man to hold his own ax and one end of each neighbor's ax horizontally in front of his chest while linking arms as shown in Fig. 20-1. Even better is the long pole crossing, where each man in the team holds onto a pole (sapling) in front of his chest wrapping his arms around the pole, one arm around the top, the other underneath. In each of these methods, the tallest, strongest man will be at the upstream end, and the line is parallel to the current.

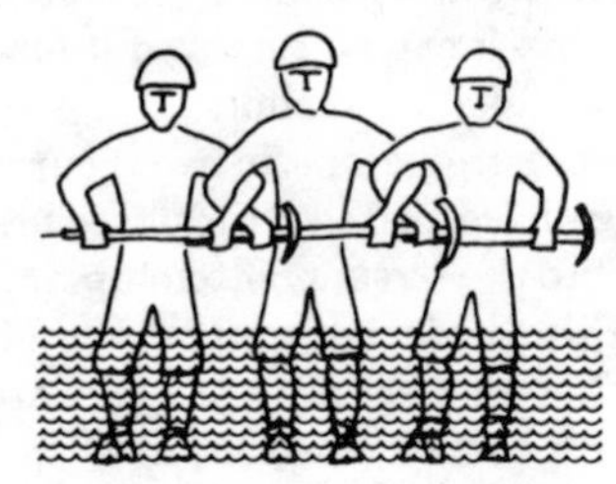

Fig. 20-1. Team crossing. Direction of flow is parallel to the line of the waders.

USE OF ROPE

If the crossing is severe and less than a rope length, one strong person with long legs should cross with the idea of setting up a hand line, belay or Tyrolean system to aid followers. When there is real danger of his being swept off his feet, this intrepid leader should not be wearing a heavy pack which may force him under water if he should lose his footing. He certainly should have a belay from a solidly anchored position upstream from the point of departure, and if he must wear a pack, it should be given a belay too. If no trees or suitable boulders are available for an anchor (say for a sitting belay), it may be possible to use a boot-ax technique in the river bank (see the chapter on snow anchors). The anchor must be solid since the forces of a swift current on a man under water or even on the rope alone are quite large. The belayer may be backed up by another man.

The tie-in used by the wader should be only a chest loop (arms passed through a simple loop across back and neck as shown in Figure 20-2) with tie-in point in front. A waist loop should never be used because there is a serious danger that the wader's head would be submerged in the case of a fall with a waist tie-in.

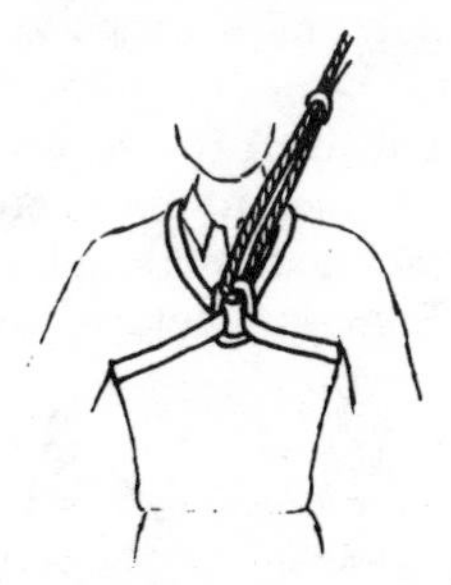

Fig. 20-2. Chest loop tie-in. The strands may cross in back.

A hand line is appropriate when the crossing is not very severe but where there is a special reason for wanting some extra steadiness in crossing, such as across an easy place above rapids or deep water, for extra aid for inexperienced members, or where one is carrying a large load. The line should be anchored firmly, and the wader crosses with his upstream arm over the rope. The hand line may be a useful aid even if the wader is belayed as below. Alternatively the wader could clip himself to the hand line with his chest loop. If the ice ax is carried in hand, it may be held in self-arrest position with the pick over the rope, but must be held in such a way that it cannot tangle with the hand line in case of a fall.

BELAYED CROSSING

The belayed crossing is made by the first wader tying in and crossing in a diagonal downstream path. He may lean against the rope for support. If he loses his footing, he will pendulum into the near bank. The ford should be chosen in a location free from boulders and snags which might catch the rope and prevent the fallen man from swinging all the way back to the bank for easy recovery. Also, it might be worth having rescuers on the bank at the end of the swing to give assistance as needed. If conditions are suitable and time is available, a Tyrolean system could be set up so that only the first man has to wade. The following paragraphs assume that everyone will wade.

When there is plenty of rope available, the following method illustrated in Figure 20-3 is most secure. The best river man (A) goes first, belayed by the second best (B) who goes last. When A gets across, he moves upstream and sets up a belay opposite B, and the next wader (C) ties in at B. Then C pendulums across taking about the same path as A, while B lets rope out, and A keeps the rope taut. If C falls, he should be pendulumed to the most favorable bank (hopefully to A so that the crossing is accomplished). In a severe crossing, A will not wear his pack, which can later be pendulumed across by A and B. Of course all packs should be securely tied shut and have no gear dangling loose on the outside. Finally B crosses, belayed by A only.

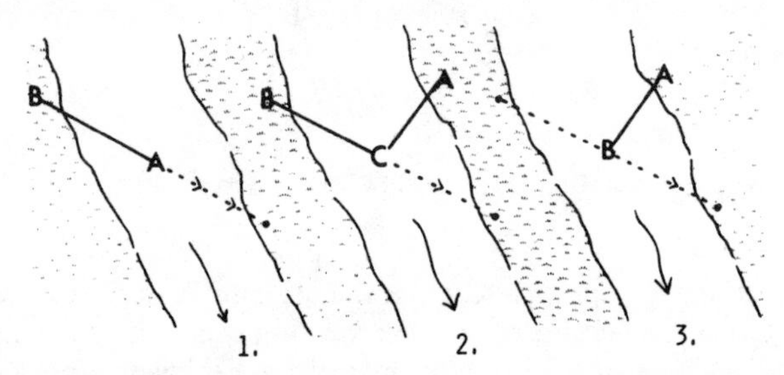

Fig. 20-3. Technique of belayed river crossing. A, the best river man, goes first, and B, the second best, goes last.

If only enough rope is available for a belay from one bank, A crosses as above, C ties into the main belay rope and also ties on a light retrieving cord held by B and is belayed by A. This retrieving line is necessary since it would probably be impossible to throw the rope back to B after C crosses.

RIVER CROSSING EVACUATION

If the crossing is quite easy, a victim who can walk but is not up to wading may be carried across by a rescuer using a tragsitz or improvised rope seat with the rescuer making use of a hand line and belay for added safety. For best security when a litter is being carried, two taut hand lines should be set about 2 ft (.6 m) apart, and the litter bearers walk between these with the ropes under their armpits. The hand lines should be secured 10 ft (3 m) or more back from the bank so that the litter bearers can make use of the lines as they start and complete the crossing.

If the litter can be lashed to long poles, the litter bearers are spread out and thus perhaps not all in the strongest current at the same time.

If belays or team techniques are needed for the crossing, carrying a victim in a litter will be extremely dangerous and is best not attempted. In this situation, a Tyrolean should be used if possible, or a helicopter should be summoned. A day or so waiting or finding an alternate safe route is preferable to losing the victim.

REFERENCES

1. *Safety in the Mountains*, Federated Mountain Clubs of New Zealand, 1967.

PART III

The subject matter of this part constitutes the heart of mountain rescue. Any organization skilled in mountain rescue will have its members so well trained in these techniques that application of the methods on a mission will be routine.

First aid is usually the most important activity at the scene of a rescue. The chapter here discusses only some points pertinent or peculiar to mountain rescue. Mountain rescuers are likely to encounter major trauma and are encouraged to get advanced training as offered by emergency medical technician (EMT) courses and practical experience in large city hospital emergency rooms.

Most of the evacuation techniques are based on nylon rope rather than steel cable largely because the mountain rescuer should first of all be a mountain climber and thus will be familiar with rope properties and climbing techniques, and thence be able to quickly learn the specialized techniques of evacuation involving rope and rock climbing hardware. Some knowledge of fifth and sixth class climbing techniques is assumed throughout these chapters. Because of the nature of many mountaineering accidents in Colorado, the emphasis here is on rock rescue and evacuation techniques, and rescuers skilled in these methods should find that most of the snow techniques are readily learned.

CHAPTER 21

FIRST AID

First aid (and second aid too) is of course extremely important in mountain rescue, but the subject is so lengthy that we will not give here even the usual brief summary. Instead, we refer the reader to two fine references (1, 2). This chapter will include only a few selected topics of special concern to the mountain rescuer which are not emphasized in the usual first aid books although some of these points are made in reference 1.

First aiders who have completed a course such as Advanced First Aid by the American Red Cross (reference 3) and who are not familiar with mountaineering may find that the added problems of weather, terrain, and distance to professional care are sizable. Performing first aid indoors is quite a contrast to doing the same at night in a freezing rain in the mountains. Also, an injury which would be some minor inconvenience in town may require litter evacuation in the mountains due to the more difficult terrain. Another form of first aid which can be serious in the mountains is the care of the uninjured but "shook" partner of a victim of a serious injury. Such a person may require the full attention of one or more rescuers.

Traumatic Shock. Traumatic shock, which is the relative or absolute lack of blood perfusion to the body's tissues, may become a critical problem in the mountains even with only minor injuries due to the possibility of low air temperatures, wind, precipitation, dehydration, and long transportation times to hospital care.

A principal requirement in the treatment of shock is keeping the body warm; this requires the best sleeping bags and other insulation to provide protection from the elements. The sleeping bag carried by a mountain rescue unit is preferably one with good insulating coverage everywhere and designed for rescue. It should have a zipper all the way around giving access to any part of the body for first aid. The bag should be on a thick foam pad in the litter.

Another requirement in treating shock is the placing of the victim in a prone position, with the usual recommendation to have the feet elevated somewhat. However, the optimum position for carrying a badly injured victim in the mountains is *not* head down. The idea of letting gravity push blood to the head is a fallacy; a better position is to have the body sloped so that the head is about 6 in. (15 cm) above the hips, allowing the diaphragm to descend and give more efficient use of the lungs which is particularly important at high altitudes, especially with chest or abdominal trauma which decreases respiratory exchange. The legs can be raised slightly to push blood from this area resulting in the victim's being slightly jack-knifed, head and feet both raised perhaps 6 or 8 in. (15-20 cm).

Intravenous Solutions (IV's). The use of intravenous solutions (IV's) may be called for in some cases. Even if properly trained personnel are available, the administration of IV's in the mountains is often difficult due to a variety of problems. Maintaining sterility of the various necessary items backpacked to the scene may be difficult. Breakage of IV bottles is also a problem. A few types of solution are available in plastic bags instead of bottles, but these can be punctured and do break when frozen unless handled with care. Low temperatures cause great problems in administering IV's due to freezing of the solution, first while being transported to the victim and second, in the actual administration; to solve these, first, a rescuer can transport the solution by carrying it inside his clothing next to his body, and second, the tubing through which the solution flows from bottle to patient can be passed down a rescuer's sleeve, thus it is hardly exposed to the cold. The solution must ideally be near body temperature when being administered, preventing further cooling of a victim who is either hypothermic or in great risk of hypothermia. Even though some solutions such as Normasol are not affected by freezing, others including Mannitol are very difficult redissolve after being precipitated at low temperature. The manufacturer should be contacted for specifics on each solution.

Even if the above problems are overcome, there is still a difficulty administering an IV to a victim being carried along a trail. A method which appears attractive and which in fact turns out to be very difficult is to have a rescuer carry the IV bottle at the side of the litter. One problem with this is the need for an extra long IV tube, another is that it is difficult to hold the bottle high enough (overhead) to depend on gravity for the feed, and still another is the danger of having the needle jerked out from the victim. A better method is to carry the IV bottle in the litter and to use a blood pump to provide the necessary pressure for feeding; but then care must be taken not to force the solution too fast or to let air in the IV line. If the solution is contained in a plastic bag, the bag itself may be squeezed for necessary pressure. Also, one must be careful to avoid damaging the tube; even the smallest hole is unrepairable, and a spare should be carried.

Immobilization. The immobilization of body parts as required by first aid must be done thoroughly and securely to prevent further injury during what is likely to be a rough evacuation to medical care. The need for a stable and complete job is very likely to be underestimated by a person who has performed first aid only on victims to be carried a few feet to a waiting ambulance. The Stokes litter is well suited for body immobilization because its tubular and open construction allows body parts to be immobilized directly, or splints to be secured. An orthopedic stretcher may be nicely used in conjunction with a Stokes litter. Air splints are easily applied and effective, but rescuers should be aware that some varieties of plastic get brittle and break at subzero temperatures. Great care must be taken in cold weather to avoid frostbite of immobilized limbs due to the pressure of splints compromising circulation.

Generally the body as a whole must not be allowed to move around in the litter. This may be accomplished with the aid of good litter tie-in straps (Chapter 22). Much padding is usually required, with packs, wool sweaters, etc., being much more desirable than down-filled clothing which is too compressible for this service.

Various means can be used to prevent the victim from sliding downwards if the litter is tilted head up. The need for such immobilization and the means to achieve it vary with the injuries. If the victim is in a Stokes with a leg divider, he may be placed with his feet resting against the foot end rail if he has long legs; otherwise a firm object may be put between his feet and the end rail. Another method is to arrange a sling clipped to a side rail passing around a foot of the victim so that the victim in essence "stands" in the sling.

The problem is considerably more difficult if both of the victim's legs are injured. A wide sling may be passed through the victim's crotch (taking appropriate precautions in the case of an unconscious male) and clipped to the upper part of the litter, but even with a good climbing seat sling or harness, the victim will be quite uncomfortable, and circulation in the legs will be seriously impaired if the litter is tilted head up. Similar problems exist in attempting to immobilize the victim at the arm pits. One effective method is to immobilize the victim's pelvic area by placing a firm barrier just below his buttocks; a large coil of rope essentially surrounding the entire trunk can be secured well to serve as the barrier. Then cross ties can be passed from the litter side rails over the victim's hip bones holding his pelvis firmly in place with little discomfort.

A fractured femur should be put in traction. It is nearly impossible to satisfactorily immobilize the entire body in the litter well enough to use the litter itself as a traction splint. A separate splint should be improvised if not carried by the rescue team. The victim and splint should be in a sleeping bag due to shock, which often accompanies major bone fractures.

In the case of back and neck injuries, a cervical collar will be found invaluable. A backboard can be very nicely improvised from a pack-frame with suitably placed clothing as padding, and packs and sleeping bags used to further support a victim with back injuries in a sitting position. Large quantities of adhesive tape will be found useful for body and head immobilization, especially for taping the forehead and chin to the litter. The primary rule to follow in these cases is to not transport the victim until he is properly immobilized.

The victim of a head injury who may be delirious needs to be thoroughly trussed up in the litter. Restraints may be easily improvised from webbing; overhand loops tied around the ankles and elbows and secured to the Stokes are very effective. Also, adhesive tape is useful for this same purpose.

Food and Water. For the usual traumatic injury, food is not needed, and should not be given if the victim has any injury that may require an operation. Food or water should never be given to an unconscious victim, who may aspirate the food or fluid into the lungs.

If a lost person is found alive after an extended period with no food or water, special considerations are in order. The dehydrated person's water supply should be replenished promptly, but not too fast. At first a few swallows should be given, and if it stays down more can be given, with two quarts or more given over a period of about an hour.

If a person has been without water for a lengthy period, his appetite may be poor. In such a case fruit juice can serve as both food and drink. If his appetite is good, he should take in only limited quantities of easily digested food until he is under the care of a physician.

Frostbite. The classic article on frostbite is Reference 4 and should be read by all winter mountaineers and rescuers. The physiology, prevention, and treatment of frostbite are discussed clearly. We summarize here some aspects of treatment which might be performed by mountain rescuers. We are not concerned with superficial frostnip, most often on the nose, which is treated simply by applying warmth from a hand.

Deep frostbite is identified by the body part being not only white and waxy looking but also frozen hard and with minimal pain. The latter two points are not the case with superficial frostbite. The best treatment insofar as the mountain rescuer is concerned is usually just evacuation to proper medical care with *no* rewarming of the frostbitten part. In fact a victim can walk on a frostbitten foot (protected by socks and boot of course) with little if any further damage or pain, *if* no rewarming has taken place.

If rewarming has been started, the body part should be treated with extreme care to avoid any damage to the affected tissue. This is best done by the rescuer by building a "tent" around the part to keep a reasonably sterile environment and to avoid contact of anything with the body tissues, and keeping the part warm in a sleeping bag. Affected toes or fingers should be kept separated with sterile gauze or cotton. Abrasion of any sort does severe damage, and refreezing is almost certain to cause ultimately the complete loss of the body part.

The treatment of choice is a rapid rewarming of the body part in water after the victim is in no danger whatsoever of further freezing. This is normally not a field operation and is best avoided by the mountain rescuer, but the technique is well described in Reference 4.

After rewarming it is impossible to judge immediately the extent of permanent damage—only time (months) will tell.

Hypothermia (Exposure). Hypothermia is the lowering of the body core temperature below the normal 98.6°F (37°C) and is an extremely serious mountain emergency. We describe some symptoms of hypothermia and the most important causes and treatment.

In the first stages, when the body temperature has dropped a degree or so (to say 96°F or 36°C) a person shivers involuntarily and in so doing loses some coordination. There is already reduced circulation to the extremities, where heat loss is likely to be the greatest, in order to maintain core temperature. Shivering is an effective mechanism to increase heat production by the body, thereby raising the core temperature back towards normal, but such action cannot be kept up for long if the body is exhausted, that is, if the reserve stores of energy are nearly depleted.

As the core temperature drops further (say 95-91°F or 35-33°C), there will be occasional violent shivering, sluggish thinking and slowness in response to questions, slurred speech, and listlessness. Below about 91°F (33°C), shivering stops, and the body goes into occasional muscle spasm. Thinking is very unclear, and there is no realization that there is a problem of being cold. Even so a person appears to be rational. At these core temperatures, the body is incapable of maintaining or raising its temperature, thus further rapid cooling results. A person becomes unconscious or has a glassy stare and has very slow pulse and respiration when his core temperature drops to 86°F or 30°C. Few survive body temperatures below 80°F (27°C).

Hypothermia will come about when the body is in an environment such that it loses heat to the surroundings more rapidly than the body can generate heat. Air temperatures can be above freezing. The body is most prone to hypothermia when in poor general physical condition or exhausted, dehydrated and with inadequate food intake, and also inadequately protected from the environment, that is, from low air temperatures, wind, snow, or rain. Heat is lost very rapidly around the head, because of both large blood supply circulating there, and exposure of the skin to the elements. Any clothing material loses most of its insulation qualities when wet including wool, but wool does a much better job of insulating when wet than other materials. A tired person who has become wet is most highly susceptible to hypothermia, particularly if he is not wearing wool.

The treatment for hypothermia is the immediate addition of heat to the body. Merely putting a hypothermic person into a sleeping bag is inadequate because the body may be incapable of generating enough energy to heat itself; the body no longer can shiver if its core temperature is below 93°F (33°C). A second and healthy person in the sleeping bag with the victim is effective. Very efficient in reducing the heat lost to radiation is the "space blanket" or "survival blanket," which is a lightweight aluminized mylar sheet. Also essential in treatment of hypothermia is adequate insulation from the ground.

Under development is the Hypothermia Blanket (Reference 5), which amounts to a large hot water bottle which is wrapped around the victim. Warm water heated by a small stove is circulated through the blanket to raise the temperature of the victim. Also usable and much simpler is an electric blanket which could be powered in the field by a small gasoline powered generator packed to the scene. An unanswered question concerning these blankets is the following: At what rate of adding heat is there a danger that blood would be drawn from the body core putting the person into irreversible shock and causing ventricular fibrillation? There is probably no danger if the blanket is kept at or below 100°F (37.7°C). Thermal burns are likely to be caused if the temperature is higher than this.

Additional treatment is feeding the victim sugar in easily digested form. Only small amounts of food should be taken at a time.

Miscellaneous Thoughts on First Aid in the Mountains. As usual for any unconscious victim, an airway must be maintained. A great assistance for doing this is the plastic oropharyngeal airway, and a suction pump may be found very valuable.

The damage to a hardhat worn by the victim of a head injury gives valuable clues about the nature of the injury and should always be taken with the victim to the attending neurosurgeon.

Tags should be carried with the first aid supplies to record times and nature of any special symptoms, drugs administered, initial assessment of injuries and the victim's name. The tag should be tied on to the victim to be sure that the information reaches the physician. In a multiple-victim situation requiring triage (choice or priority decision where some victims will have to wait for treatment), marking victims with various colors of surveyor's tape (used as flagging on searches) may be useful.

Artificial respiration (AR) can be given to a victim during a scree evacuation or trail carryout by using a bag-mask resuscitator. To allow mobility on a steep scree evacuation, the rescuer giving AR ties himself onto the lowering rope several feet from the litter with a tie-in long enough to place him at the head of the victim. This rescuer has his hands full maintaining his own footing while giving AR, and the procedure requires practice. The job is easier though tiring on a trail carryout.

It is very difficult to administer cardiopulmonary resuscitation (CPR) during an evacuation. One method that works is for a lightweight and strong rescuer to straddle the victim on the litter during a trail carryout, giving external heart massage. The other rescuer who will be simultaneously giving AR needs access to the victim's head, thus extra litter bearers cannot be put on to ease the burden. One rescuer not involved in the carrying or first aid counts aloud, providing the rhythm for the administration of CPR.

There are various other paramedical techniques which are almost never needed by the usual EMT serving as an ambulance attendant but which may be used in mountain rescue, such as intubation and urinary catheterization. A discussion of these is not appropriate here.

Legal Aspects of Death. All climbers and mountain rescuers should be aware that the law may be concerned with possible crime, and a body should not be moved without the permission of the county coroner. Mountain rescue units may have a member who has been deputized as a coroner, thus the rescue group can legally evacuate a body upon approval of the deputy without the need to obtain formal approval from the coroner himself, although such approval is always in order if time permits. Death messages are normally not transmitted over the radios, but prearranged codes may be used. Next of kin are notified by the authorities upon positive identification.

Presumptive Signs of Death. Occasionally the mountain rescuer will have to determine from a practical point of view whether or not a victim has just died. The following, when taken together, are indicators of death:

1. No blood pressure or pulse,
2. No spontaneous breathing,
3. Pupils fixed and dilated.

The first two of these indicators are sometimes difficult to determine, especially in bad weather in the mountains. The pulse in the femoral artery is probably the strongest, with the carotid artery and direct feel over the heart being good also. A stethoscope placed on the upper part of the sternum may be used to listen for breathing, and a polished mirror at the nostrils or mouth can be observed for fogging due to breath. If the pupils react to light, the victim is still alive.

Various other signs also accompany death but are not positive indicators:

4. No response to painful stimuli,
5. Cyanosis, especially in body parts near the ground,
6. Pale surface tissue due to lack of blood,
7. Decreased body temperature relative to ambient.

Gravity causes blood to pool downwards, with final clotting being appreciable in 5 to 10 minutes. Still other indicators including rigor mortis and odor are slower coming on.

If the victim of a traumatic injury goes into cardiac arrest and if CPR and AR are administered for say 10 minutes with no indications of vital signs, especially the pupils, it is probably appropriate in a mountain rescue situation to assume that the victim is dead. Such a decision will of course be the most difficult one ever made by a mountain rescuer.

REFERENCES

1. *Medicine for Mountaineering*, J. A. Wilkerson, ed., The Mountaineers, Seattle, 1967.

2. *Emergency Care and Transportation*, American Academy of Orthopaedic Surgeons, Chicago, 1971.

3. *First Aid*, American Red Cross, Doubleday, Garden City, 1957.

4. "Frostbite," B. Washburn, *American Alpine Journal*, 1962, also available in reprint form.

5. *Summit*, March 1970, p. 2.

CHAPTER 22

NONTECHNICAL EVACUATIONS

An evacuation is a safe move of an injured victim from an accident site to competent medical care. To avoid adding to a victim's injuries, transportation in the mountains is conveniently done using a Stokes litter, which can be used for carrying over any terrain.

We assume that the victim is to be transported over terrain including trails, talus and scree slopes, open and steep hillsides, low angle bedrock, and low angle snow fields. Gravity does not aid operations under these conditions, with the consequence that litter carrying requires a great deal of physical effort. We shall assume for purposes of this chapter that the slopes are never so steep that a belay to the individual litter bearers is required.

Since this sort of nontechnical terrain is encountered on virtually all mountain rescue evacuations, all rescue group members must be familiar with the techniques used. We will first describe positioning of the victim into a Stokes litter (the chapter on first aid discusses some of these ideas more fully). Next we discuss the carrying of the litter over low angle terrain, and finally consider litter rigging and carrying with a belay to the litter (the "Scree Evac"). Except for one section of the chapter, we assume throughout that any belaying of the litter is done with nylon rope rather than steel cable. Some additional details of the Stokes litter are given in Appendix A.

SECURING THE VICTIM IN THE LITTER

Rescuers must be careful to immobilize all injured body parts to minimize the possibility of further injury to a victim during loading and evacuation. Techniques of loading, including lifting procedures and the application of traction, are part of first aid. Discussions are omitted here except to say that the most competent first aider should be in charge of loading, and that the references of the first aid chapter give further details. Normally a victim will be placed on his back in the litter on a pad, but if straightening of the body from another position involves undue pain, the victim should be placed for maximum comfort. Also, for first aid reasons the victim may be placed on his stomach. Usually, because of danger of shock, the victim will be placed in a special rescue sleeping bag. In any case he should be well padded, and injured parts should be immobilized and supported by spare clothing (wool sweaters, etc.), small packs, coils of rope or smooth tree branches. Some form of rain protection such as a large poncho may be needed on occasion. Immobilization is particularly critical in the case of back injuries, and a back board may be improvised from a packframe.

The victim must be very securely tied in so that he cannot slide around or fall (or jump) out, even if the litter is accidentally inverted. Obviously, he must not be tied in so tightly that his circulation or breathing is impaired. A convenient tie-in method is shown in Fig. 22-1.

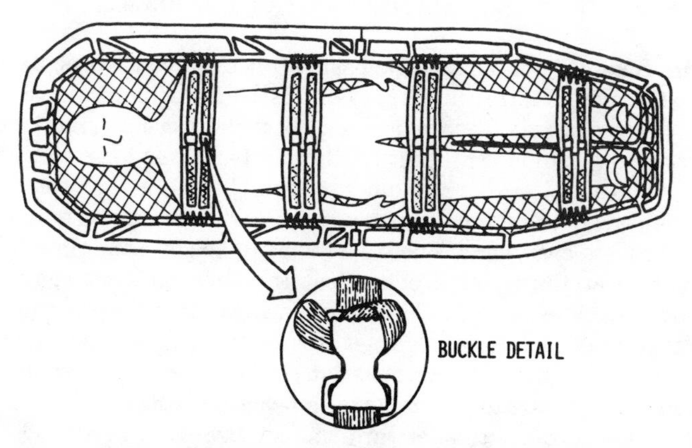

Fig. 22-1. Victim secured in the Stokes litter. His hands are under a tie-in or across his chest. The tie-in straps are made of one-inch webbing stitched to nylon duck. Some buckles may be made more secure by buckling the webbing as shown in the inset.

If the litter is not equipped with these special straps, a long piece of webbing may be passed back and forth over the victim and around an inner litter rail five to ten times. This webbing should not be wrapped around the outer rails because the webbing might become seriously weakened by abrasion if the litter rubs against rock or trees.

It is a good idea to secure the victim's hands inside the litter, because the victim has a tendency to grab the outer rails just when the rails bump into something. The victim's hands may be crossed over his chest, particularly if he is having difficulty breathing.

Normally the victim is carried with his head uphill from his feet, that is, feet first on descent, head first on ascent. First aid treatment for shock usually requires that the body be nearly horizontal. Since mountain terrain is usually steep enough that the head down position would cause the victim much discomfort, the head up position is used. Also, head up is mandatory in cases of head injury, chest injury, or breathing difficulty.

Some special precautions should be taken in the case of a fatality. Because of legal aspects, the body must not be moved or touched until the county coroner has so authorized. Special body bags will normally be used and will be carried to the scene in the case of a known fatality.

LITTER CARRYING WITHOUT A BELAY

The Basic Litter Team. The basic litter team consists of six men, three to a side. A larger number than this get in each other's way, and with fewer than six, each man's load becomes uncomfortably heavy unless the victim is very light. With only two litter bearers on each side, if one man loses his grip due to a stumble or slip, the litter might be dropped by the other litter bearer. Thus an optimum number of litter bearers carrying at one time seems to be six. Sometimes a seventh man at the forward end (or at the back on somewhat steep downhill sections) is useful. He will be an experienced rescuer and will not take part in rotation of roles (see below) but will be the litter captain during the entire evacuation. He will steady and guide the litter on rough terrain. If the trail is level, the litter can be carried head end first. Since this forward end is heaviest, it needs the extra support as provided by the seventh man, especially during rotation (below). It is also the responsibility of the litter captain to maintain the speed of movement on long evacuations where the litter bearers become tired and demoralized and tend to slow down. An additional person may walk behind the litter to administer first aid as necessary during transport.

The men in front have the only clear view of the footing ahead. They should call out any hazards or obstacles to warn the carriers behind. If the path is on the level or along a fall line, the pairs of litter bearers should be of approximately equal height and strength. But if the carry is contouring around the hillside, the downhill men should be taller.

Rotation of Roles. When more than six men are available for evacuating a litter, the extra personnel may scout and clear a route, belay the litter and carry rope, spare clothing and extra equipment such as ice axes (which for safety must have guards attached and should not be worn by the litter bearers but may on occasion be placed in the litter). If every member of the team is of roughly the same strength, the roles should be interchanged regularly. When there are extra people available, the litter bearers may be relieved regularly in the following fashion. The extra personnel are placed in pairs, perhaps every 50 to 100 yards (meters) or so along the trail ahead of the litter, one person on each side of the trail. As the litter passes each pair, they take over at the back end of the litter simultaneously with the back pair moving to the middle, the middle pair moving to the front and the front pair leaving the litter and walking rapidly down the trail ahead of the litter to be placed again by the team leader to take another turn on the litter. Normally the members of a pair will alternate sides between shifts to use a different set of muscles. In this manner the litter never needs to stop moving. A similar technique may be used if the litter is carried through terrain with downed timber or trees spaced closely enough that litter bearers and litter cannot simultaneously move among the trees. In this case the litter is passed by hand between the trees, and the back men drop off. This hand-to-hand technique is also effective on talus and glacial moraine.

Slings for Weight Transfer. If rotation cannot be performed at very frequent intervals, each man may use a web sling passed from the stretcher rail over a shoulder in front or back to the outside hand. Since considerably more weight can be carried on the shoulders than by hand and arm, it is much less tiring to carry the litter using this sling, which to some extent transfers weight from one hand to the other. Furthermore, height adjustments of the litter can be made very easily as demanded by rough terrain. The sling should be wide soft webbing, not rope, to prevent cutting into the shoulder. A 10 ft (3 m) circumference sling is quite satisfactory. For easy attachment and removal the sling may be clipped to the litter rail with an Army aluminum or large Stubai (T.M.) carabiner, other types being too small to pass over the rail. One of the small litter bars may be used to clip on a weight transfer sling as described here, but since these small bars are rather weak they should not be used as litter bearer belay attachment points discussed in the next chapter. Alternatives to this scheme are to have a straight length of sling material with a small loop tied in one end which may be clipped to the litter rail, or a long straight length looped around the litter rail, or a loop sling hitched to the rail. The sling should never be allowed to dangle loose outside the litter, getting underfoot, but should be removed or placed in the litter when not being used. During the unbelayed evacuation, the sling never ties the litter bearer to the litter. If rotation is being used, there usually will be no need to use slings since no one litter bearer will be carrying the litter for more than perhaps 300 yards (meters). However, a sling might be helpful for height adjustments, and in winter the slings may be useful since the litter rails are cold to carry, even when wearing mittens or gloves.

THE BELAYED LITTER ("SCREE EVAC")

Many times the terrain will be steep enough that the litter will be belayed for safety and steadying, but not so steep that the litter bearers need to be belayed themselves. Under these conditions, uphill carrying is very exhausting but may be necessary. We ignore for now the problem of moving a litter uphill using mechanical advantage or hauling techniques, and consider only downhill travel. Our discussion will deal with rigging, carrying, and belaying the litter, emphasizing nylon rope belays.

Rigging the Litter. A belay rope can be attached to the end of the litter as shown in Fig. 22-2, taking five turns around the litter rail. The reason for multiple turns is that the litter rail is not continuous through the end but is butt welded at the center, and under heavy loading this weld could break, allowing the middle turn of the rope to slip out. Thus if only one turn of rope were used around this middle section, it could come out under heavy loading, losing the belay.

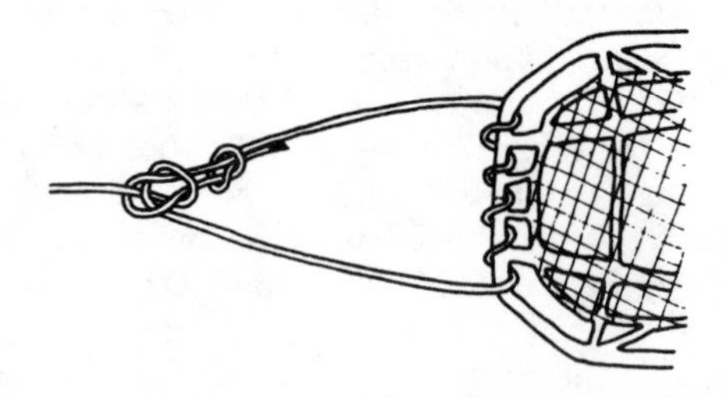

Fig. 22-2. Showing method of tying belay rope to the end of the litter.

If the belay is needed for more than one rope length and if a second anchor is placed to provide the additional belaying, the evacuation may be kept continuously moving by tying a sling to the litter as shown in Fig. 22-3 and using a strong locking carabiner between sling and lowering rope. The second belay rope from the lower anchor may be clipped into this sling, which should be of very stout nylon webbing or rope, by the second belay team as the litter approaches the lower anchor. Then, as the litter passes by this lower anchor, the upper belay rope is removed, and the litter continues on belay without stopping. The first belay rope may then be set up ahead of the litter downslope.

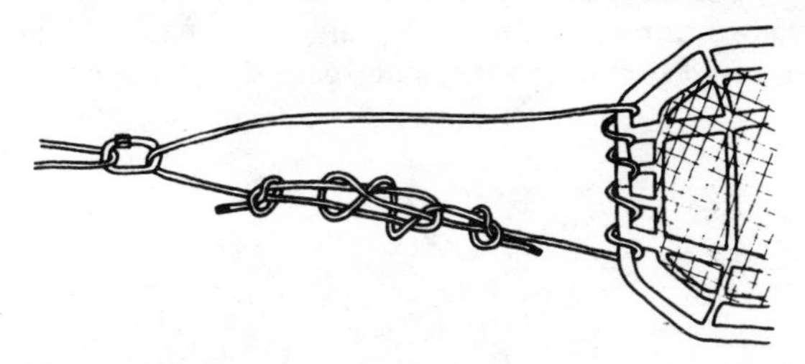

Fig. 22-3. Showing method of tying yoke to end of litter. The double sheet bend should be cinched down, with safeties, and the carabiner should be of very high strength and locking.

Carrying the Belayed Litter. We assume that the litter is being lowered downhill on a taut rope attached to one end of the litter. If the rope is loaded heavily due to a steeper slope, the litter team should be reduced to four, as discussed in the next chapter, to avoid high stresses in the belay system. Under these conditions the litter is easier to carry than on the level. For good footing the litter bearers should hold onto and lean out against the belayed litter. They should not make an effort to stand vertically, but should be nearly perpendicular to the underfooting, using techniques similar to keeping one's footing during rappelling, that is, keeping the body perpendicular to the rock and leaning downhill somewhat, holding onto the litter while looking downhill. The position is shown in Fig. 22-4. The litter bearers should always let the belay control the downward motion of the litter. If a litter bearer slips, he should hang onto the litter. The belay is of great assistance to the litter bearers on steep terrain.

Communication between the litter and the brakeman is important since the latter, not the bearers, controls the speed of descent. A pair of radios solves the problem very well. The radio at the litter will be carried by the litter captain, who gives all commands regarding the motion of the litter. The calls "Stop," "Slow," "Faster" are used. If the bearers find it necessary to stop themselves, the belay rope may go slack, and then "up rope" should be requested before continuing. Because the front men are the only ones with a clear view of the footing ahead, they should warn the others of obstacles coming up.

Any time that the rope makes a bend around a rock projection (or past a very small tree or bush) in going from the brakeman to the litter, the litter bearers, and particularly the litter captain, must be aware that the rope might slip over the rock knob if they change their direction of descent. Such a slip of the rope could result in a sudden drop of the litter and consequent shock loading of the belay system and is to be avoided. Direction-changing pulleys or carabiners can be used, keeping in mind that a knot does not pass through.

Fig. 22-4. Carrying the litter. Showing only 3 of the 6 litter bearers.

Litter bearers should strive for smoothness and speed. It is easier to carry the litter rapidly over somewhat rough terrain with feet slipping and sliding a bit than to carry it slowly with firm placement of the feet at each step.

The litter bearers should be aware of the elastic nature of nylon rope. The loading on the rope varies with the steepness of the slope, since the rope supports none of the weight of the litter and bearers on level ground, and progressively more and more of it as the terrain steepens. Thus, as the belayed litter goes from a relatively level spot to a steeper slope, the rope stretch will become markedly greater, and the litter may drop several feet. This problem becomes very severe with more than about 200 ft (70 m) of belay rope out. This stretch can be overcome by preloading the rope on the level. The litter captain calls for "Stop" while the litter is on level ground and then has the litter team move forward, pulling hard against the rope; thus, the rope will be heavily loaded as the litter reaches the steep section. This technique gives a smoother and gentler ride for the victim and is easier for unskilled litter bearers to execute than simply to charge downhill with the litter, although a sharp litter team can smoothly and speedily make such a descent. (The comments of this paragraph do not apply to steel cable belays.)

Belaying the Litter: Basic Systems. Under very moderate conditions, a belay rope back to an individual walking behind the litter may be useful for steadying the litter on the trail. If the route is through timber, this person may walk perhaps 20 to 30 ft (5 to 10 m) behind the litter and can quickly set up a tree anchor and brake system as described below. Since the belay rope is likely to be much longer than 30 ft (10 m) the excess may be carried conveniently in a coil over the shoulder, but not around the neck, to prevent strangulation if a pull should come suddenly. To pull on the belay rope and to steady the litter, the system shown in Fig. 22-5 is good. Any pull then comes on the hips.

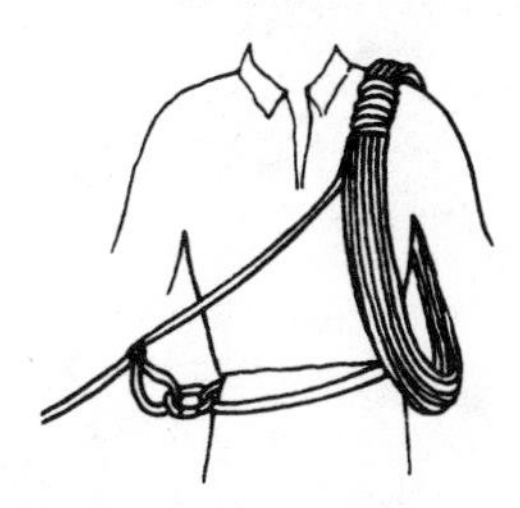

Fig. 22-5. Method of carrying extra belay rope. A pull on the belay rope is taken on the waist loop.

On somewhat steeper terrain, a very strong belay will be necessary. The anchor used for the belay system must be extremely solid since loading may approach 1000 lbs (450 kg) in a steep scree evacuation. See a separate discussion of anchors. Here we will describe some suitable braking systems.

Tree Anchor-Brake. When the evacuation is to be done through timbered terrain, a sturdy tree may be found to serve the dual role of anchor and brake system. The lowering rope from the litter is wrapped usually once or twice around the tree and held by the brakeman, who is normally in a standing position. He can readily control the amount of friction by walking around the tree one way or the other, and thus the tree should be chosen with a clear space all around and with no low branches. If the brakeman cannot run around the tree, he may pass the rope around his hips for greater control of the friction. The rope should be wrapped around the tree in such a way that the bottom turn goes to the litter. Then if the tree bark is quite smooth and hard, the turns cannot be driven into the ground by the rope from the litter pulling down nor can the turns be self-jamming (this is especially important when passing a knot). On a long evacuation, the rope could cut through the bark to sap wood. This should be avoided to prevent permanent damage to the tree. Above timberline, the technique described here can be used on a smooth solid boulder, and less than one turn around provides plenty of friction.

Carabiner-Brake-Bar Brake. A normal rope brake may have to be set up and attached to a suitable anchor in the absence of usable trees. Anchor systems, such as rope around a large boulder, are described later (Ch. 25). A tree strong enough for a tree brake would make a fine anchor if for some reason, such as branches or sappy bark, it is not appropriate for a tree brake. A suitable brake system is shown in Fig. 22-6, with many modifications possible.

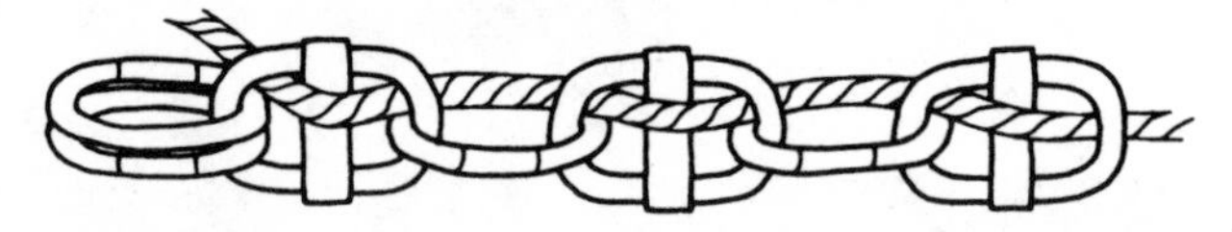

Fig. 22-6. Triple-brake-bar brake. The gates on the doubled carabiners to the anchor are opposed.

Note that there are two carabiners with gates opposed for safety connecting the brake to the anchor. The figure shows three brake bars, but two will be sufficient if the terrain is not steep. Although any brake bars may be used, the rescue bars have been modified to flip freely rather than snap onto and off the carabiner. This modification is useful to ease insertion and removal of the rope from the brake, but has a danger that if slack develops, the brake bar could fall open. Thus the brakes should be placed with the bars on top so that the bars will not accidentally fall open. Then the ropes are fed into the brakes from the underneath side. As a brakeman becomes more experienced and skilled he may wish to feed the rope in from the top, with the brake bar underneath, but he must be aware that the bar can fall open if the rope is slack in the brake. With the brakes inverted in this way, rope changes (Ch. 24) are easier to do quickly, but there is the potential danger of the brakes opening at the wrong time.

Brake Plates. The special and excellent brake plates illustrated in Ch. 24 are very well suited for use in evacuation as described here. Discussion is left to that chapter.

Handling the Ropes and Brakes. For any braking system, the brakeman should feed the rope smoothly and at a uniform speed as desired by the litter captain. This is easily done if the brakeman must grip the rope with a moderate grasp to control the litter. If the brake has too much friction, the brakeman will have to push the rope into the brakes and may have kinking problems; if the braking action is too small, the brakeman's grip on the rope for full control may tire him out too rapidly.

A rope handler is very useful to assist the brakeman and frequently is essential for smooth operation of the brakes. Ideally the rope is laid out in a straight line from the brakeman, but more usually the rope is coiled or heaped on the ground. The rope handler should provide to the brakeman several feet of slack and unkinked rope. Kinks may be anticipated by twisting the slack rope in such a direction as to unlay it. Kinks may be worked away from the brakeman by spinning the rope. If the rope handler is sloppy in his function, he will slow down the entire evacuation.

If the evacuation goes over terrain such that only two of the three brake bars are needed, the upper bar may be eliminated from action if the loading on the rope can be removed. Because of the weight of the rope to the litter, there will still be some tension on the rope even when the litter is off belay. If the rope and a carabiner below the upper brake bar are grasped together by one hand, the stress in the rope in the upper bar is eliminated, and the bar can be flipped open. To maintain best dexterity the brakeman need not wear gloves (but when skilled he may find the gloves are worthwhile), and thus he must be careful to not grab a brake bar which may be hot. If the terrain crossed by the litter could steepen again after reducing brake friction, the brake bar should not be flipped open in the first place, but a rope handler should pull slack through the upper brake bar; the brakeman lowers by feeding the rope only into the lower bars. Then, when more friction is needed, the slack around the upper bar is let go, and lowering is done using all bars. This procedure eliminates the need to reset the upper brake bar. For more friction the brakeman can pass the rope around his hips.

Several Rope Lengths. When the belayed evacuation needs to be continued beyond one rope length, a second rope can be tied on, or the anchor and brake system may be moved downhill.

Second Rope. A second length may be tied onto the first using a double sheet bend with safety overhands. If a tree anchor-brake is used, the knot is easily passed around the tree. The litter continues without stopping, but the litter bearers should be prepared for an increasing amount of rope stretch thereafter due to the extra length of rope.

If a brake bar system is used, a knot joining the rope lengths will not pass through the brakes, but may be passed by if the litter bearers find a secure spot to set the litter down and release the belay allowing the brakeman to remove the rope from the brakes. If this is to be done, the brakeman must inform the litter bearers when, say, only 50 ft (15 m) of rope remain before a stop will be necessary. A similar warning is given at 20 ft (6 m) and at 5 ft (1.5 m), at which time the brakeman stops and awaits the instructions from the litter captain, such as "Four more feet" or "Off belay." It is not necessary that the litter go off belay to pass a knot, but more complex rigging will be needed as described in Ch. 24.

Whenever extra ropes are tied onto the first to lengthen belays, several precautions should be taken. First, the knot should be a double sheet bend with several safety overhands. Other knots are as strong or stronger but either tend to jam after heavy loading or else are more complicated to tie. Also, the knots should be tied before the rope is removed from the brakes to prevent accidentally dropping the rope. A knot may be worked past a trouble spot such as around a corner or past a tree by clipping a carabiner around the rope near the knot and pulling out on the rope as the knot moves. Also, it is a good idea to have someone follow the knot down the slope to prevent the knot from jamming or hanging up in timber or rock. The problem of rope stretch becomes very severe when more than one extra rope is tied on. It is preferable to set up a second anchor-brake system lower down the slope. The next paragraphs discuss the techniques of shifting the belay from one brake to another down the slope to keep an evacuation moving smoothly.

Second Anchor-Brake. The second anchor-brake system should be prepared by a second belay team while the litter is being lowered from above. Then, as the litter approaches the lower anchor, the second lowering rope can be attached by the rope handler to the sling on the litter rigged as shown in Fig. 22-3 above. The second brakeman takes over as the litter passes below this new brake. The upper brakeman provides slack, and this first belay rope is removed from the litter sling by a rope handler. Then the first belay station can be moved downhill to a third position. Using this leap-frogging technique, the litter can be kept moving continuously on a long evacuation with only a minimum of personnel and equipment, if each member of the evacuation team works fast to maintain continuity.

Running Tree Belay. When tree brakes are available, the following technique may be used to easily move the anchor downhill and continue the evacuation using just one rope. We assume that the litter may be taken off belay below the site for the lower anchor. The upper brakeman releases the rope, which remains stretched out up the hill, and the second belayer immediately wraps a long bight in the rope around the lower tree as shown in Fig. 22-7 and puts the litter on belay again. The rope is shown with two wraps around the tree and going to the hips of the brakeman, giving a great deal of friction. The brakeman may wish to use only one wrap, or not pass the rope around his hips. The turns on the tree should not cross one another. It is now essential to have at least one and better two rope handlers to feed the slack rope around the tree to the brakeman's braking hand. Here again, when the second brakeman has control, the first belay team can move quickly downhill, after removing any knots from the end of the rope, to set up a third position.

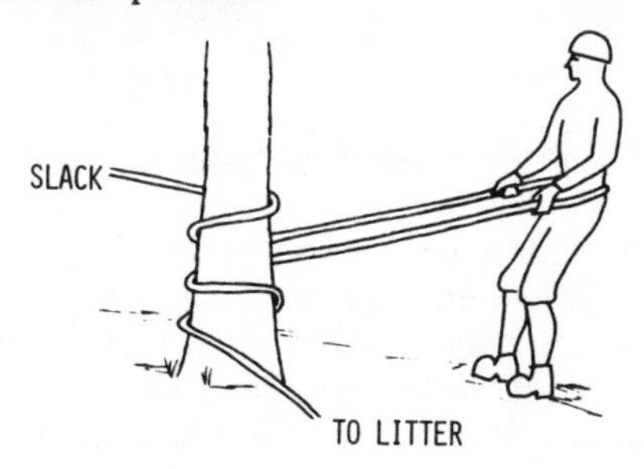

Fig. 22-7. The running tree belay. A rope handler is essential to feed slack rope to the belayer, who may just hold the rope in hand rather than pass it around his hips.

STEEL CABLE OPERATIONS

The lowering operations described in the previous section could be done with steel cable instead of nylon rope, making appropriate changes in the braking system. The rigging on the litter is the same as shown in Fig. 22-3 with the addition of a shock absorber to the cable. A strong steel (chrome-vanadium locking) carabiner clips the eye of the cable to the rigging. The cable is never tied in knots, and a carabiner should never need to bear directly on the cable since the cable eyes should contain thimbles. Because steel cable will cut into a tree, the tree anchor-brake cannot be used. A hardwood brake block is used with three turns of cable, allowing the brakeman (wearing heavy gloves) to control loadings of up to 700 lbs (300 kg). Considerable difficulty will be encountered in smooth lowering if the brake block is wet. Cable handlers reel cable off reels. If the evacuation is long, the handlers also attach connectors, which can pass around the brake block with little difficulty.

The litter bearers on a cable scree evacuation have about the same job as with nylon. Due to the lack of elasticity of cable, they need not worry about going for a sudden "ride" when descending a markedly steeper incline. On long descents when a connector is out, the litter captain should be sure that the cable runs in a path that will not hang up the connector. One difference from nylon rope is that cable passing over a rock edge or around a tree can cut a deep groove causing the connector to be jammed. If this situation is likely to arise, the litter team should stop to place a large direction-changing pulley carried for the purpose.

MOVING THE STOKES LITTER OVER SNOW

Movement of the litter over snow may be very easy on both the victim and the litter bearers if snow conditions are optimum. If it is anticipated that some travel will be over snow, a poncho or other waterproof material will be placed under the victim on initial loading in the litter. This is a "must" since a wet sleeping bag is very cold.

On low angle snow the litter bearers drag the litter in the snow using slings hitched to the litter rail. The litter moves easily if it is fitted with a smooth bottom and if the snow is reasonably firm. A belayer may move with the litter and may tie in around his waist with the belay rope, clipping a small loop to the waist loop, as shown in Fig. 22-5 above. Thus any pull by the litter on the belayer is on his hips, and he can pull back harder than by just gripping the rope in his hands.

On somewhat steeper or harder snow the litter may move readily by itself and will have to be held back at all times by the litter bearers and belayer. A belay rope may be held by several people while two to four men go with the litter guiding it by pulling on slings. On still steeper snow, an ice ax or some other anchor and brake system will have to be set up. The discussion of snow techniques is left to a later chapter.

SPECIAL SITUATIONS

Several Litters Down the Same Path. When a belay station is to be reused, there is no need to pull the rope up after the first litter is off belay, but instead, the rope end which was free during the first evacuation is attached to the second litter. On a tree brake, the direction of travel of the rope is reversed for the second evacuation. It will be necessary to reverse the wrapping of turns to ensure that the rope to the litter comes from the bottom turn. Also, to prevent serious damage to the tree, the turns should be moved slightly on the trunk.

With a carabiner-brake-bar brake, the system will be simply reversed, that is, the end which was towards the litter is attached to the anchor. In both cases, the free end of the rope is straight downhill from the brake, and no knots tied at the bottom end. The litter bearers should never step on the slack rope.

Boats. Occasionally the situation arises where transport of a victim around a high mountain lake is necessary. If the path around the lake is poor, through talus or along a steep wall such that the litter carrying may be difficult, a portable rubber raft or other boat can be used to advantage, if available. For example, a six-man raft is quite stable when loaded with a litter and one oarsman, but a strong wind tends to blow the boat around. An eight-man raft will nicely hold the loaded litter and four rescuers, allowing two men to paddle and two to tend the victim. A tag line to shore might be useful. Life jackets should be worn by all sea-going members because the water is likely to be quite cold, and a person does not survive long in ice water. Also, although the victim is left in the litter, he should not be strapped in since the litter would make a very nice anchor in the case of capsize.

Wheeled Litter. Because litters are available with a large single wheel (the Stokes can be so modified), some comments on the use of a wheeled litter are in order. The use of the wheel depends on the nature of the victim's injuries. Even when used carefully the wheel will result in a more jarring ride for the victim than will a hand carried litter on all trails except one paved or exceptionally smooth. Thus almost any injury will be worsened more by a ride on the wheeled litter than the hand-carried one. The wheel is in somewhat widespread use for mountain rescue, and is for the convenience of the rescuer at the expense of a rougher ride for the victim. The main value of the wheel arises when there is a serious manpower shortage, since two litter bearers can handle the litter for an extended time. However, travel with the wheel is slower and requires a great deal of discipline on the part of the litter bearers to prevent unnecessary jarring of the victim. The procedure with the wheel is for the front litter bearer to observe the trail for objects and call out "up" to carry the litter over the rough spots and then "down."

Tragsitz. In the case of a lightweight victim with only very minor injuries or none at all, the tragsitz (see Chs. 7 and 31) may be used to carry the victim "piggyback." A tail rope belay to the carrier is useful even on a trail, which could be steep or with poor footing. The carrier can lean against the belay for added security.

CHAPTER 23

TECHNICAL ROCK EVACUATIONS I: THE SCREE EVACUATION

Technical evacuation is an evacuation of an injured victim off terrain so steep that a fall or slip of a rescuer would result in injury, and special methods are used to protect the personnel. We will assume that the reader is familiar with the ideas given in the previous chapter. The present discussion is concerned with the high angle scree evacuation, which is just like a nontechnical litter evacuation but on terrain steep enough that the litter bearers will be tied into the litter itself. Except for the last section of the chapter, we assume that nylon rope rather than steel cable is used. We shall consider only lowering of the litter; raising and hauling are discussed later. The high angle steep wall evacuation will be the subject of the next chapter.

Scree Evacuations on Steep Slopes. On low angle terrain, gravity is a hindrance to evacuation operations, and a litter with the victim is carried by usually six litter bearers. As the angle becomes moderately steep, a belay of the litter becomes advisable, since it may be difficult for the litter bearers to maintain their own footing and carry a heavy load as well, as discussed in the previous chapter. On still steeper terrain not only will the litter movement need to be controlled by a belay, but also the litter bearers themselves will need a safety tie-in since a fall of one of them could be serious. Because the belay takes only part of the weight of the loaded litter, it is still necessary to use say six litter bearers. But as the slope steepens more, to about 40° or more, the belay takes more of the load and some of the weight of the bearers too, and the stresses in the belay system become large, sometimes over 1000 lbs (450 kg). Since the belay rope takes more of the load as the terrain steepens, fewer litter bearers are needed, and their number should be reduced to four to reduce the stresses on the belay or lowering system. On very steep or vertical walls there will be only two litter bearers, who do not need to support the litter at all, as discussed in the next chapter.

We assume that the litter is belayed by a rope tied to the end of the litter using the rigging and lowering techniques already discussed in Chapter 22. It is now particularly important to be sure that the victim is very well secured in the litter, especially preventing sliding downwards, as discussed in the chapter on first aid. The loading on the lowering rope may be very large since as many as eight people may be supported in part by this rope on steep terrain which occasionally may be encountered. Because of this loading, the lowering rope should be attached with multiple wraps around the head end (uphill) main litter rail as was shown in Figure 22-2.

Litter Bearer Tie-Ins. On steep scree evacuations, litter bearers are individually tied to the litter. Each litter bearer wears a normal waist loop or seat sling onto which his tie-in sling can be clipped, with locking carabiner or two with gates opposed. The sling should be attached to the upper half of the litter, by hitching or with an army aluminum carabiner or equivalent large one. Thus if a litter bearer slips or falls, he will be held by his tie-in to the litter. The reason for clipping into the upper half of the litter is that there is a possibility that under very heavy loading by the litter bearers, the bottom half could break loose from the upper belayed half with resulting disaster. As we describe below, the litter bearer may wish to lean back against his tie-in, thus the tie-in sling should be no longer than necessary to reach from the litter attachment point to the litter bearer himself. For convenience in adjusting the length of the tie-in, the sling may be a long (10-12 ft or 4 m circumference) webbing or 1/4 inch (7 mm) rope which can be doubled, tripled, or quadrupled as needed. A more complicated alternative is the special adjustable tie-in shown in Figure 23-1. The prusik shown may be moved to make necessary adjustments. The attachment point on the litter may be moved for tie-in length adjustment too, but should be kept out of the way of the other litter bearers' grips. The small diameter litter bars are only brazed in place and are not very strong, and thus should not be used for tie-in points. On very long evacuations, the litter bearers may use belay seats for added comfort.

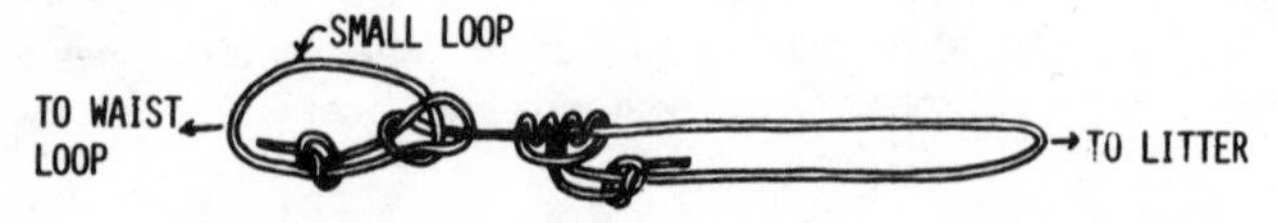

Fig. 23-1. Adjustable litter bearer tie-in. The small loops at each end of the sling could be spliced rather than tied.

Handling the Litter. For good footing on steep terrain, the litter bearers hold onto and lean out against the litter, as in Figure 23-2, making no effort to stand vertically but instead staying nearly perpendicular to the underfooting. This holds particularly true as the terrain steepens to the point where one would have to find footholds. To save rapidly tiring arms, the litter bearer may let his tie-in support some or occasionally most of his weight especially as the terrain approaches the vertical as could happen over a very short vertical wall. The general technique is similar to the footwork of rappelling but with the speed of descent controlled by the belayer (brakeman) from above. For this reason communication between litter and brakeman must be adequate, using the calls as discussed in Chapter 22: "Stop," "Slow," "Faster," "Five feet," etc. Also, since only the foot end litter bearers have a good view of the approaching underfooting, they should keep the others informed.

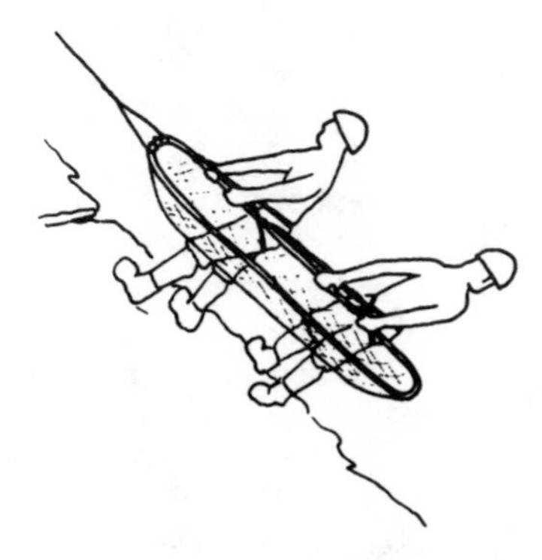

Fig. 23-2. Litter bearers on a steep scree evacuation. Showing only two of the four litter bearers.

Rope stretch on terrain of varying slope is a much more severe problem than for nontechnical evacuations or for vertical walls, since the stretch varies in proportion to the rope loading, and the loading in this case varies a great deal with slope. As the litter goes over a sudden steepening in the slope, the added rope stretch with say 100 feet (30 m) of belay rope out could easily be 10 feet (3 m) or more. The litter bearers must be prepared for this. One way to prevent the sudden stretch is for the litter bearers to have the belayer hold firm on the rope say 10 feet (3 m) before the litter reaches the steep section. Then the litter bearers pull, preloading the rope as they approach the steep part, and call for "Down slow" as they go over. Rope stretch with very long belay ropes is a severe problem that can be avoided by setting up a new anchor and belay position lower down the hill.

Belaying the Steep Scree Evac. Belays here will be similar to those on nontechnical evacuations, except that the stresses applied to the brake will be quite large, larger in fact than those encountered in any other type of evacuation. Two or three wraps of the lowering rope from the litter around a very sturdy green tree near the roots and to the hips of the belayer who wears gloves makes quite a nice anchor and brake system as described in Chapter 22. Lacking trees, some other anchor such as a big solid boulder will be used along with a carabiner-brake-bar system or brake plate as described in Chapters 22 and 24. The brakeman must be prepared for great changes in loading. He may readily control large loads by passing the rope from the brake around his hips to his braking hand. The descent from the anchor should not be so long (200 ft, 60 m) that a knot joining two belay ropes will have to be passed by the brake system because of the problem of rope stretch. But should the occasion arise anyway, the litter bearers try to find a place to securely set the litter down and go off belay while the brakeman passes the knot (or the technique of knot passing discussed in Ch. 24 could be used), or while a Running Tree Belay (Ch. 22) is set up at a new belay station. The knot, always the double sheet bend with safety, must never be allowed to actually reach the brake system or it will be jammed, and it should be tied on by a rope handler at the brakes well before the end of the rope is reached. The tree anchor-brake does not have this problem since the knot passes readily around the tree.

The Scree Evac on Loose Rock. A scree evacuation on loose rock requires considerable care and skill on the part of the litter bearers. They should *use* the litter to stay perpendicular to the underfooting, otherwise they tend to push rock loose in getting their feet placed. If a rock is set loose, either by a litter bearer or from above, the rock may safely pass under the litter if it is not bouncing. The litter bearers must be prepared to move quickly to avoid rockslide and to protect the victim, while giving the victim a smooth ride. All personnel on the slope should be wearing hardhats, including the victim.

Rescuers not on the litter or belaying should be either well to the side of the litter or below but not above, to prevent accidentally kicking rocks loose onto the litter. Someone to the side with a loudhailer at a vantage point can direct personnel and give warning of sliding or falling rock. Hand lines may be set up to aid personnel.

Knots in the lowering rope are to be completely avoided, since knots set loose rocks sliding very easily, directly down towards the litter. Thus to extend a belay for more than one rope length, new anchor points should be found rather than tying on a second rope. Since all too frequently anchor points are not available when desired on large scree slopes, advantage must be taken of those available.

Steel Cable. Steel cable may be used in place of nylon rope for the lowering operations, again making some obvious changes. The rigging to attach the cable to the litter should always include a shock absorber on steep evacuations. If the litter or a cable connector should get hung up for any reason and some slack develop in the cable, disastrous shock loads could easily develop in the system if the litter should suddenly drop a little. A securely anchored wooden brake block will be used to provide friction on the cable. Most existing brake blocks can take up to three turns of cable, allowing the brakeman to control loads no greater than about 700 pounds (300 kg), thus no more than four litter bearers should be used for steep scree evacuations since loadings can easily rise above 1000 pounds (450 kg) with 6 litter bearers. If the brake block is wet, friction rises, the block tends to wear or groove rapidly, and smooth control is more difficult; passing a connector may become quite a problem.

Since steel cable does not have the problems of elasticity present in nylon, it may be used very successfully for long steep scree evacuations by simply joining on multiple lengths. When a long evac route has poor anchor points along the way, the entire evacuation may be run from one belay station. Evacuations as long as 5000 feet (1500 m) have been done this way. Cable handling at the top is a large problem; one effective scheme is to have the cable laid out straight in long lengths to allow connectors to be attached without having to stop the evacuation. On evacuations longer than one cable length and particularly on very long evacs, thought must be given to the possibility of connectors causing rockfall. It may be appropriate for rescuers to be stationed along the evac route looking out for such problems.

CHAPTER 24

TECHNICAL ROCK EVACUATIONS II: HIGH ANGLE EVACUATIONS

In contrast to the scree evacuation, where gravity must be overcome by the several litter bearers supporting the litter, the high angle evacuation on vertical walls is performed by only two litter bearers with the litter fully supported by the lowering ropes. When an injured victim is on a steep wall, a third man will normally rappel to the victim before the litter is lowered and will administer first aid and then be of great assistance in loading the victim into the litter. In fact this "Third Man" may perform the technically most difficult part of the evacuation in loading the injured person. His job is sufficiently complex, important, and specialized to warrant the separate discussion in Ch. 32. Except for one section on cable, we assume throughout the chapter that the evacuation is a lowering of the victim with nylon rope.

GENERAL DISCUSSION

The job of the litter bearers is to get the litter to the victim, to see that the victim is properly loaded and secured, to give the victim a smooth evacuation by preventing the loaded litter from knocking against the rock, and to administer first aid to the victim if necessary. For first aid reasons the litter should normally be horizontal. Two litter bearers should be used rather than one for a number of reasons. One litter bearer cannot come close to matching the performance of two in smoothness, speed, and safety of handling a litter on a wall with structures such as overhangs and dihedrals. Likewise, one litter bearer is unable to load an injured victim into the litter without doing more injury, except in the very simplest cases, and if first aid needs to be administered during the evacuation, one litter bearer cannot do this and handle the litter simultaneously. Also, one litter bearer alone is almost certain to knock the litter against the wall during the evacuation. Such banging around is very hard on a victim who has undergone major trauma.

Obviously essential in the evacuation is proper operation of the brakes controlling the lowering. We will discuss in detail only the system where the brakes are fixed in position at the top of the cliff with a brakeman controlling the lowering. This is in contrast to the technique of travelling brakes and fixed ropes, where the brakes are attached to the litter and operated by the litter bearers. We will briefly describe and compare the two systems, illustrated in Figs. 24-1 and 24-2. With travelling brakes, the two belay ropes are fixed to anchors at the top, whereas with fixed brakes, the brakes are attached to the anchor, and the ropes move.

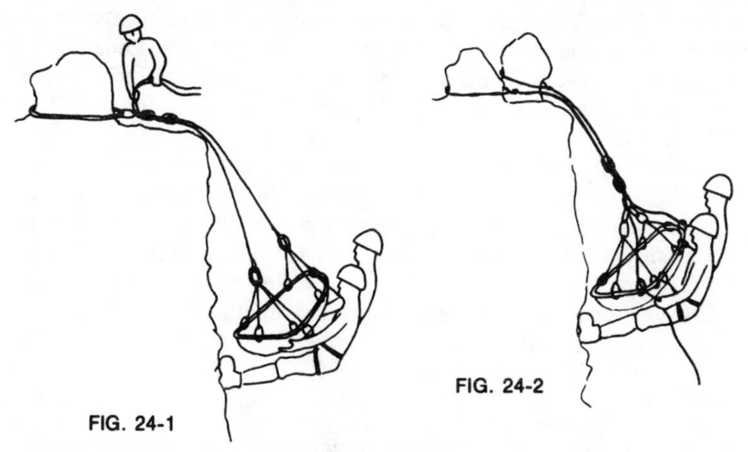

Fig. 24-1. Two litter bearers on a high angle evacuation, fixed brakes, moving rope method (preferred). **Fig. 24-2.** Two litter bearers on high angle evacuation, travelling brakes and fixed ropes, (not the preferred method).

Some advantages of the travelling brake system are the following. Since the ropes are stationary, there is little wear on the rope except at the lip of the cliff where the wear could be very severe without padding. Similarly, the fixed rope is less likely to knock rocks down onto the litter. If the evacuation is longer than one rope length, the knot joining the two ropes is perhaps not so likely to jam as with fixed brakes. It may appear that the travelling brake system has better safety against anchor failure because two anchors could be used independently, but equalization techniques (Ch. 25) can be used for the fixed brakes.

There are, however, numerous complications and major disadvantages of the travelling brakes/fixed rope method. In order to control the brakes the litter bearers will have to be attached directly to the litter. This eliminates the mobility of the litter bearers around the litter and thus their ability to control and maneuver the litter and to load the litter or to administer first aid. If the handling of the litter is tricky, the litter bearers may have an extremely difficult time controlling both the brakes and the litter simultaneously. Of course the fixed brake system does require excellent communications between the litter bearers and the brakeman on top, as is readily provided by radio if voice is not sufficient. Knots may be passed by travelling brakes without much difficulty on easy short evacuations, but sometimes the litter bearers may have their hands full in just handling the litter. Furthermore, it will take complex rigging at the litter to permit this operation to be done at all with travelling brakes on very long evacuations, due to rope stretch. On the other hand, a knot is easily passed by the team running brakes on top. Separating the operations of handling the litter and the brakes greatly simplifies the training of skilled rescuers even though all rescuers should be taught the techniques of both braking and litter handling. Finally it may be difficult to extend the lowering ropes down the cliff ahead of the litter without tangles or hangups occurring. Since the disadvantages of handling the litter with travelling brakes are so major, we will discuss the system no further, but assume that the fixed brake technique will be used.

We now consider the details of the elementary rock evacuation, including rigging the litter, special considerations of anchors, belaying, and litter handling techniques.

LITTER RIGGING

The system to be discussed involves two litter bearers descending with a Stokes litter horizontal and parallel to the wall. The brakes will be in fixed position at the top of the face. The litter must be assembled with the two halves locked together. Two 7/16 in. Goldline ropes are used for the lowering, each terminated in a bowline (with safety overhands) attached to a large locking steel carabiner. These ropes should be of matched length for ease in rope changes (below), and ideally the ropes will be also matched in elasticity, being out of the same manufacturer's lot and of similar wear. A short length of rope may join the two carabiners for added security in the case of a failure of one lowering rope. Also clipped to each of the steel carabiners will be three sling rope loops or spliced lengths each about 20 in. (50 cm) long terminated in a large carabiner which is clipped over the outer rail of the Stokes litter, as shown in Fig. 24-3. (Recall that only a few types of carabiners will clip over the litter rail.) These are the litter "Spiders." Equalization systems allowing the litter to be leveled if the pull is not vertical are undesirable since the litter may be then tilted and upset when the pull is vertical, and loading the victim is made more difficult. When the nonequalizing system shown in Fig. 24-3 is used, one of the side connections of each spider may be removed to facilitate the loading.

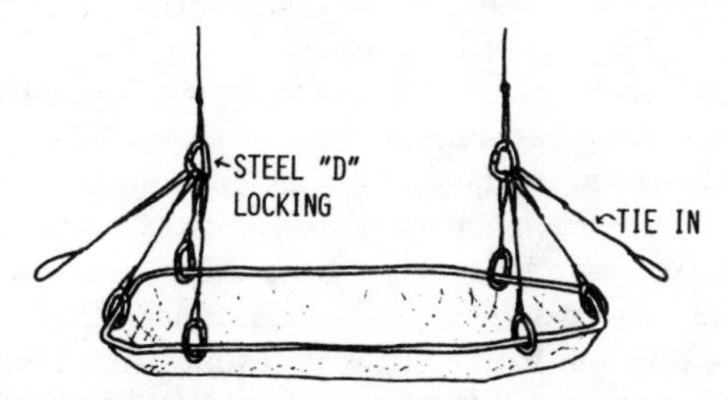

Fig. 24-3. Showing the Stokes litter rigged for high angle evacuation.

The carabiners which attach the spiders to the litter rails should be left with the gates facing in to prevent the litter bearers from inadvertently being clipped in at that point. Also attached to the steel carabiner at the top of each spider is the adjustable litter bearer tie-in which is a loop approximately 1.5 ft (.5 m) long at the shortest. The free end may be tied with a bowline as shown in Fig. 24-4 or may be eye-spliced. The prusik (which could be replaced with a tent hitch) allows for adjustment of the loop length. The litter bearer clips into the bowline, and the loop is always left clipped to the steel carabiner. By being tied

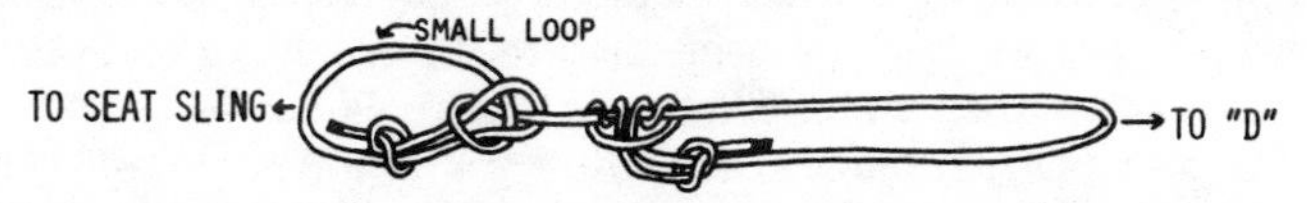

Fig. 24-4. Litter bearer tie-in. The small loops at each end of the sling could be spliced rather than tied.

into the carabiner over the litter rather than to the litter directly, the litter bearer is able to maneuver around to the end of the litter as needed to negotiate structures on the rock wall. The litter bearers should use locking or doubled carabiners to clip to the tie-in to prevent being accidentally attached to the litter or other rigging and for safety. The litter bearers will use comfortable seat slings; for long evacuations or those with loading problems, a belay seat may be used also for added comfort.

After the evacuation is complete, the lowering ropes should be removed from the spiders and the knots untied to allow the ropes to be hauled back to the summit without a knot jamming. The spiders themselves should not be dragged up the cliff because of the danger of jamming. Normally the ropes will be pulled up and carried down rather than dropped, because of the possibility of snagging or damage.

ANCHORS AND BRAKING

Anchors. The anchor location should be as directly as possible above the victim. For an evacuation on a large face when visibility is good, a spotter on the ground with a plumb bob can direct an accurate job of alignment of the anchor over the victim by communicating to the people on top. If the cliff is not vertical, the observer must observe the cliff "head-on": he must be in the vertical plane containing the fall line through the victim. If the cliff is irregular, the plumb bob technique may be unreliable, but the observer may still be the best source of information in locating the anchor. The anchor system itself is discussed in Ch. 25. If the anchor is placed in such a way that the rope will have to pass over a sharp corner of rock at the lip of the face, the corner should be "softened" by breaking the edge with a hammer and by securing padding such as a cotton duck pack (not nylon, which will be damaged by heat and friction from the ropes). Alternatively, a direction-changing pulley can be placed, but it will cause extra problems if a knot must go over the edge.

Brakes. Here we discuss braking using a double rope in a double brake bar system shown in Fig. 24-5 to lower the litter. The brake bars are normal ones which have been filed to flip freely on and off the carabiner rather than snap. This modification is useful to ease removal of the rope from the brakes as during a rope change (below) but has a potential danger (see below). The two carabiners connecting the brake system to the anchor should have the gates opposed for safety.

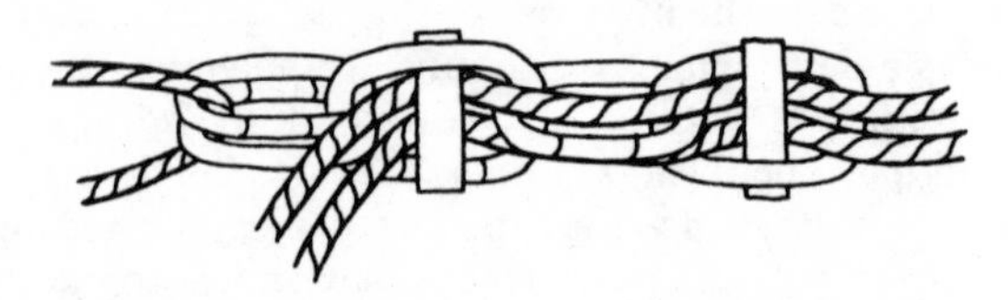

Fig. 24-5. Carabiner-brake-bar brakes for high angle evacuation.

There is only one carabiner between the two brake bars because if two 'biners were used in parallel, the friction on the ropes would be so great that the litter could not be lowered. The brake system as shown normally has the brake bars on the top so that the bars do not fall open if the ropes through the brakes go slack. However, if the brakeman is sufficiently skilled, he may feed the ropes in from the top and have the bars underneath, keeping in mind that the bars will fall open if the rope goes slack. This "upside-down" method may be found more convenient for feeding and rope changes.

Rope Management. The proper management of the rope by the team at the top is essential for efficient evacuations, and in fact the overall job on top usually involves more thought and skill than is needed by the litter bearers. The operations on top are best accomplished by at least three people: the brakeman, who directly controls the speed of descent, and at least two rope handlers with prime duty of providing slack rope with no kinks to the brakeman, and sometimes assisting on the brakes. The rope handlers' jobs are crucial since the evacuation comes to a rapid halt if they allow the ropes to become snarled. The ideal situation on top is to be able to lay the lowering ropes out in a straight line for their entire length. Then the rope handlers have an easy time assisting the brakeman. If space is limited, the ropes can be stacked separately and neatly. There may be a tendency for the rope to kink at the brakes, in which case the rope handlers will keep busy twisting and spinning the slack rope. If a knot will have to be passed by the brakes, one of the rope handlers may man the auxiliary brake system (below).

Brakeman. The general goal of the brakeman is to lower the litter smoothly and safely as directed by the litter captain. The commands to be used are as follows: "On belay" has the usual meaning and is used before the evacuation begins. "Down" means for the brakeman to feed the lowering ropes equally through the brakes at a moderate speed. "Head" means that the brakeman is to feed only the rope going to the head end of the litter, holding firm on the foot rope, and "Foot" means to lower only the foot end. Due to unequal loading on the two lowering ropes, the head or foot end may tend to be lowered faster, but the litter is normally kept horizontal for first aid reasons. The brakeman will continue to lower the head or foot end until the countermand "Down" or "Stop" is given. "Stop" of course may be given at any time. When the litter reaches the ground, the litter bearers call for "Slack" to disconnect the ropes, and finally call "Off belay."

If the brakeman is in an exposed position, he should be clipped in to an anchor himself. He may use either the main anchor or a separate one for this purpose. If the main anchor is self-equalizing (see Ch. 25), he must clip directly to the point of attachment of the brakes since this point can move as much as several feet with respect to the rock if one of the anchor points fails.

The brakeman obviously plays an important part in the successful evacuation. Let us consider here some of the details of his job. Best manual dexterity is achieved without gloves, but the skilled brakeman may wish to use them for added safety. He will not grab a brake bar which may be hot. To maintain full control of the lowering, the brakeman never lets go of the ropes until tied off (see below) or "Off belay." The brakeman should keep the descent smooth and steady, feeding the ropes equally into the brakes, never allowing a kink to form. A kink may jam in the brake and be extremely difficult to release. Smoothness is easily produced if the loading by the litter is steady and sufficiently large that the brakeman must maintain a moderate grip on the ropes holding both ropes together in one hand and letting the litter do the pulling. However, if the loading is too light (say two lightweight litter bearers and an empty litter), two brake bars provide too much friction, and the ropes must be pushed into the brakes. If the loading is very light, the upper brake bar can be temporarily bypassed but kept ready for immediate use by having a rope handler feed slack through the upper brake bar while the brakeman controls the lowering by using only the lower bar. The upper bar is kept in place and may be brought back into service by releasing the slack rope between the brake bars.

The litter should normally remain horizontal, and thus the two lowering ropes should be fed equally into the brakes. One rope may tend to feed faster than the other due to unequal loading or unmatched ropes. The ropes may be grasped together by one hand and fed equally, even with unbalanced loads. It is often a help to the brakeman to have a rope handler pull the rope which is not feeding rapidly enough through the brakes. This is particularly useful when the litter is lightly loaded. In an extreme case of unequal feeding, one rope may be slacked around the upper brake bar and fed into the lower brake while the other rope passes through both bars. The brakeman must have an assistant to use this technique.

If the command "Stop" is given and will apply for only a short time, the brakeman simply holds the ropes. For added friction he may increase the angle of wrap of the rope around the upper brake bar to the point of having the slack side parallel to the loaded ropes to the litter, as shown in Fig. 24-6. If quite a bit more friction is desired, the brakeman may pass the rope around his hips; three bars with the doubled rope will provide too much friction for any normal evacuation. For a longer "Stop," as during a loading problem, the brakeman may tie off the lowering ropes as shown in Fig. 24-7.

Fig. 24-6. The direction of pull on the ropes by the brakeman may be as shown for added friction.

Fig. 24-7. Showing a method of tying off the brakes for lengthy stops.

When the litter reaches the ground and the call "Slack" is given, the brakeman should rapidly feed the rope through the brakes, perhaps with an assistant pulling the ropes towards the litter. To ease this job, one brake can be released. One brake is to be left on since otherwise there is some danger that the rope could get away. The upper brake is easily released if the brakeman grasps the ropes and the carabiner joining the brakes thus preventing the ropes from sliding through. It helps to be wearing gloves. The tension on the ropes at this time should be little more than rope weight, and the brakeman should be able to hold this load easily by gripping the rope against the carabiner. However, if he cannot hold the rope readily, he can get more friction by grasping the lower brake bar, carabiner and ropes by one hand, remembering that the brake bar may be hot. Then there is no tension on the rope passing through the upper brake, which can be released by pushing slack rope into the brake and flipping the bar open.

If the brake bars become quite hot, as upon lowering of a heavy load or during any high speed descent, the ropes should not be allowed to come to rest under tension in the brakes, otherwise there may be some melting of the rope surface. If such a situation can be anticipated, an auxiliary system can be set up exactly as for the rope change, described below. The cool auxiliary brakes can take the load when the main ropes stop.

On a very high speed descent, say greater than 120 ft/min (40 m/min) (speed useful in training but not in an actual evacuation), the ropes should not be brand new, and the brakeman must be very careful never to allow kinks to get into the brakes. Since kinks can form only if there is some slack in the rope between the brakeman's (gloved) hand and the brakes, the minimum friction for which the brakeman can control the lowering should be used. The ropes may be fed rapidly by holding the ropes together in one hand about 2 ft (.6 m) from the brake and feeding this two-foot length into the brake smoothly. As the first hand approaches the brake, the other grasps another 2 ft (.6 m) and feeds it, and so forth. With this technique the ropes move continuously, never stopping or jerking. During such high speed lowering, precautions regarding hot brakes as discussed above should be taken. Water may be poured on the brakes to keep them cool.

BRAKE PLATES

Special brake plates may be used to provide friction on the lowering ropes, instead of using carabiner and brake bars or the equivalent improvised from carabiners alone.

One type of brake plate has been developed for belaying a climber and can be used for rappelling. This plate, called the "Sticht" plate, is sketched in Fig. 24-8 and is shown in use in Fig. 24-8[An alternate form is a chain link. A load of up to about 350 lbs (160 kg) may be readily held. The plate is satisfactory for occasional holding of loads in climbing but is not recommended for use in rescue because it causes rapid wear on the rope and does not have the load or heat capacity needed.

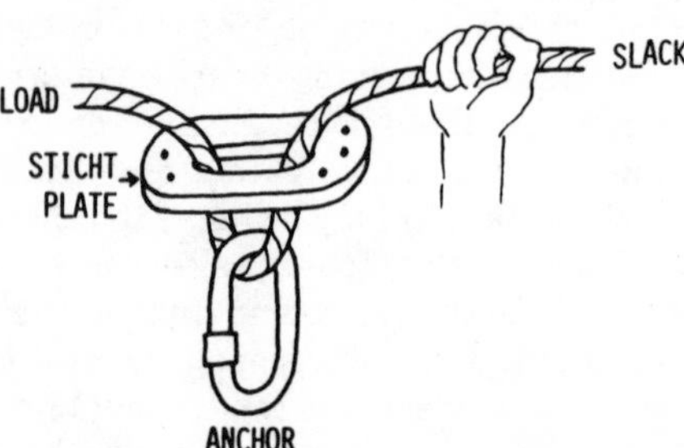

Fig. 24-8. The Sticht plate, showing method of use.

Another type of brake plate, ideally suited for rescue, is shown in Fig. 24-9a, and is about 11 in. long, 3 in. wide and .5 in. thick (28x7x1.2 cm) made of hard alloy aluminum. It is highly specialized but quite versatile in its job of replacing the carabiner brake for nylon rope as used in rescue. Because of the large mass and surface area of the plate, it dissipates heat readily, and the brakeman need not worry about the plate heating enough to damage the rope. This is in contrast to the carabiner-brake system which can get quite hot and melt surface fibers of the ropes if the ropes come to rest on the hot brake bars. Another significant advantage of the brake plate is the ease with which the total friction can be adjusted. Fig. 24-9a shows the plate fully wrapped with double lowering ropes for maximum friction, allowing the brakeman to hold over 1000 lbs (450 kg) with moderate grip on the ropes. Wraps may be readily removed and added as needed at the anchor end even with tension on the ropes, and the pattern may be altered with ease, giving a large range of usable friction.

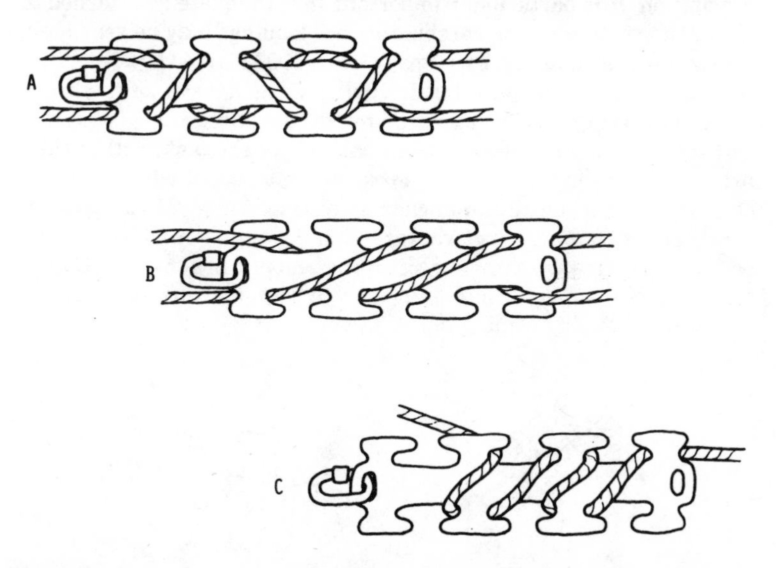

Fig. 24-9. Rescue brake plate. a) Wrapped for maximum friction, b) improperly wrapped—too little friction, c) wrapped for single strand lowering, as on a scree evacuation.

In use the plate is attached to the anchor system by one chrome-vanadium locking carabiner or two opposed aluminum ones, side-by-side. The ropes should be wrapped as shown in Fig. 24-9a if the initial loading on the ropes may be large; friction is easily reduced. The brakeman feeds the ropes equally by gripping both ropes together, just as for the carabiner-brake-bar system. If the ropes are unbalanced, the wrapping pattern may be altered to increase or reduce the friction on one rope. Reducing the angle of wrapping greatly reduces friction, as can be seen by comparing Fig. 24-9b to 24-9a. In the case of small loading, wraps should be reduced to the point where the brakeman has to grip the rope a moderate amount. With too much friction, control is not good, and it is difficult to feed the ropes equally and smoothly. Also, there is danger of the ropes twisting out of the slots with kinking. The typical high angle evacuation with two litter bearers and loaded litter will require use of two of the three slot-pairs on the plate, for a loading of say 400 lbs (180 kg), and up to about 650 lbs (300 kg) may be held with this pattern. One slot-pair is about equivalent to one carabiner-brake-bar.

The plate may also be used for single rope lowering, as on a scree evacuation. It is particularly important that the plate be attached to the anchor with a strong carabiner, since loadings may be very high. The wrap pattern in Fig. 24-9c easily holds 1000 lbs (450 kg). Note that this pattern is not a spiral but is applied from one side of the brake plate only. Wraps can be added or removed as needed.

If the brakeman prefers to be to one side of the plate rather than behind it, the direction of the ropes can be changed with the extra carabiners attached to the anchor as shown in Fig. 24-10. Such an arrangement has the disadvantage that friction cannot be altered easily. The extra carabiners reduce the amount of tension required from the brakeman to maintain smooth running and prevent the ropes from possibly coming out of the slots.

Fig. 24-10. The brake plate with carabiners for guiding rope.

KNOT PASS (ROPE CHANGE)

A belayed evacuation longer than one rope length (200 ft or 60 m —the length of the standard rescue rope) can be continued in one of two ways: either by setting up a new anchor and brake system lower down the evacuation path, or by tying in another length of rope. Here we will consider only the second situation since it is usually less practical to use the first technique on a high angle wall. We assume that the brakes are fixed at an anchor, that there are two lowering ropes to the litter being lowered, and that the litter is always fully supported by the ropes. Since the knot used to join the second set of ropes to the first cannot pass through the carabiner-brake-bar or brake plate system without jamming, the load must be taken temporarily on a second (auxiliary) brake system, allowing the first (main) system to be released and the main lowering ropes removed while the knots are passed. After the main brakes are put back on the ropes, the litter is lowered by the auxiliary system until the slack is out of the main ropes and the main system can take the load. Then the auxiliary system is released and removed. Note that the auxiliary system must be able to actually lower the load and relieve tension on itself so that it can be removed. The details of the procedure are now given.

It should be known in advance that the rope change will be necessary. The main lowering ropes to the litter should be of matched length so that both knots can be passed at the same time. Preparation can be made by connecting the complete auxiliary brake system shown in Fig. 24-11 to the anchor with the auxiliary ropes placed in the auxiliary brakes. Only about 10 to 15 ft (3-5 m) of lowering rope is needed for each auxiliary rope. Ends from an anchor rope, or even the far ends of the second main lowering ropes, may be used. A small bowline with safety overhand is tied into the end of each auxiliary rope, and a carabiner is clipped into each loop. These carabiners will be clipped to short slings which will be tied as prusik knots on the

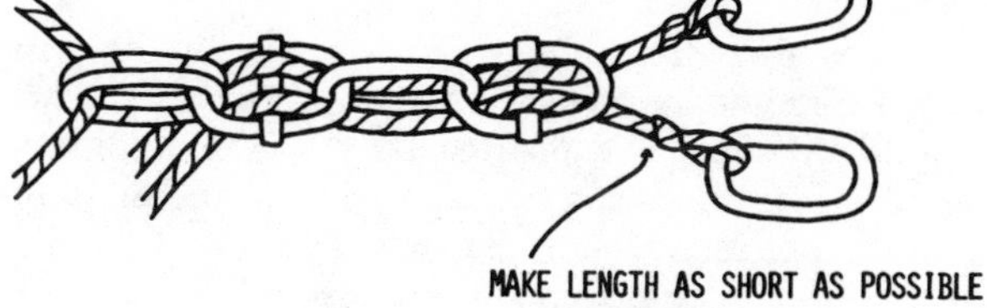

Fig. 24-11. Auxiliary brakes for knot pass. The loops are tied small.

main ropes. Finally the bowlines are pulled back as close to the brakes as possible to minimize rope stretch. The setup should be completed well in advance of the actual knot pass (rope change).

When there are 6 to 10 ft (2-3 m) of main rope left, the second set of main ropes can be tied to the first main ropes, using a double sheet bend with three safety overhands on each tail. When there are about 3 ft (1 m) but no less than 18 in. (.5 m) of main rope between the main brakes and the double sheet bend knots, the lowering is stopped. These knots should never be allowed to reach the brakes, or the rope change will be made extremely difficult. At this time prusiks can be placed on the main ropes between the litter and the main brakes, using three wraps. (Jumars should not be used because of inadequate margin of safety.) The prusik slings are clipped to the carabiners on the auxiliary ropes, and the prusiks are pulled towards the litter and set tight, with all of the slack out of the ropes in the auxiliary brake system. For faster rope changes, the prusiks may be placed loosely on the main ropes well in advance of stopping these ropes. They must be kept from setting themselves too soon, however. The overall setup is shown in Fig. 24-12.

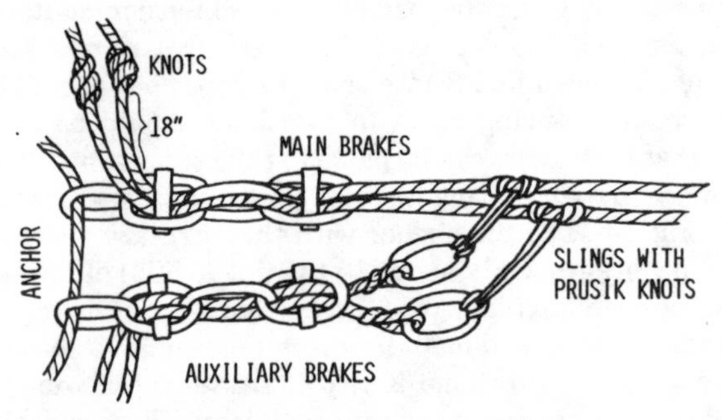

Fig. 24-12. Showing complete setup for knot pass. Three-wrap prusiks should be used, and the knots joining main ropes are double sheet bends with safeties. A separate anchor may be used for the auxiliary brakes.

With a second brakeman holding firmly on the auxiliary ropes, the main ropes are gradually released, making sure that the prusiks do not slip, until the litter is supported fully by the auxiliary brakes. Then the first main ropes can be removed from the main brakes so that the knots are immediately below the brakes. CAUTION: The knots must be tied in the main ropes before the ropes are removed from the main brakes. This is necessary to prevent the end of a main rope from passing through a prusik if the prusik should inadvertently slip on a main lowering rope during the period when the ropes are removed from the main brakes. The auxiliary brakes are released gradually with the main ropes held tight until the litter is once again supported fully by the main ropes. The prusiks are removed, and the evacuation is continued.

The prusik slings are best made of 5/16 in. diameter nylon rope, and preferably spliced to form loops of about 1.5 ft (.5 m) circumference. The three-wrap prusik suggested above will usually slip on 7/16 in. Goldline at over 1000 lbs (450 kg). The slings are short to minimize stretch, and are spliced rather than tied to ease tying and particularly removal of the loops from the main ropes. The spliced sling may be removed from the rope very easily by simply pulling on the sling at the center of the prusik knot after the knot is loosened. A prusik set by loading can be broken loose by hitting its end hard with the heel of the hand.

The prusiks should not be allowed to scrape over the rock for several reasons. If they go over the edge of the cliff, recovery may be difficult. Also, if a prusik is pushed from its end, it may slide on the rope (this property may be used to release the knot at the appropriate time). If space is limited and the knot must pass over the rock, the knot can be lifted by clipping a carabiner around the rope near the prusik and lifting as the knot moves along. This same technique also may be used to ease the movement of the double sheet bend over the rock.

If a mistake is made and a knot joining main ropes is allowed to jam into the brake, a great deal of effort will be required to pull up on the lowering rope to free the knot and move the brake bar. If the knot is just barely into the brake so that sufficient slack (6 in. or 15 cm) is unavailable to lift the brake bar, an angle piton may be inserted immediately next to the brake bar and used for added leverage to pry up on the rope, allowing the brake to be opened. But if the knot is jammed tightly into the brake, it may be necessary to set a prusik on the main rope and to use a hauling system with mechanical advantage. This is best done using the main anchor system for the hauling anchor to avoid having to overcome the stretch in the anchor rope itself. If the hauling system is effective, sufficient slack can be brought up on the main ropes to release the knot from the brakes. About 6 in. (15 cm) of slack is needed for opening a brake bar and somewhat less for knot removal from the brake plate. But if only say 2 in. (5 cm) of slack is available easily from the hauling system, the main brakes can be unclipped from the anchor itself and the jammed knot removed.

HANDLING THE LITTER

We will consider here only the elementary techniques of handling the litter. The general goal is to descend safely and smoothly with the litter.

Safety covers many items. 1) The litter bearer will always wear hardhat and pack. The reason for the latter is that in the case of small rock fall towards the helpless victim, the litter bearers can lean over the victim, shielding him, and the packs and hardhats protect the litter bearers. The victim might wear a hardhat too. A plastic or fiberglass shield could be used to cover and protect the victim, but is a nuisance to transport to the scene, and may greatly hinder loading and first aid. 2) A redundant litter bearer tie-in is sometimes used for safety, and locking or doubled carabiners should always be used both to prevent the litter bearer tie-in from being released accidentally and to prevent the litter bearer from inadvertently being hitched directly to the litter or rigging. Also, the litter bearers should be sure that the gates of the carabiners attaching the spiders to the litter rails are all facing in. Only during the first stages of the evacuation is this a problem, that is, in working the litter over the lip of the cliff. Once the weight of the litter is fully supported by the lowering ropes, these carabiners stay put. 3) Smooth handling of the litter by skilled litter bearers is the best way to insure a safe ride down for the victim, since banging the litter against the rock is very hard on the victim, and poor handling of the litter may result in dangerous positions for the litter bearers.

In starting the evacuation the litter bearers may have to carry the litter a short distance at the top of the face taking care that the ropes are positioned over a smooth rounded edge of the cliff and that the spider carabiners have gates facing in. Once their weight is on the lowering ropes, the litter bearers' main job is to hold the litter away from the rock, using their feet against the rock as in rappelling to maintain footing. The litter bearer's position on a nearly vertical wall is to be hanging from his tie-in which may be a comfortable seat sling, or even a belay seat too, for added comfort during a long evacuation. This tie-in is adjusted to a length such that the litter bearer can easily reach the rock with his feet under the litter. For visibility and maneuverability on high speed descents the tie-in would be extra long. The litter bearers are normally on the outside of the litter (away from the rock), gripping the outer or an underneath rail to hold the litter away from the rock, as in Fig. 24-13. The inside underneath rail may be used to pull the litter still farther off the rock to clear projections, etc., or to level the litter if loading is uneven. Occasionally the rail at the cliff face is grasped, but care must be taken to avoid getting crushed hands.

Throughout the descent, there must be good communications between the litter bearers and brakeman. Normally the most competent litter bearer is the litter captain. The bearer at the head end should be lighter in weight to better equalize the loading on each lowering rope, since the victim is heavier at the head end. The litter captain will give the commands as described above: "On belay," "Down," "Head," "Foot," "Slow," "Faster," "Stop," "Slack," "Off belay."

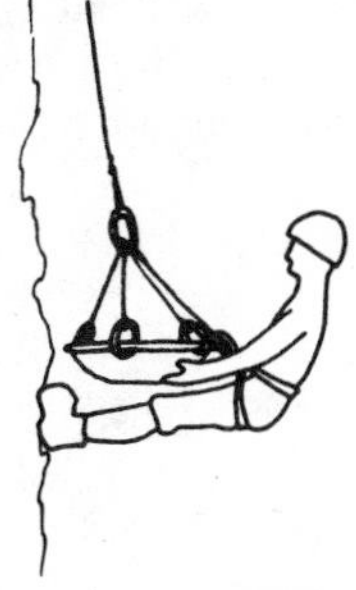

Fig. 24-13. Showing position of one of the two litter bearers. The litter bearer tie-in may be longer for better visibility underfoot.

If voice and radio communications fail, hand signals by the litter bearers on descent may be used. A spotter stationed with a good view may be needed as a relay. Suitable signals, given with one hand only, are: Wave overhead for "Stop;" point repeatedly to foot (head) (down) for "Foot" ("Head") ("Down").

The descent is easy on flat, smooth, vertical walls. On a wall with structure, footwork techniques as in rappelling are used, that is, the litter bearers try to keep their legs essentially perpendicular to the wall and spread comfortably apart. To negotiate a small overhang, the litter bearers go to the ends of the litter and try to get their feet on the rock below the lip of the overhang, still holding the litter at their sides away from the rock. On a big overhang where the rock below cannot be reached, just before the litter is at the overhang, the litter bearers again go to the end of the litter and keep their feet on the lip of the overhang, holding the litter at their sides away from the rock. As the litter descends past the overhang, the litter bearers may have their feet above their heads. When the litter is below the overhang, the litter bearers push off with their feet and let the litter swing in, but they must not do this too soon. Dihedrals are trickier yet. A litter bearer may get between the litter and rock with his hips at the litter and his feet on the rock wall. Fancy techniques such as swinging the litter through a 180° turn may be used. *Experience is the best guide to technique.* A litter bearer cannot become expert by reading a book.

BASIC LOADING TECHNIQUE

The basic technique of loading a helpless victim is to stop the litter a short distance above him, allowing for the slow inevitable stretch of the ropes which takes place over several minutes. The litter should be stopped high enough so that when the victim is in the litter, his weight is fully supported by the litter and not by his tie-in to the rock, or else the litter bearers will have problems releasing this tie-in. Also, the litter must be properly oriented head and foot with respect to the victim, rotating either the litter or the victim if necessary. The litter may be rotated well in advance of the litter reaching the victim by some aerobatics on the part of the litter bearers, or by having the brakeman lower only one end of the litter until it is vertical. The rotation is then easily performed, and then the high end is lowered until the litter is once again horizontal.

If necessary one or two inside spider connections are removed from the litter rail to load the victim. To get a stance to lift the victim, the litter bearers stand on the litter rails (but not the chicken wire mesh), or in stirrups clipped to the litter rail or lowering rope, or go to the rock. They must, of course, be careful not to dump the litter when any of the spider connections are removed. They then load the victim, who must be securely padded as required for first aid, and secured with his hands inside. There is a tendency for the victim to grab the litter rail just at the wrong moments and have his hands injured. At all times the victim must be tied in, either to the wall or to the litter, most especially for panicky victims. When the victim is loaded, the spider connections are replaced, and the evacuation continued.

Further details of loading are given in Ch. 32.

STEEL CABLE EVACUATIONS

With steel cable, the litter rigging can be the same as shown in Fig. 24-3 with the addition of a yoke to join the spiders to the single lowering cable. The yoke must not allow the litter to tip head to foot or side to side. A pole about 4 or 5 ft (1.5 m) long can be used to hold the main spider carabiners apart over the litter, but this is not essential. If the two litter bearers both clip their tie-ins to the same point on the rigging, they tend to be always bumping into each other. As on the steep scree evacuation, it is very important to insert a shock absorber at the litter end of the cable; if the litter or a connector hangs up and then suddenly releases, the shock absorber will prevent disastrous loadings. At the top of the evac, the rigging will be about the same as for the cable scree evacuation, but a direction-changing pulley and possibly an A-frame (Ch. 27) might be needed at the lip of the cliff.

The litter bearers must be careful to avoid putting shock loads on the cable. Because there is only a single cable and thus no ability to have head and foot lowered independently, they may have a more difficult time maneuvering the litter over rock faces with structure such as dihedrals and overhangs, and they may find that the litter rotates if it hangs completely free from the rock face (see discussion of swivels in Ch. 10). There is also a psychological problem of security, comparing the thin single cable to the two substantial-appearing nylon ropes.

LOWERING THE VICTIM WITHOUT LITTER

Tragsitz. In cases where a victim is uninjured or slightly injured, rescuers may use the tragsitz to perform the evacuation rapidly instead of using a litter. The Austrian tragsitz is a canvas and leather affair, and newer versions have been made of the more modern materials, nylon cloth and webbing. Shown in Fig. 24-14, the tragsitz looks somewhat like a backpack, and is designed to be worn like a pack, carrying the victim "piggyback" on a rescuer. The victim is to be seated with not only his buttocks but also his thighs well supported by the large pouch. If the victim is not placed properly in the seat, circulation in his legs will be impaired; an extra sling to a foot of the victim may be used so that occasionally he can transfer some of his weight to the foot. If the seat is unavailable, one can be improvised from rope alone (see below).

If the victim is on flat ground or on a wide ledge, the tragsitz may be loaded by the rescuer sitting and the victim getting in; then the rescuer rolls into a kneeling position with the victim "riding" on the back of the rescuer, at which time the rescuer can stand up.

Since the weight of the victim is far greater than that which the usual rescuer can carry on his back easily, the tragsitz is designed so that the victim's weight is taken largely by the lowering rope once the rescuer gets onto a steep wall. Thus, both the rescuer and the victim are supported by the lowering rope, and the rescuer just controls the motion of the victim and keeps the victim from bouncing against the wall. There must be an adjustment of the tie-in from either the victim or the rescuer to the lowering rope so that the victim rides at a comfortable place on the rescuer's back.

If the victim is loaded on a large, steep face with considerable amount of lowering rope out, his weight may be transferred to the rope before he is released from his tie-in to the wall by the crew on top pulling up on the rope after the victim is loaded. If this procedure is not done, the rescuer and victim will go for a sudden ride when the extra weight of the victim is added to that of the rescuer supported by the lowering rope.

Two techniques of lowering may be used, either fixed brakes anchored at the top of the evacuation, or travelling brakes at the rescuer. In using the first technique, a loop (bowline with safety) is tied in the lower end of the single lowering rope, and the rescuer ties into this loop with a sling from his seat sling so that the end of the rope is just above his head during lowering. Also, the short support tie from the tragsitz is clipped to this loop, resulting in rescuer and victim both suspended from the lowering rope. The brakeman, using double or triple brake bars or equivalent (tree wrap, brake plate), merely lowers the victim and rescuer down the cliff. The only difficult part of the evacuation is in getting started, because the rescuer must carry the full weight of the victim and must simultaneously work his way over the edge of the cliff. This general method also works well using steel cable for the lowering operation, making the obvious changes in braking.

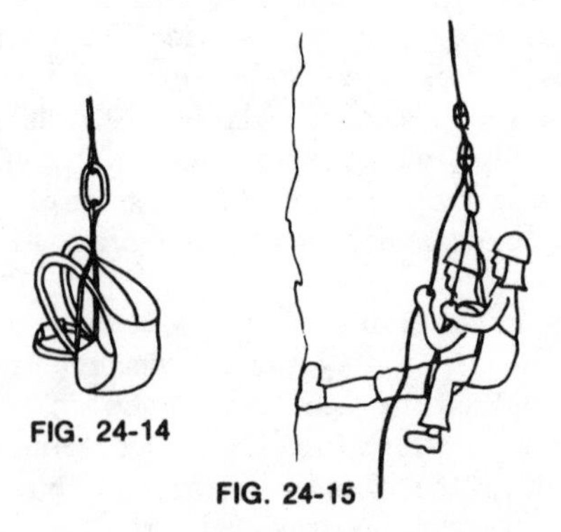

Fig. 24-14. Tragsitz. Worn like a pack. **Fig. 24-15.** The tragsitz in use.

Instead of having the brakeman lower rescuer and victim, the rescuer may lower himself and rider just as in rappelling. But the brake system must now be positioned over the rescuer's head, and both victim and rescuer are suspended from the brakes, as shown in Fig. 24-15. The rescuer controls the speed by pulling on the slack rappel rope. This travelling brake system may be preferred (using nylon rope, not steel cable) when the cliff face is rather uniform without overhangs and dihedrals, etc., and thus is an easy rappel. The brakes used should provide somewhat more friction than needed for the usual single man rappel. The rescuer is well advised to use a belay. Fixed brakes should be used if a knot needs to be passed.

Rope Seat Lowering. If a victim is uninjured but merely stuck and is able to help himself to considerable extent, he may be lowered using the three loop system (triple bowline) shown in Fig. 24-16. The victim sits in the loops as shown in Fig. 24-17, with chest sling for safety, and is lowered by a brakeman using any convenient brake. The leg loops as shown provide much more comfort for the victim than does just a bowline on a coil waist loop. A waist loop alone should not be used if the victim's entire weight is to be on the rope.

The discussions of the tragsitz and rope seat are continued in Ch. 31.

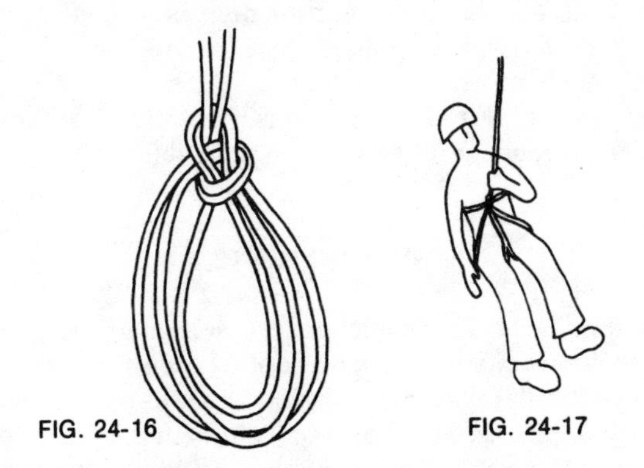

Fig. 24-16. Triple bowline. **Fig. 24-17.** The triple bowline as an improvised seat.

CHAPTER 25

ANCHORS FOR RESCUE I: ROCK

Every technical evacuation requires an anchor. Often the anchors used are very simple, such as a tree or boulder; at other times a system involving several relatively weak anchor points will be used. Anchors for rescue must be completely safe and will usually support loads larger than normally encountered in rock climbing. The rock climber does not need very solid anchors in aid climbing, and he may be willing to use weak anchor points (pitons etc.) all too frequently in fifth class climbing, since he trusts that he will not often fall. However, the loadings in mountain rescue are relatively predictable and rather large; the rock climber seldom encounters the 1000 lb (450 kg) stresses that are routine in mountain rescue systems.

This chapter will deal first with anchor points, ranging from elementary to unusual. The second section discusses equalizing systems, which are used to distribute the stresses of the load among several independent anchor points, any one of which may be too weak to support the full load. Finally, some considerations of anchor location are given. The discussion of snow anchors is left to Ch. 29.

ANCHOR POINTS

The basis for an evacuation anchor system is an anchor point. Some anchor points are very simple, such as a sling around a tree or boulder; others involve the standard rock climbing hardware including pitons, nuts, etc. Still others used in rescue include such miscellaneous forms as anchoring to a car. Most of the anchor points discussed below are familiar to the rock climber skilled in fifth and sixth class techniques. The discussions are not intended to be a text for rock climbers but are given as a review and as background to predicting anchor strengths.

Natural Anchor Points. If a very sturdy green tree is available, two or three turns of 7/16 in. rope low around the tree tied to form a loop (double sheet bend or fisherman's) or a climber's loop sling of suitably strong material passed low around the tree will serve. One complete turn should be taken directly around the tree to prevent the loop from sliding up or down the trunk. The tree anchor-brake has already been discussed in Ch. 23.

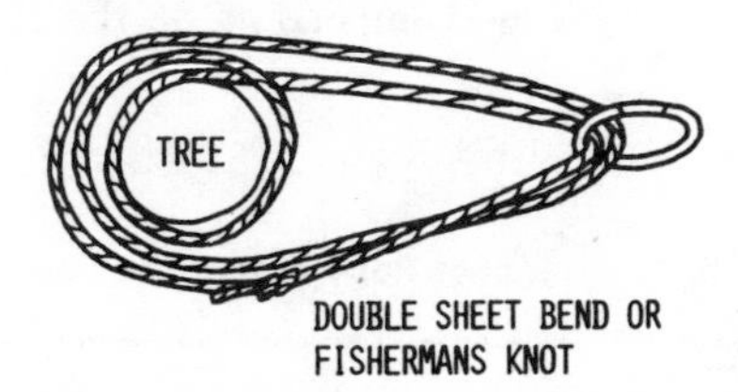

Fig. 25-1. Anchor rope on tree. An extra turn should be taken directly around the tree.

Instead of a tree, a very large boulder that will not roll, a solid chockstone, or a rock projection will serve as the anchor. A strong loop sling can be used, or two or three turns of 7/16 in. rope may be passed around the rock, using as much as 50 to 100 ft (15-30 m) of rope if necessary. The following precautions should be taken: a) The rope must not slip off when pulled in the direction of the evacuation. Extra slings and carabiners may be required to hold the anchor rope in place. b) There must be no sharp corners which could cut the rope. Such corners can be padded with spare clothing, a packsack, etc., or may be rounded off using a piton hammer. c) The lengths of all turns should be equalized to distribute the load between the loops. d) The angle between strands at the brake system attachment point should be less than 90°, as shown in Fig. 25-2, to prevent larger loading in the anchor

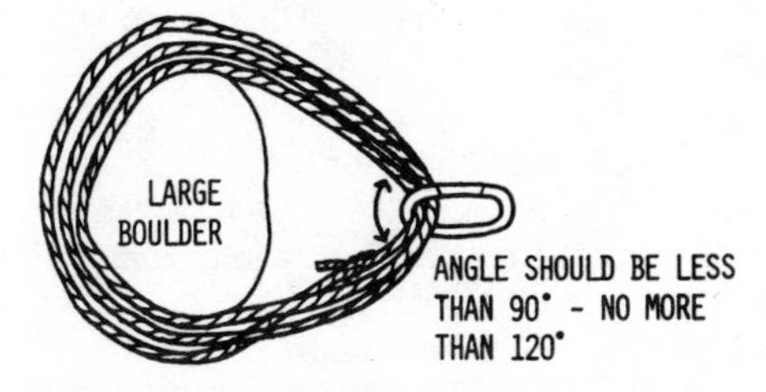

Fig. 25-2. Showing anchor rope on boulder. Sharp corners on the rock should be padded.

than in the evacuation belay rope. Table 25-1 shows the relative stress in the anchor rope when a single turn of rope around a boulder is used, where the angle is that shown in Fig. 25-2 or in Table 25-1.

Piton Anchor Points. When natural anchors are unavailable, pitons will be the primary form of anchors for rescue. Their strength depends first on the intrinsic strength of the piton itself as discussed in Ch. 7, and, second and most important, on the placement.

Table 25-1

Ratio of Anchor Rope Tension to Load

Angle θ	2-Piton Anchor
150	1.94
120	1.00
90	.71
60	.58
45	.54

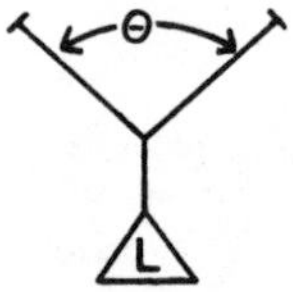

The holding power of a piton depends to a great extent on the nature of the crack. The ideal situation is a horizontal crack in sound rock into which is driven a horizontal piton (angle or blade) which is loaded downwards perpendicular to the crack. Holding powers of well-driven chromoly pitons are typically in excess of 800 lbs (360 kg) up to the limit of the eye or blade of the piton (see references at the end of the chapter). The corresponding figures for soft iron pitons range upwards from only a few hundred pounds (100 or so kilograms) with the piton failing by oozing from the crack. Thus, the chromoly pitons may be much more reliable in holding large loads. In vertical cracks with downward pull, the holding power again ranges upwards from a few hundred pounds. If the placement is not good, the holding power may be far below these figures, and sometimes an apparently good placement turns out to be very bad. All the figures assume that the load is attached to the piton with a carabiner. If a rope or web sling is used directly on the piton, the sling will fail at only a few hundred pounds (perhaps 200 or so kg) due to the relatively sharp edge of the piton cutting the sling.

The conclusion of numerous field tests is that it is rather difficult to predict quantitatively in advance the actual holding power of a piton. However, a rough estimate of the overall quality of the piton/crack system is made by experienced rock climbers for chromoly pitons by driving the piton in most of the way, then tapping downwards and sideways on the head to observe any shifting, then driving to the eye and retesting. Very hard driving is the best security in solid crack systems, but it is possible to overdrive a piton and weaken the anchor point. For example, if the crack is bottoming, hard driving may kick the piton out of the crack. Also, overdriving may stress the surrounding rock so greatly that it fractures. Furthermore, driving a piton hard into an expanding crack may greatly lessen the holding power.

As rock climbers know, a piton which is too big for its crack and cannot be driven in to the eye should be tied off next to the rock with a sling and should not be relied on to hold a load attached to the eye. The sling will break at the blade at perhaps 500 lbs (230 kg). Also, if a crack is too big for available pitons, two or more pitons may be nested, sometimes with considerable security.

As mentioned above, soft iron pitons are inherently much weaker than chromoly, but they have good use. If a piton must be abandoned as an anchor, the cheaper soft iron might be preferred, since there is a factor of about five in cost, but cost is seldom a consideration in rescue. A more significant use for soft iron is for anchors in rather loose rock or twisty cracks. The soft iron, being malleable, tends to be somewhat sticky and soft compared to chromoly, and is able to follow bends and conform to the crack. Thus soft iron may be better than chromoly in cracks where the rock may shift somewhat, and also for rotten rock.

The placement of pitons for safe anchor points requires judgment which is acquired only from extensive climbing experience. For safety in rescue, pitons should always be used in combination with an equalizing anchor system described below, never trusting one piton alone.

Nuts and Chockstones. To hold a load, a nut must obviously be placed in a crack which narrows in the direction of pull, and the pull must not rotate the nut out of the crack. Not all crack structures are suitable for nuts, but vertical cracks and deep rounded cracks in granite are often quite good, the latter being poor for holding pitons. Sound rock may hold both pitons and nuts very well. But in a less than ideal situation, if the rock crumbles at the point of contact or moves slightly under sudden loading, the nut may settle to a new solid position, whereas a chromoly piton is likely to give way completely.

When using nuts under high load conditions, the sling on which the nut is threaded should not be used since the sling may fail at less than 1000 lbs (450 kg). (Steel cable is stronger.) Instead, the nut should be treated as a chockstone (next paragraph) with a separate web sling or rope placed around the nut in the crack. After heavy loading the nut may be very difficult to remove.

In very large cracks or grooves, small boulders or even tree limbs may be placed and used as very effective natural chockstones. However, the material for the chockstone should be chosen carefully, keeping in mind that soft sandstone and some conglomerates often crumble easily, and other rock such as slate may fracture or cleave on loading. The chockstone should be placed with its smallest dimension across the crack, as shown in Fig. 25-3; otherwise it could rotate and fall out.

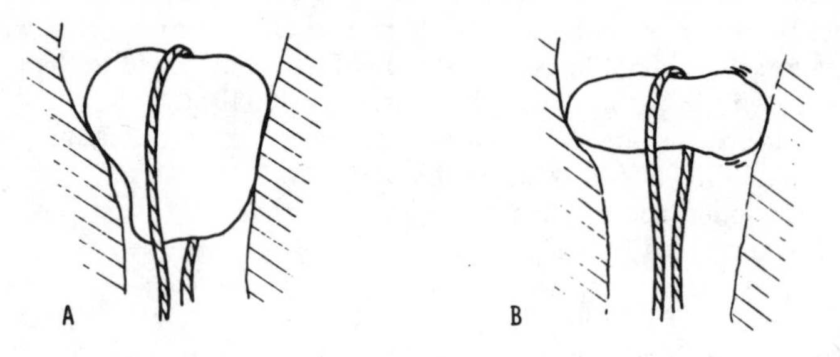

Fig. 25-3. Chockstone, showing a) correct, and b) incorrect placement.

Bolts. Characteristics of various types of bolts suitable for use in mountain rescue have been described in Ch. 7. We discuss here some aspects of bolt placement.

In drilling the hole with either a self-driving bolt or percussion drill, the drill should be rotated slightly between every blow of the hammer, and the hole should be cleaned out using the blowtube after every five to ten hammer blows. Throughout drilling, the drill should be kept perpendicular to the rock face to avoid unnecessarily enlarging the hole diameter. The teeth of a self-driving bolt may need to be cleared during driving, and, if the rock is very hard, the bolt may have to be replaced before the hole is completed. Likewise, the teeth of a percussion drill will need to be sharpened occasionally.

In the case of a self-driving bolt, the hole should be deep enough that the end of the bolt is flush with the face of the rock; however, the hole for a Rawl drive must be deeper than the length of the bolt. The self-driving bolt is set by inserting the expansion pin and pounding with very few hard blows. Additional pounding will usually loosen the bolt. The hanger is attached snugly with a cap screw, but not extremely tightly to avoid rotating the bolt in its hole. The cap screw may be weakened by use and should be discarded rather than reused.

Bolts should be placed such that the pull will be across and not along the axis of the bolt, to prevent the bolt from being levered out of the hole by the hanger when the load is applied. See the discussion in Ch. 7 regarding types of hangers. Since a single bolt should not be trusted for a complete evacuation anchor, several should be placed, and an equalizing anchor system (below) used. Each bolt should be placed at least 1 ft (.3 m) from the nearest bolt or rock edge to prevent major fracturing of the rock when the bolt itself is set.

A hole drilled in soft rock tends to become very enlarged, often so much that the normal size bolt for the drill used will not hold in the hole. Thus for soft rock, either extra-large bolts will be needed, or an extra-small drill must be used. An effective alternative is to drive a small angle piton into the hole instead of using a bolt.

Deadmen and Pickets. Occasionally a rescue anchor must be set up in a location without rocks or trees, but in just earth at the top of a large cliff. The following paragraphs deal with setting up an anchor in dirt. The techniques are similar to those used for snow anchors (Ch. 29) and may also be used with effort in loose scree.

The classic deadman in dirt consists simply of a log or other suitable object (the deadman) buried in perhaps 2 or 3 ft (.6-1 m) of dirt, in the configuration of Fig. 25-4. The log is placed and buried in a trench cut at right angles to the direction of pull, as shown. The anchor rope is tied around the log. This rope goes in a small slot cut in the ground from the log to a few feet (meters) in front of the log. If it is desired to prevent the rope from cutting deeper into the ground, a small log

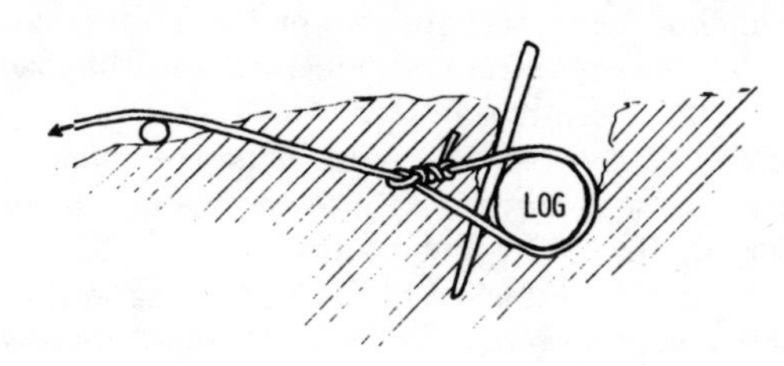

Fig. 25-4. Showing placement of deadman in earth. A slot is cut in the ground for the rope to the load.

or other object may be placed under the rope where it comes to the surface. In case the dirt is somewhat loose, stakes can be driven next to the log as shown in Fig. 25-4 for additional security.

A large suitable log very likely may not be available for the deadman, but any reasonably large object may be used instead. In the absence of such a large object, several small ones could be used either tied together or independently, with an equalizing anchor system (described below). The concept of the deadman is very useful, and the key to success in its application is *improvisation.*

Pickets may be faster and easier to set up than deadmen if the ground is not rocky and if the pickets are available. As shown in Fig. 25-5, the pickets are simply stakes driven into the ground. These stakes should be sizable; an ice ax would be the minimum size. It is unlikely that one stake could be sufficiently solid, and several are used in tandem as shown, placed in the line of the pull. For extra security, two or more sets of pickets could be used together with an equalizing anchor system (below).

Fig. 25-5. Pickets. Showing method of using pickets in tandem.

Miscellaneous Anchor Points. The rescuer should have an open mind and develop the ability to improvise anchor points from available materials. The ideas of this section are merely typical.

Tie Off the Mountain. The entire top of a pinnacle may be tied off forming an anchor using perhaps two or three rope lengths. There may be considerable rope stretch in the anchor as the load is applied, but the anchor is generally solid.

Several Sitting Bodies. Several rescuers may be able to sit in secure positions with legs well-braced. With padding and a little pain, each can hold over 200 lbs (100 kg) in a sitting belay.

Car Axle. A car axle (attached to the car) works well as an anchor point but care must be exercised to pad the rope wherever it passes over a sharp corner. A car parked on dry pavement slides with a horizontal pull about equal to the weight of the car. This figure is reduced considerably when the car is on gravel, dirt, or wet pavement. Obviously the parking brakes should be set and the car left in the lowest gear.

SELF-EQUALIZING ANCHORS

When a single anchor point is not strong enough to give a reasonable margin of safety for an evacuation anchor, several such points may be rigged together forming a system known as a self-equalizing anchor. Such a system distributes the load among the various anchor points, and if any one point fails, the load is automatically redistributed among the remaining sound anchor points. The self-equalizing technique places an equal load on each point; simply passing the rope from one anchor point to the next in a large loop and attaching the brakes to this loop does *not*. Also, slings or fixed lengths of rope from each point to the brakes will not make a self-equalizing system.

For the sake of discussion we assume below that each anchor point is a piton, but the self-equalizing technique may be applied to any type or combination of anchor points.

The pitons should be placed in separate noninteracting cracks, and all must be carefully tested after driving all pitons (that is, care must be taken that a second piton when driven does not loosen the first which may be in an expanding crack). Fig. 25-6 shows the general setup.

The knot shown in Fig. 25-6 is quite convenient and provides the requirements of a very large loop and a small one, both pointing up, and another small one pointing down for attachment of the brakes. To tie this knot a single large loop, about 10 ft (3 m) larger in circumference than is needed to run the rope from knot to piton to knot, etc., is tied with a double sheet bend and safety. The rope is then arranged as shown in Fig. 25-6a. A Figure-of-Eight knot is tied with the four 2.5 ft (.75 m) lengths shown. The result is shown in Fig. 25-6b.

A carabiner is placed in each piton, and another is placed on the rope between each piton, as in Fig. 25-6b. Then each of the latter carabiners is also clipped into the small loop at the knot, Fig. 25-6c. When the pull is applied downwards as shown, the loading on each piton will equalize. When the large knot is moved sideways or if a piton fails, the rope should move through the numerous carabiners to maintain the equalized load distribution among the solid pitons. The carabiners at the small loop may be pyramided as shown in Fig. 25-6d to prevent crowding and reduce friction.

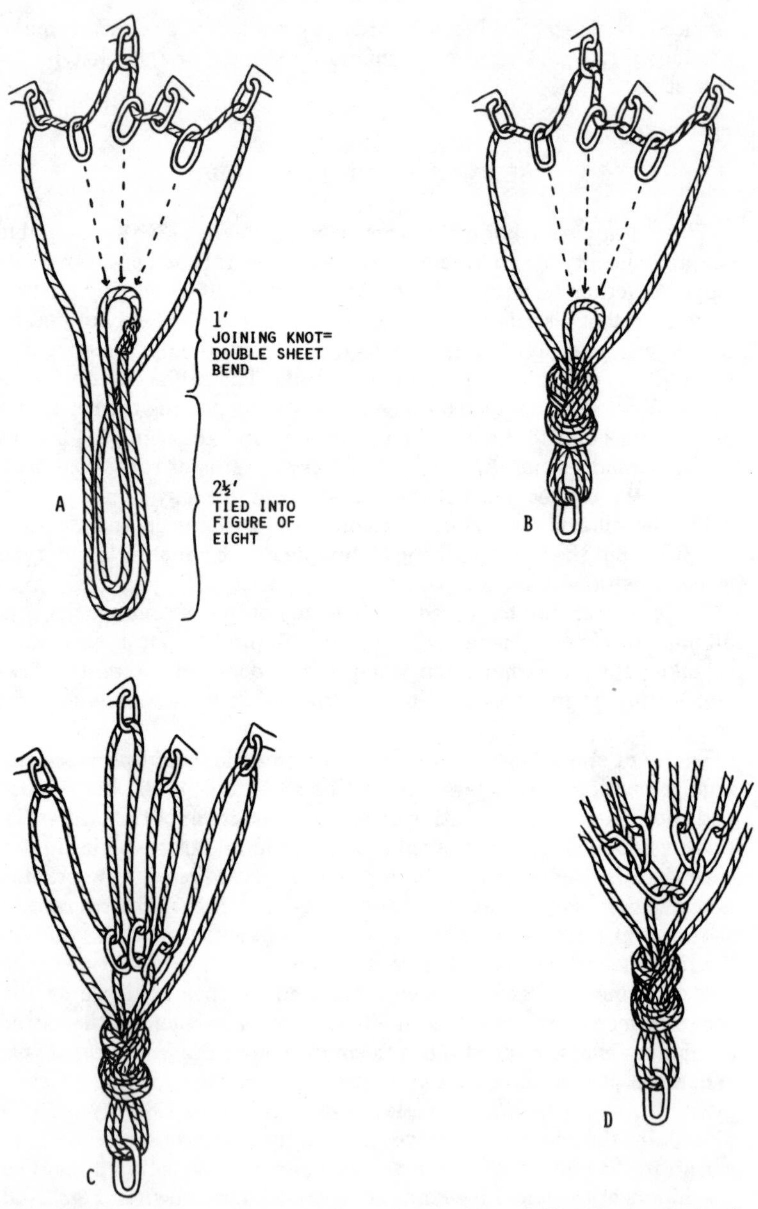

Fig. 25-6. Equalizing anchor. a) Method of tying. b), c), d) Showing methods of assembling the rigging.

The point was made earlier that the angle between the various strands must be less than 120° and preferably less than 90°, as shown in Fig. 25-2; now this becomes particularly important. If only two pitons are used and if the angle between the ropes from the knot to each piton is 120°, the stresses on each anchor point will be the same as the load. To be safe the knot should be as far below the pitons as the pitons are spaced apart. Table 25-2 gives the relative force per piton for symmetrical two-piton and three-piton anchors as shown.

Table 25-2

Ratio of Piton Loading to Total Load

Angle θ	2-Piton Anchor	3-Piton Anchor
150	1.94	.66
120	1.00	.50
90	.71	.41
60	.58	.37
45	.54	.35
0	.50	.33

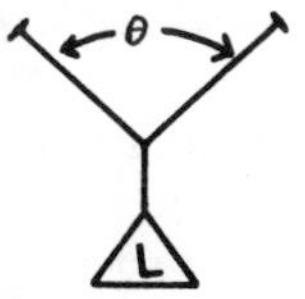

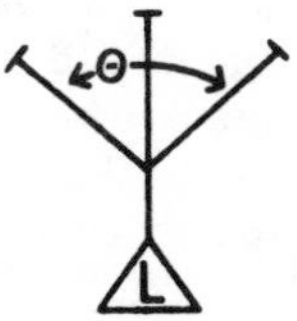

For self-equalizing anchors placed in a position so exposed that the rescuers will be tied in, the brakeman should clip into the anchor system itself, to either small loop shown in Fig. 25-6, rather than to the rock. The reason for this is that if one of the pitons does pull out, the point at which the brakes are attached to the anchor moves relative to the rock. Thus if the brakeman is attached to the rock, the brakes may be no longer accessible to him. If he is attached to the anchor, he may be moved but at least he will be at the brakes. He should not use a short redundant tie-in to the rock.

ANCHOR LOCATION

In the usual scree evacuation, the exact location of an anchor and descent path is usually not critical, but in the case of a high angle rock evacuation where a victim will have to be loaded into the litter on the face, the line of descent will need to be very nearly directly down to the victim unless complex traversing techniques are used. Since the victim may not be visible from the top of the face, a spotter on the ground out from the face may be essential. For relatively short evacuations (say 200 ft or 60 m) the spotter can accurately "eyeball" the proper location on the top for starting the descent. On longer faces he may find a plumb bob (easily rigged from a small stone and a piece of light cord) very useful for determining the vertical line above the victim as described in the previous chapter. Obviously the spotter must have excellent communications with the party on top. If visibility is bad, a rescuer will need to descend to find the victim. The anchor location is not very critical if only one rescuer is lowered to the victim, unless the rock is quite slippery from water or snow, making a pendulum difficult.

For convenience and safety in operating the brakes, the anchor and brake location should be a relatively flat, secure and safe location, 5-10 ft (1.5-5 m) or more back from the lip of a cliff, with room for the brakeman and rope handlers to work, and for the litter and litter bearers to start the descent.

It is possible that the correctly located descent path does not start at a point with a suitable anchor site. If this is the case, the anchor will have to be placed in the nearest adequate location, and the lowering ropes may be directed to the descent route around a rock projection. There must be no sharp rock corners which will severely damage the rope. If such corners exist, they can be "softened" with a piton hammer and well padded with a durable pack or equivalent that will take the abrasion from the sliding rope. If the rope cannot be directed using rock knobs, it may be necessary to place pulleys. Anchors for these pulleys must be secure, using the techniques described above. The loading on a pulley may be greater than on the brake itself; if the rope makes a 180° change of direction, the pulley will support twice the rope load. A carabiner alone is a suitable substitute for the pulley, particularly in a lowering operation where the added friction does no harm. If a knot needs to be passed through the direction-changing pulley, the knot pass techniques described in Ch. 24 may be used.

REFERENCES

1. *Summit,* July 1966, p. 24; June 1967, p. 10.
2. *Belaying the Leader*, Leonard et al., Sierra Club.
3. *American Alpine Journal* 1967, p. 334.

CHAPTER 26

HAULING SYSTEMS

Mechanical advantage and/or direction changing systems which may be used to raise loads using nylon rope or steel cable are described. The basic systems using nylon rope are discussed, and then refinements and special applications are considered.

A knowledge of efficiency of each system is easily calculated assuming that the tension in any rope is not altered when the rope passes through a pulley, that is, for frictionless pulleys. It should be remembered that the greater the theoretical mechanical advantage, the more rope will be hauled in to raise the load a given distance.

BASIC HAULING SYSTEMS

Simple Direction Change. Shown in Fig. 26-1, the system is useful in raising loads when sufficient lifting power is available, for example in raising a loaded litter when many people are available to pull. The ratchet is highly desirable to prevent the load from falling when the pull is released; it will be discussed below. The simplest system, using only the carabiner as shown in Fig. 26-1a, is significantly less efficient than the pulley system when a good pulley is used. Efficiencies are indicated in Tables 26-1 and 26-2.

Two-to-One. The simplest 2:1 system is shown in Fig. 26-2a, and a more practical one in Fig. 26-2b. The latter works by 1) raising the load with the prusik a short distance, 2) releasing the pull so that the load goes to the ratchet, 3) sliding the prusik towards the load, 4) pulling again with the prusik taking the load. If the pull is to the side rather than vertical, some mechanical advantage will be lost.

Three-to-One. As shown in Fig. 26-3, the system is a practical one working much like the 2:1 above. The prusik is set as close to the load

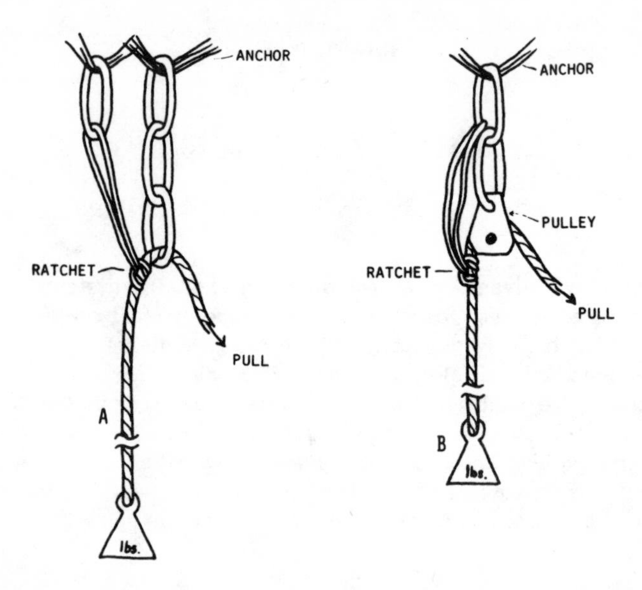

Fig. 26-1. The basic direction-changing system, with ratchet. a) Inefficient, with carabiner only. b) Efficient, with pulley.

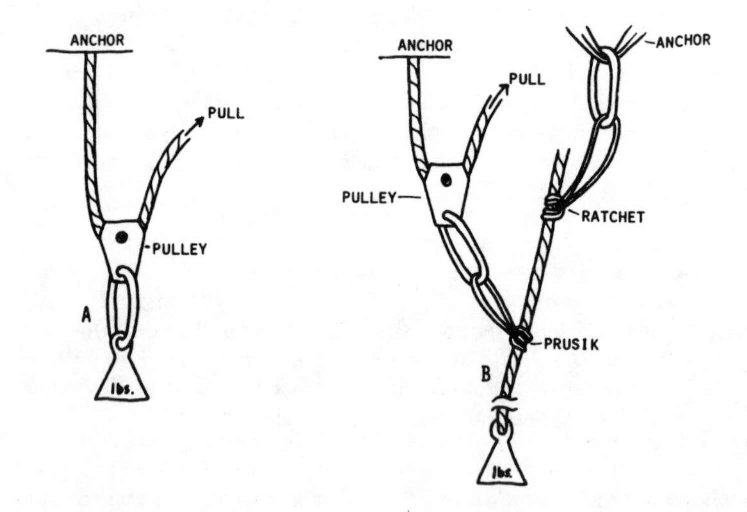

Fig. 26-2. Two-to-one system. a) Basic. b) System rigged for use with a short hauling rope.

as rope and space permit. Pulling must be stopped before Pulley 2 reaches Pulley 1, or else suddenly the mechanical advantage will be lost; that is, as long as the rope forms a Z, the 3:1 advantage will be present, but if the rope straightens out, the pull equals the load force.

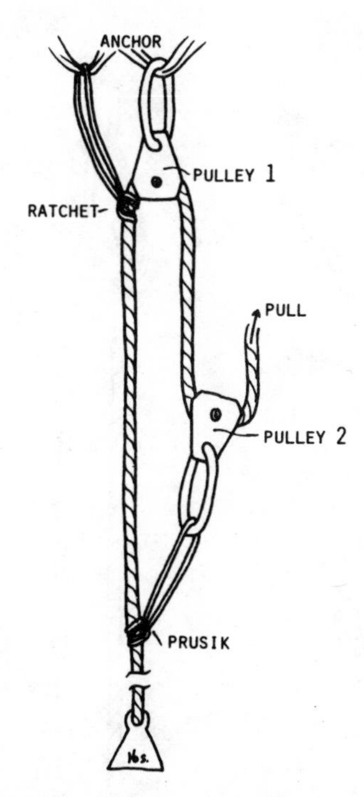

Fig. 26-3. Practical three-to-one system rigged with ratchet.

Additional Mechanical Advantage. For mechanical advantage greater than 3:1, the systems described above may be ganged, as shown in Fig. 26-4 for 6:1 or Fig. 26-5 for 9:1. The ropes must remain in Z's to keep the mechanical advantage. The use of nylon rope in these high mechanical advantage systems is not very practical for long hauls because of the large rope stretch which must be overcome in the hauling system itself and the effort to reposition the prusik. A great deal of hauling at "pull" in Fig. 26-4 or -5 is required to raise the load even a short distance. Since the pull is quite a bit less than the load even including the loss of efficiency as shown in Table 26-1, it might be thought possible to break the main load line, but the prusik will normally fail by slipping first. A 5/16 in. three-wrap prusik on 7/16 in. Goldline usually will slip at about 1200 lbs, (550 kg), the two-wrap at about 800 lbs (360 kg).

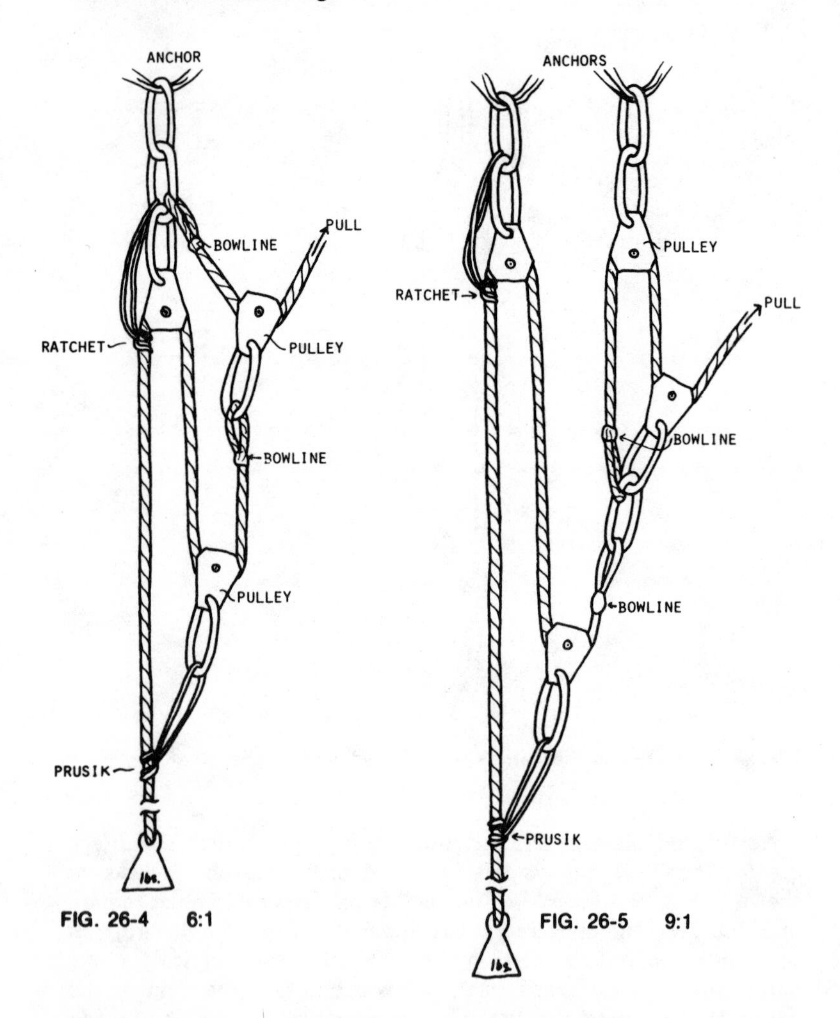

Fig. 26-4. Six-to-one system. **Fig. 26-5.** Nine-to-one system.

Table 26-1

Mechanical Advantage = Load/Pull to Raise

System	Pulley Type		
	Frictionless	"Rescue"	Ball Bearing
Fig. 1b	1	.73	.91
Fig. 2	2	1.7	1.9
Fig. 3	3	2.3	2.7
Fig. 4	6	3.9	5.2
Fig. 5	9	5.1	7.5

Table 26-2

Pulley Efficiency

50 lb load, worn 7/16 in. Goldline, 180 wrap

$$\text{Efficiency} = \frac{\text{load}}{\text{pull to raise}} = \frac{\text{pull to allow lowering}}{\text{load}}$$

Pulley Type	Efficiency
1. "Rescue"	.73
2. REI all nylon on Army carabiner	.74
3. Army carabiner only	.56
4. High efficiency, ball bearing	.91

RATCHETS

On most of the above hauling systems, it is often advisable to use a ratchet, which allows the main load line to be pulled up, but prevents it from dropping when the pull is released. In its simplest form as in Fig. 26-2b, the ratchet is simply a prusik on the main rope with the knot sling clipped to an anchor. Someone must continually pull the slack main rope through this prusik and keep the prusik set firmly on the main rope. The prusik sling should be as short as possible to prevent excessive stretch when the load comes on the ratchet. For security the prusik should be of three turns.

A ratchet which operates without attention is shown in Figs. 26-1 and 26-6. Again, the ratchet knot is a prusik tied with a very short sling with no slack to the anchor. As the load is raised, the knot is pulled against the pulley (or carabiner). With no tension on the sling, the main rope can slide in the direction of the pull. But if the pull is released, the load tends to drop, and the ratchet knot moves down away from the pulley causing the short sling to become taut. Then the ratchet grips the main rope and holds the load. When this automatic ratchet is set up properly, the load drops less than 2 in. (5 cm) when the pull is released.

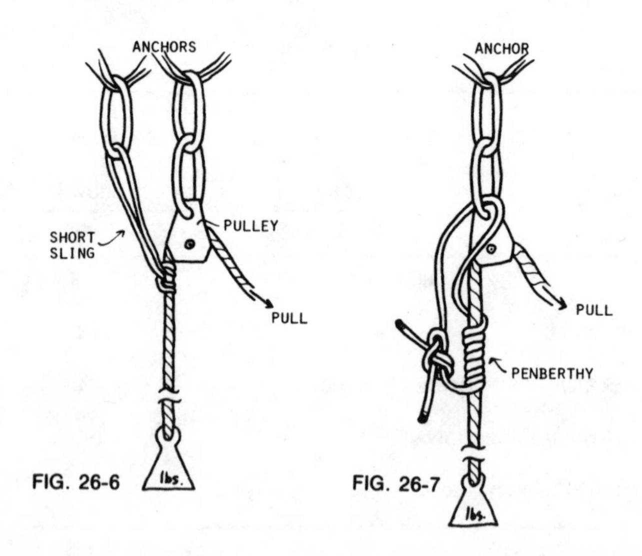

Fig. 26-6. Practical ratchet, using prusik. **Fig. 26-7.** Ratchet, using Penberthy knot.

Other knots or devices may be substituted for the prusik knot as shown. For example, the Penberthy knot, shown in Fig. 26-7, may be used, but this knot is tied from a straight length of sling rope rather than from a loop sling which is the usual form of sling carried and is considerably more time consuming and complex to set up and release than the prusik. Instead of using a rope knot, mechanical devices may be used for automatic operation next to the pulley or carabiner. Jumars may be placed upside-down anywhere on the main load line and anchored top and bottom, forming very efficient ratchets as described below (Yosemite haul). Jumars should not be trusted to hold large loads.

USE OF THE SYSTEMS

Uphill Scree Evacuation. If it is necessary to pull a loaded litter with four litter bearers up a steep slope, the simple direction-changing pulley system shown in Fig. 26-1b may be satisfactory if there are sufficient personnel on top. Smoothness of pulling requires considerable coordination between haulers and litter bearers for control of speed. A major problem which will be encountered on long hauls is the stretch of the rope, but this is not a problem with steel cables. Mechanical advantage systems are usually not very practical because of their complexity. On very steep terrain where the litter bearers may desire a belay, careful attention must be given to the strength of the ratchet. Jumars are not adequate. Also, the anchor will have to withstand more than just the load weight.

High Angle Rock Evac. If it is necessary to lift a loaded litter just a few inches or cm (for example, to release a knot which the brakeman may have accidentally allowed to reach the brakes), sufficient manpower on top may do the job by attaching prusiks on the lowering ropes and hauling lines onto these prusiks. If the litter is to come up many feet (meters), these hauling lines will be passed through a mechanical advantage system. For safety the main lowering ropes should be left in the main brakes, and slack taken up by the brakeman and rope handlers as the litter is raised. Good coordination will be required between the haulers and the litter bearers to allow the litter bearers to negotiate structure in the rock face. Long hauls are best done with steel cable, as discussed below.

Tensioning Tie. If a rope needs to be pulled taut and tied, such as for a traverse system or for tying loads onto a packframe, a very elementary form of the 3:1 system may be used as shown in Fig. 26-8. A small loop is tied in the rope to be tensioned. A hard pull as shown will make the rope quite taut, and the pulled end may be readily tied off without losing tension because of friction. More details will be given in Ch. 27. For increased tension, the rope can be pushed sideways at point A while pulling; when the sideways pushing is released, additional rope can be taken up by continued pulling. Further increases in the rope tension may be achieved by clipping another rope onto the first as at Point A or farther from the anchor and applying a mechanical advantage system to this second rope.

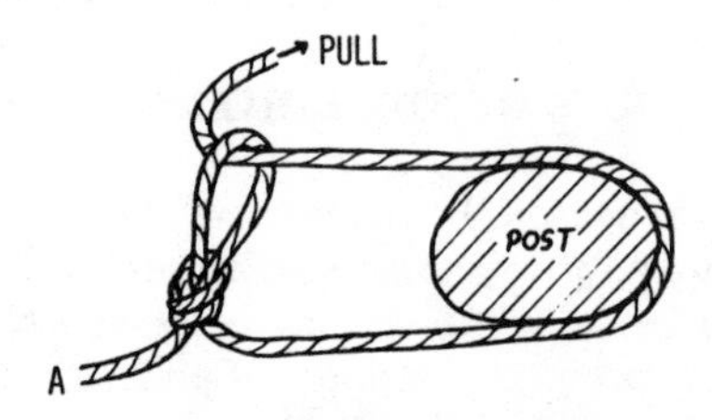

Fig. 26-8. Line-tightening system, high friction due to nylon-on-nylon contact. Most useful for lashing.

YOSEMITE HAULING SYSTEM

A system for hauling moderate (say 50 lb or 25 kg) loads is shown in Fig. 26-9 and is known as the Yosemite hauling technique. The system works with no mechanical advantage, but is efficient and relatively effortless to use since the raising is done using leg muscles rather than arms. The Jumar on the left is upside-down and is anchored securely so that it will not move up or down. Its purpose is to hold the load while the rope on the other side of the pulley is slack. The other Jumar is clipped to the rope near the pulley, and the operator simply stands in the attached stirrup, raising the load a short distance. When the operator steps out of the stirrup, he can raise this Jumar by hand towards the pulley again, and repeat the operation. The ratchet Jumar needs no attention during the operation.

Either Jumar could be replaced by a prusik knot with resulting additional effort needed to operate the system. Also, the pulley could be replaced by a carabiner with sizable loss of efficiency. To prevent loss of height gained during raising, the ratchet Jumar must be anchored so that it cannot move up or down; any amount that it moves up during raising is lost when hauling tension is released. The lower anchor may be simply some gear clipped to the Jumar as shown, space permitting. Likewise, any amount that the sling on top of the ratchet Jumar stretches when the Jumar is loaded must be overcome on the next raising operation.

More than body weight can be lifted with considerable effort if the operator stands in the stirrup and simultaneously grips the rope down to the load and lifts by hand. This procedure is tiring and is not to be relied upon to lift a load more than a short distance.

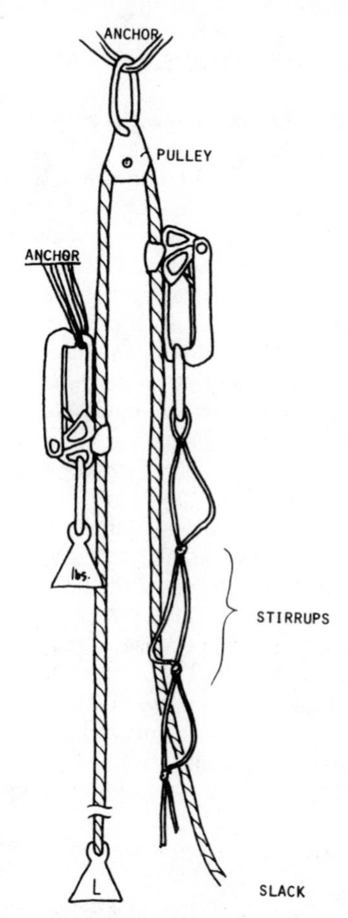

Fig. 26-9. Yosemite hauling system. The upside-down Jumar may be anchored at both ends.

Another variation may be used for heavy loads or bad (low angle) hauling conditions. The hauling Jumar is attached directly to the hauler's waist loop, and the pulley is secured as closely as possible to the anchor. The hauler then places his feet on either side of the pulley with bent knees, and presses out, walking down the wall a bit as he succeeds in pulling up some of the haul rope. A safety tie-in of appropriate length stops him, and he repositions himself to repeat the process. This technique only works when the hauling force needed is large, and it will work when body weight alone is not sufficient.

HAULING WITH STEEL CABLE

All of the rigging used for lowering with cable as discussed in previous chapters is used for lifting, and some additional rigging is needed at the top end as shown in Fig. 26-10. For safety, the cable to the litter should always be passed around an anchored brake block, and the hauling system is attached to the cable with a cable clamp below the brake block. Then the cable around the brake block may be taken up and kept loose but with no excess slack, and if the cable clamp to the hauling rigging should fail, the brake block would hold the load. A completely independent nylon belay to the litter may be desired.

The hauling system is usually of nylon rope for convenience in handling, and depending on personnel available may have simply a direction changing pulley or might have a 2:1 or 3:1 mechanical advantage shown in Figs. 26-2 and 26-3 with the load shown there replaced by the cable clamp. The 3:1 system is advisable if the load is a litter with bearers on a high angle wall, to keep the litter speed down. Rather than use a ratchet on the hauling system, a second cable clamp is placed on the cable just below the brake block as shown in Fig. 26-10. Instead of this ratchet, the cable could be tightened around the brake block, but only at the expense of some height gained and extra effort to release the friction. The clamp does not work automatically and must be attended. There should be 10 ft (3 m) or more space below the brake block and ratchet clamp to allow the hauling clamp to be moved and give a reasonable lift on each pull by the hauling team. As much as 50 ft (15 m) or more space on top may be used by the hauling team.

The operation of the system requires considerable coordination among all personnel. The hauling team (5 to 10 men is typical) should be directed by one and only one designated person; otherwise, various yells will be misinterpreted. The communications with the litter team go through this hauling captain. Team practice is required to make the operation run smoothly. Litter bearers may have a difficult time negotiating structure in the slope or rock wall when the pulling is jerky, and it seems that frequently the hauling team will be just finishing one round of pulling when the litter reaches an awkward spot to pause.

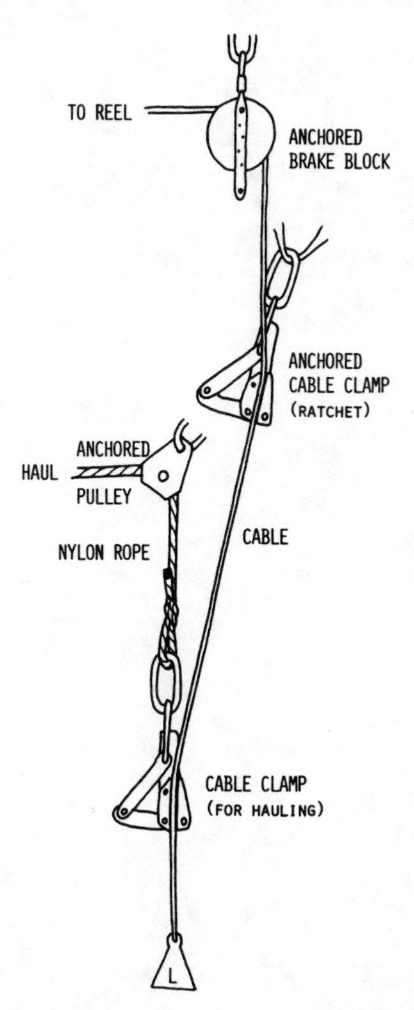

Fig. 26-10. Practical hauling system for use with steel cable to the load.

Instead of having a large hauling team with all members simultaneously pulling, one man at a time could operate a hand-powered winch such as a Come-Along or a more efficient capstan winch, and the team members take turns. It has been found that the fastest way to run such a system is for each man to exert himself hard for a short timed period (15 seconds) and then be relieved, rather than for each to work until quite tired.

CHAPTER 27

SUSPENSION SYSTEMS

A suspension system, with which a load is transported off the ground along a taut (static) line, may be very useful when it is necessary to cross streams or gorges or other such difficult terrain. Such systems can be used to aid the movement of teams or for transport of victims. These systems, also known as tyroleans, aerial tramways, or high wires, are often seen at rescue exercises and demonstrations since they look spectacular. They are time-consuming to set up, but in spite of the complexity, the techniques are occasionally very worthwhile to employ in rescue; however, time should not be wasted waiting for the system to be set up. Sometimes the rigging may be done by team specialists while the victim is being transported to its site, and then the system is used with essentially no delay. Since system stresses are often large, the margin of safety is smaller than usual or desirable in rescue, and the rigging should be supervised by someone experienced in the techniques.

Line Tensions. The tension in the main static line may be much greater than the weight supported, with the worst case being a horizontal traverse with the load at midspan, as shown in Fig. 27-1. For this situation, elementary mechanics gives the result that the line tension T is related to the supported weight W and the angle θ which the line makes with the horizontal by: $2T\sin\theta = W$. Operationally, it is usually desirable to minimize sag and θ so that the load does not hit the ground, but this raises T. Table 27-1 shows the ratio T/W for several representative span/sag ratios and corresponding angles θ, and the line tension T for a load weight W of 250 lbs (110 kg), and the weight W for a tension T of 1000 lbs (450 kg). For reasonable safety, T should not exceed about 1000 lbs (450 kg) for 7/16 in. Goldline or 3/16 in. wire rope.

Table 27-1

Angle θ (deg)	$\frac{\text{Span}}{\text{Sag}}$	$\frac{T}{W}$	T (lbs) for W = 250 lbs	W (lbs) for T = 1000 lbs
3	40	10	2500	100
6	20	5	1250	200
11	10	2.6	650	380
22	5	1.3	320	750
30	3	1	250	1000

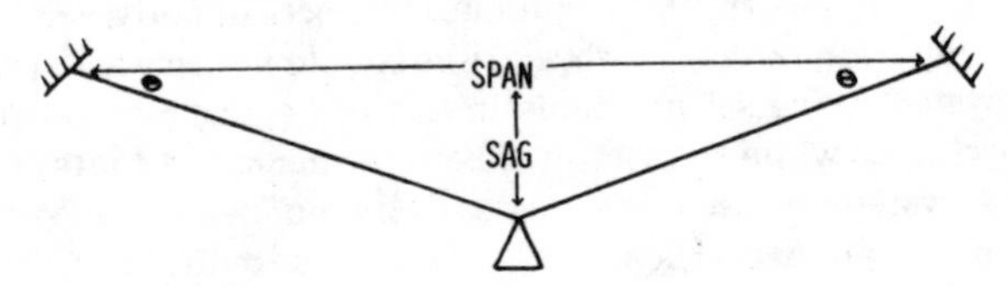

Fig. 27-1. Showing idealized suspension system. Geometry assumed in Table.

It is seen that the sag should be at least 5 ft (10 ft preferred) per 100 ft of span for suspending typical loads of about 200 lbs (90 kg). Much greater sag is usually not tolerable operationally.

Anchors. A major requirement for any suspension system is the availability of secure anchors at each end. Anchors have to be as strong for this use as any in mountain rescue, including the steep scree evacuation. To withstand the high line tensions, the anchors may have to be a combination of several anchor points rigged to be self-equalizing, as described in Ch. 25. For reasonable safety, each anchor system should be able to hold at least ten times the load to be transported.

The anchors must be suitably placed in addition to being satisfactorily strong. To prevent the load from "bottoming out," or to be able to minimize line tension T by increasing sag, the anchors will have to be placed in a high location. If the rope would bear against any sharp rock, the rock edges must be padded with anything suitable, such as leather gloves, a pack, tree branches, etc., since a taut rope can be very easily cut. The anchors should be 6 to 10 ft (2-3 m) back from the edge of the stream or cliff to allow room for loading and unloading. The rope should be 3 ft (1 m) or more off the ground at these positions, and if good anchors do not allow this, A-frames could be improvised from sturdy tree trunks as shown in Fig. 27-2.

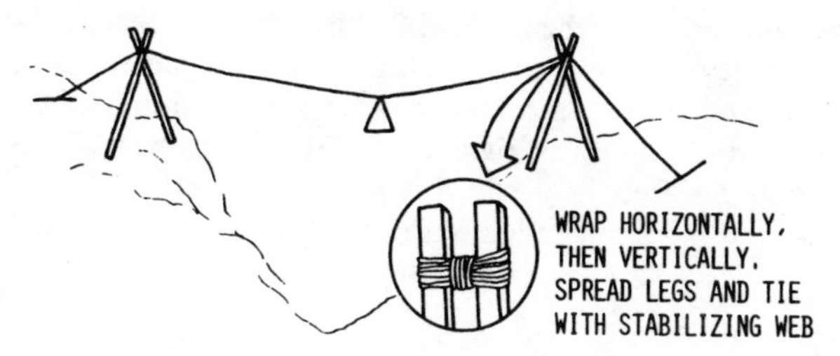

Fig. 27-2. Suspension system with A-frames, which should be set back from each lip.

Pretensioning and Sag. Pretensioning of the main static line is often done with a mechanical advantage system such as described in Ch. 26. Since stresses are high, some precautions are in order. If the line to be tensioned is 7/16 in. Goldline, a Jumar should not be used as the load-holding device due to its inadequate safety factor for this service. A prusik is much safer because it usually fails by sliding, not catastrophically. It is nearly impossible to overtension 7/16 in. Goldline rope in a suspension system using a prusik for holding the line tension; this is for two reasons. First, the prusik normally will slip at about 1200 lbs or 550 kg (three-wrap, 5/16 in. diameter) which is not an unreasonable line tension, and second, even if the line is tied firmly and tensioned to 1000 lbs (450kg), the nylon stretches so much as it is loaded with weight W that the sag (Fig. 27-1) increases considerably, and tension T increases only moderately with reasonable loads W. Very high initial line tensions do not tend to reduce sag very much. This sag from elasticity is an effective built-in safety factor but is a practical nuisance. The safety is not present in less-elastic materials such as manila or hemp rope or steel cable. The natural fiber ropes are much weaker than nylon for a given diameter or weight, and thus, new rope at least 3/4 in. (2 cm) diameter would be needed for adequate safety; such rope is completely impractical for mountain rescue use. On the other hand, the 3/16 in. steel cable is admirably suited for suspension systems in mountain rescue because of its good strength and weight, and its inelasticity is a practical convenience for use as a static line. However, if the wire is pretensioned heavily and then loaded, the wire tension may easily rise to the breaking point. In fact, so little effort is needed to tension the line that some caution must be taken to avoid overtensioning. A safe method of tensioning the line is to include a shock absorber at one anchor, and to tension the unloaded line taut by hand. Then 1.5-2 ft per 100 ft of span are let out. The result is a sag/span ratio safe for loads of 250 lbs (110 kg). Steel cable static lines should never be tensioned with a mechanical advantage system.

As mentioned above, a mechanical advantage system will be needed for pretensioning the nylon rope. One of the systems of Ch. 26 with a ratchet could be used, or perhaps more convenient is one of the tensioning tie systems shown here in Fig. 27-3. The crudest form is a high

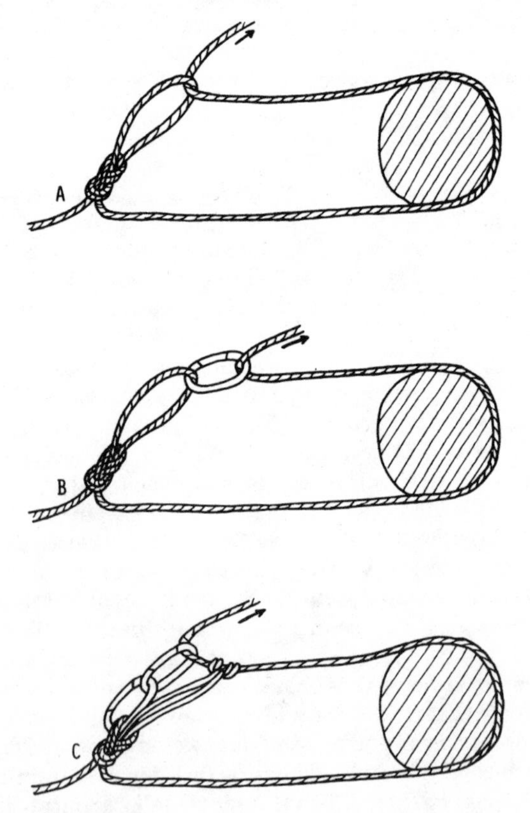

Fig. 27-3. Tensioning system. a) Inefficient, high friction, b) more efficient, c) includes ratchet.

friction 3:1 system (*not* recommended for tensioning suspension system lines due to nylon-on-nylon rubbing contact and excessive friction but quite convenient for lashing gear to packframes with nylon webbing), shown in Fig. 27-3a. The knot is a Figure-of-Eight; a Butterfly is a little stronger, but is harder to untie after tensioning. Much better for suspension system use is the same sort of arrangement but with a carabiner added, as in Fig. 27-3b. Fancier yet is the technique of Fig. 27-3c. There a loop about 1 to 1.5 ft (.3 to .6 m) long (that is, about 2-3 ft or .6-1 m circumference after tying the Figure-of-Eight) is formed into a prusik through which is fed the free end of the main rope. This free end is also passed through a carabiner which is clipped into the Figure-of-Eight knot. The prusik then acts nicely as a ratchet, and one man alone can tension the rope by repeated jerks. In Fig. 27-3, the distance from the anchor to the knot needs to be 10 to 20 percent of the span prior to tensioning to allow for stretch in the rope.

If the knot is pulled up close to the anchor before pretensioning is completed, a prusik may be placed several feet out on the taut rope and anchored temporarily to hold the line taut while the knot is retied further from the anchor for additional tensioning. If the knot is left a few feet from the anchor after tensioning, the load on the static line will be prevented from colliding with the anchor.

Once the rope is pretensioned initially, it should be loaded for several minutes during which time it stretches more; then the load is removed and the rope can be pretensioned further. This loading can be done by suspending a weight as in use or by pushing sideways on the rope. The system should always be tried by a heavy rescuer before sending a victim on the line.

At least one end of the main static line should be tied off in such a way that it can be readily untied while the rope is tensioned and preferably in a manner that allows a controllable slackening of the tension. A brake system using a carabiner or brake plate is satisfactory, but it is also effective to simply wrap the rope a few times around a tree and then tie off with a secured slip knot. If the main static line can be let out controllably, the load may be set down as needed anywhere between the ends of the traverse system.

Use of the System with a Nylon Static Line. A rescuer can cross the suspension system most conveniently by wearing a rappel seat and clipping into the main static line using two carabiners in series (to prevent damaging heat transfer from the 'biner on the main line to the seat sling.) If the static line is high off the ground, stirrups may be attached to the line with a prusik to aid individuals getting clipped onto or off the line. The most stable but slow method of crossing is for the rescuer to hang under the rope and go head first with heels crossed over the rope and to pull himself hand over hand. Speedier is to place a pulley instead of a carabiner over the main line and let gravity aid transport where possible. To control speed, the rescuer must not grab the rope with his hands while moving (or he will get his hands burned, even through gloves). A better method is to clip a carabiner onto the rope and twist the 'biner to increase friction and be slowed down. If the line is steep up or down or has a long uphill part, it may be worthwhile to use a hauling and/or brake line to the rescuer's pulley on the static line and have team members at each end control his motion.

A litter may be suspended from the main static line using the standard litter spiders described in Ch. 24 or the equivalent improvised ties of Ch. 31. The victim gets a significantly smoother ride if the litter is clipped onto the main rope using pulleys instead of carabiners; also, any upwards pulling will be easier with pulleys because of reduced friction. Except for very short traverses, hauling (tag) lines will be needed on each end of the litter to allow full control of the motion by pulling each way. If the main line is far overhead at the loading point, the line may be pulled down by tying on a sling or stirrup with a prusik over the loading area; a rescuer (or two or three) stands in the stirrup to bring the line down and hold it for loading.

There is seldom a need for a rescuer to cross with the victim and thereby place a very heavy load on the line. Even when the victim requires steady first aid such as AR or CPR, a brief pause in first aid during a smooth and speedy crossing (less than 30 seconds is typical) should be tolerable and is probably better than a rougher and longer ride with a rescuer aboard. The rescuers with the tag lines should perform a trial run to assure smoothness and speed.

Cable Systems. If steel cable is used for the main static line, special pulleys will be needed for suspending the load. A carabiner should never be allowed to drag against the cable. The engine-powered winch may be put to use in hauling loads suspended from the static line, using the configuration of Fig. 27-4. The idler keeps the pull low on the engine capstan.

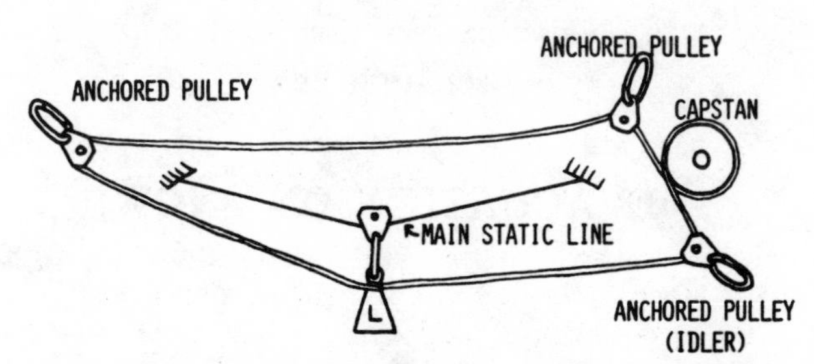

Fig. 27-4. Suspension system with engine-driven capstan winch. Steel cable is used for both the static line and the hauling line.

CHAPTER 28

EVACUATION ON SNOW

This chapter deals primarily with methods of hauling a sled, akja, or litter over snow by hand. The techniques are merely suggestions that work and generally will be modified to suit the circumstances. Rescuers equipped with web slings will be able to make necessary adaptations. When the evacuation must go at all uphill, at best considerable effort will be expended by the rescuers.

Some special problems of loading the victim will be given, as well as a brief discussion of improvised sleds, indicating general methods.

Over-snow vehicles may be the fastest and easiest means of performing an evacuation over snow. Some of the advantages and problems of using snowmobiles were discussed in Ch. 17.

Loading. Immobilization of an injured victim is made more difficult in cold weather due to the very large amount of insulation required. Waterproof material (e.g. poncho) should be placed under and perhaps over the victim. Difficulties are compounded when the victim is placed in a sled or akja rather than in a Stokes litter, because of the lack of convenient tie points. It is possible to lash a Stokes down on a sled or akja, but care must be taken during the evacuation, because the load becomes quite top-heavy. The Austrian akja is too small to load even a medium sized victim, especially if injuries prevent the victim from being placed on his back. Then a Stokes litter may be more desirable even though difficulties of over-snow travel may be greatly increased; the Stokes with a smooth bottom may be the best overall compromise and will be the choice if some of the evacuation is not over snow.

Pulling a Load with a Tow Rope. Skiers and snowshoers can pull a tow rope by attaching the rope to a wide hip or chest strap as a tow harness, allowing freedom of the hands to use ski poles. Attachment of the tow rope to the bottom cross bar of a frame pack with hip strap also works. Snowshoers may have the use of their hands and can directly grip the rope, but holding a loop, knot, or prusik sling is easier. An ice ax or ski pole can be hitched to the rope with a half hitch or clove hitch; the rescuer can then push or pull on the ax or pole. Personnel on skis will need to be about 10 ft (3 m) apart, but snowshoers can be a little closer together.

A short uphill haul may be easiest if most rescuers climb to the top and haul the load up hand-over-hand. Another possibility is to install a pulley (and ratchet if needed) at the top and pull the rope downhill.

On descents, one man will be at the rear with a tail rope, braking as needed. If the descent is steep enough that the load slides by itself, most rescuers will be above the load, holding it back. One man in front can control the direction of movement. On still steeper terrain, a snow anchor evacuation system (Ch. 29) would be used.

Sidehilling with a sled is difficult at best. An akja may be handled directly, but a tail rope may be essential to keep a sled from sliding sideways downhill. If the slope is quite steep, the load may be attached to a yoke and pendulumed at the end of a long belay rope. Alternatively a Tyrolean suspension system (Ch. 27) could be employed with the load always on the snow.

The Akja, Sled, and Litter. *Akja.* When the akja is used on gentle descents or contouring even a fairly steep hillside, two skiers can control it splendidly. Sidehilling works very well in reasonably soft snow since the akja can be steered and kept level using the handles. On somewhat steeper hills, a brake will be needed; one effective form of brake is a chain attached to the akja near the front, which may be released by the front man and allowed to slide under the akja providing friction. Considerable skill must be developed through practice in handling the akja.

On still steeper slopes, the akja requires a belay and some form of lowering system. The lowering rope may be attached either to the points of attachment of the rear handles or with a yoke arrangement to the handle rings themselves. If in timber, the downhill movement may be nicely controlled by the tail rope wrapped around a tree; otherwise, a snow anchor system as in Ch. 29 will be needed. The akja can be handled by one man in front, or one front and one rear, both tied in. A piece of webbing can be tied between the rear handles to prevent the back man from knocking his shins against the akja.

On flat terrain or gentle ascents, the akja can be pulled by four men, one to each handle, preferably wearing snowshoes rather than skis. Those in front may find that the handle rings are so high that they tend to pull the bow end of the akja down into the snow; if this happens, they may grip the tubular handle lower down or attach a towing rope or sling. The haulers should rotate positions frequently, alternating sides to tire all muscles equally. More than four may share the burden of hauling by rotation (Ch. 22) or by using a long tow rope in front.

Anytime that the akja may have to cross snowless terrain, a minimum of four men should be available to carry it. Such a carry is very difficult since the akja has no carrying handles although the steering handles may be gripped near their point of attachment. Also, the akja is not built for stresses of suspension from its ends. Clumsy but better is to pass some slings under the akja to work as handles or carrying slings. The small rings on the sides of the akja are too weak to be trusted for carrying.

Sled or Army Snow Boat. A sled such as the Army snow boat with 200 lb (90 kg) capacity is typical, having a solid smooth bottom with runners, means of attaching tow ropes front and rear, of lashing the load in securely, and of being nearly useless except on snow. Some hints on loading the sled are given in Ch. 17.

The sled is very easy to slide on level ground but is awkward on sidehills and is very difficult to carry over snowless terrain since it has no handles or side rails. Wide lengths of webbing passed underneath can, with some difficulty, serve as handles.

Modified Stokes Litter. A Stokes litter modified to have a smooth bottom as described in Ch. 7 may be dragged through the snow but only with much more effort than a snow boat or akja. However, slings may be easily hitched to the rails for hauling, and the Stokes may be carried with relative ease. In cold weather, litter bearers carrying the Stokes may want to use webbing to transfer weight to their shoulders (see Ch. 22) so that their hands do not have to grip the cold metal side rails continuously.

Improvisation. There are many configurations of improvised sleds or toboggans which can be put together using two or four skis. Often if skis are available at all, the rescuers must wear them for their own mobility, and thus improvisation will be only with the victim's skis and poles. We describe here a two-ski sled and a two-ski plow. A well-constructed sled, with skis parallel, is maneuverable and relatively easy to slide compared to the plow, with ski tips lashed together, but is more difficult to build. In all cases if the skis were predrilled with a small hole near each tip, improvisation would be made easier.

Two-Ski Sled. The sled is built with the skis parallel and about 1-1.5 ft (.3-.5 m) apart, lashed in place using cross braces (rucksack stiffeners, tree branches, ice axes, etc.) at the tips and at the bindings. Rigidity is increased by lashing down the ski poles in the form of an X from tips to bindings, as in Fig. 28-1. The sled is pulled by rope or additional ski poles from the front cross brace.

Two-Ski Plow. The plow is readily constructed as in Fig. 28-2. The handle of one pole is passed through the basket of the other, and each pole is lashed to the bindings, using a clove hitch. Tow ropes may be attached at the bindings and passed through the pole baskets or tied on at the tips. The victim's comfort is aided by lashing on a packframe or two from ski to ski or by passing a rope back and forth from pole to pole.

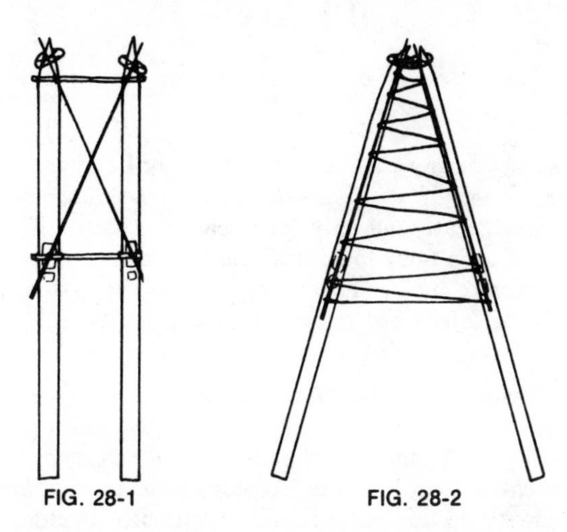

Fig. 28-1. Sled improvised from skis and poles. **Fig. 28-2.** Plow sled improvised from skis and poles. A packframe or more cross members on top would be needed for the comfort of the victim.

CHAPTER 29

ANCHORS II: SNOW ANCHORS AND BELAYS

The reliability of any snow and ice anchor or belay is very difficult for even experienced mountaineers to judge because snow and ice conditions vary greatly not only from season to season but also from day to day and even hour to hour. Generally, a rock belay or anchor will be preferred to one on snow or ice. Each of the systems described below should be considered to lack desired security.

SNOW ANCHORS

Deadman. The deadman anchor technique has long been known and used in earth (Ch. 25) but only recently has been applied specifically to snow with the commercially available Deadman and the smaller version, the Deadboy. The basic deadman, shown in Fig. 29-1a, is a stiff aluminum plate approximately 8 in. (20 cm) square with a steel cable attached. One refinement is a reinforcement of the top of the deadman to withstand pounding. Another is to bend the plate slightly about a vertical axis as shown in Fig. 29-1b. Still another is to drill many holes in the plate to lighten it. The cable yoke may be a loop passed through two holes to allow rotation of the vertical axis of the plate with respect to the direction of pull, or the yoke may be solidly attached at two points. The deadman is readily placed in snow, forming an excellent anchor in a wide variety of snow conditions, but its placement is somewhat critical as described below.

The deadman is inserted into the snow at about a 45° angle from the intended direction of pull (Fig. 29-2a). A slot should be cut for it in firm snow, and a slot should also be cut for the cable. As the load is put on the cable, the deadman is pulled deeper into the snow until it sets firmly (Fig. 29-2b). If the snow is too powdery, the deadman will not hold solidly but may drag through the snow. If the deadman is inserted too nearly at right angles to the pull, it will not dig into the snow and set, and if it is put in at too small an angle, it will not be driven deeply but will come to the surface. Also, if there is a harder layer of snow below the surface, the point of the deadman may stop as the deadman is pulled, and the top of the plate then moves in the direction of pull causing the deadman to travel immediately towards the surface and pull out. There is still controversy regarding merits of fixing the cable yoke at two points compared to the loop form of yoke. The bent plate shown in Fig. 29-1b is more stable than the flat plate with respect to rotation about the vertical axis.

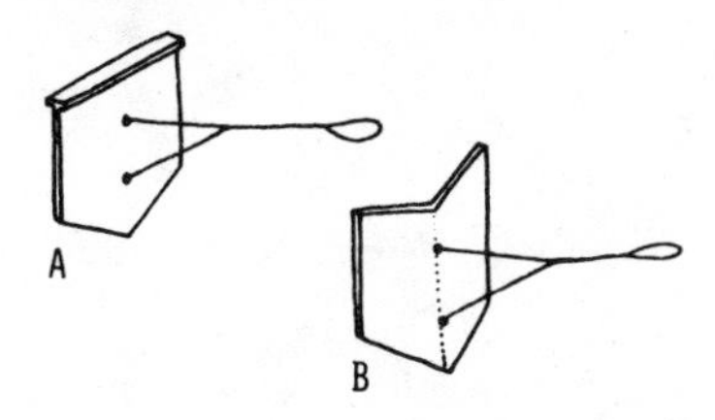

Fig. 29-1. Deadmen for snow. The plates may be a) flat or b) bent, reinforced or not.

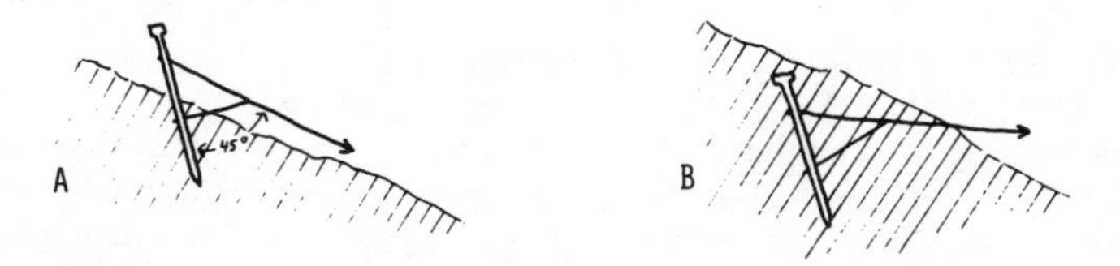

Fig. 29-2. Deadman in snow. a) Placement, b) set in place.

The properly inserted deadman makes quite a solid anchor, easily holding several hundred pounds. Since placement is critical, the deadman should be tested vigorously before being put to use.

Snow Pickets. Another form of snow anchor is the snow picket, which is simply a length of hard aluminum tubing or bar of X or T cross section with a hole near one end into which a carabiner may be clipped. (Webbing passed through the hole is liable to be cut by the metal edge.) The required length is very much dependent upon snow conditions likely to be encountered with 2-6 ft (.6-2 m) being typical, the longer ones needed for softer snow. A typical cross sectional dimension is 2 in. (5 cm), and the bar may be lightened by drilling numerous holes, any of which could be used for clipping on the load.

The picket is driven into the snow with a hammer after the surface snow is stamped down; if the picket can be pushed in to its upper end by hand, it will fail by moving in the direction of the load at rather small loading. The load should never be applied to the end if the end is much above the surface of the snow since the typical lightweight picket will bend and fail. For best reliability, pickets should be used in tandem, as shown in Fig. 29-3.

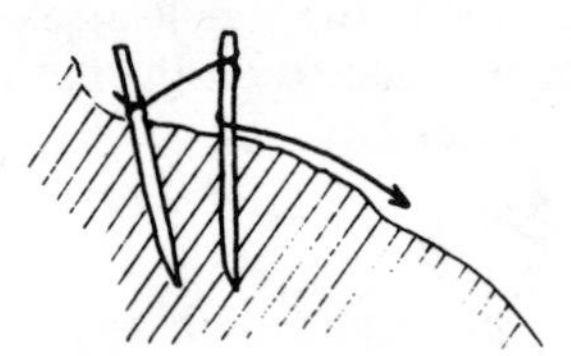

Fig. 29-3. Snow pickets, in place. Normally used in tandem.

The snow picket can form a solid rescue anchor, but it has now been largely replaced by the deadman, which is much more convenient to carry, even though the deadman does require somewhat more care in placement.

Bollards. A bollard is a horseshoe-shaped, short pillar of ice or snow as shown in Fig. 29-4 and is constructed by cutting with the ice ax or by stamping with the boots. When made in solid ice, it will be perhaps 1.5-3 ft (.5-1 m) across and 4-6 in. (10-15 cm) thick. In snow, it will be much larger, as much as 10 ft (3 m) across and as deep as the boots can stamp it out. It appears that an anchor could always be made in snow from a bollard, but care must be taken: if the snow or ice is laminated, particularly parallel to the top surface of the bollard, the entire pillar may cleave off. Also, a single strand of rope around a soft

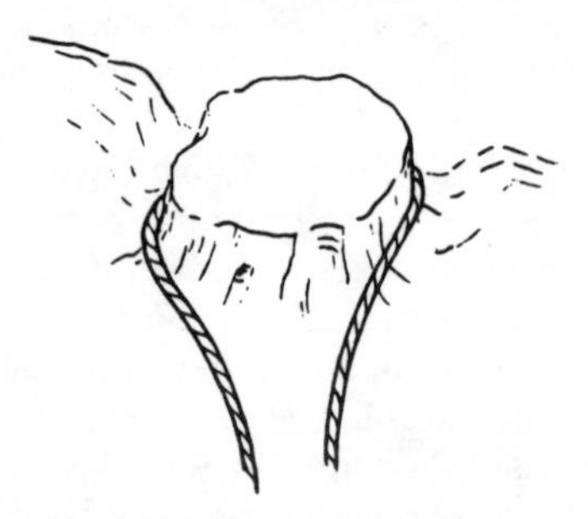

Fig. 29-4. Snow or ice bollard. Size depends on snow or ice conditions.

snow bollard may tend to cut through, but several turns of rope around the pillar padded with clothing, etc., may be reasonably secure. Bollards are seldom used in rescue.

Unattended Ice Ax. An ax alone pushed vertically into the snow to its head makes a very convenient although rather weak anchor useful for a belayer's tie-in or for temporarily anchoring gear such as a pack or spare rope, etc. An ax with a carabiner hole in the head is convenient, but makes a particularly weak anchor. Better, the load may be clipped to a sling passed around the ax. This form of anchor should never be counted on to hold more than a small load.

Ice Pitons, Tubes, and Screws. Fallen snow becomes compacted and after a season of settling turns into *firn.* This is further compressed by gravity into glacier ice into which a deadman or picket cannot be driven, and an ice piton or screw will be used. The hardness of the ice may range from rather porous as found on a glacier under the surface snow or in crevasses to very hard clear or black water ice or gully ice. The choice of piton or screw will depend on the nature of the ice. Ice pitons are solid pointed bars of steel 8-12 in. (20-30 cm) long with rectangular or U cross section and an eye or ring at the head end.

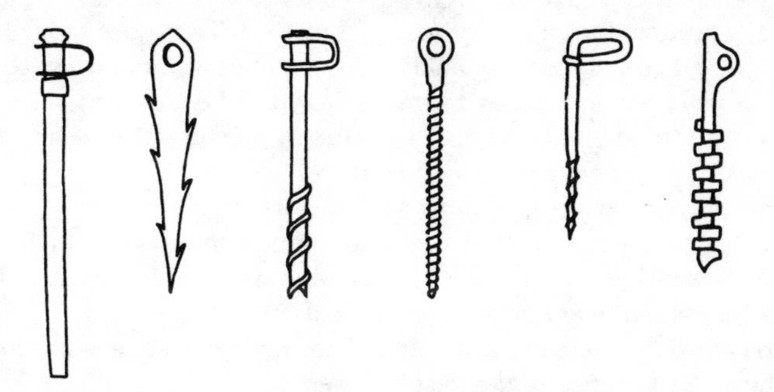

Fig. 29-5. Ice pitons, tubes, and screws. Strength depends on metal quality and placement.

Tubes are similar, with modern types made of stiff alloy steels. Screws take on a variety of shapes, including pointed bolts, corkscrew-like or sturdy tubes with rugged outside threads, such as shown in Fig. 29-5.

The piton, tube or screw is driven in all the way to its head. It is very important that the pull on any of these devices be nearly at right angles to the shaft; any outward component of force is likely to make the device fail by pulling out. All of these devices should be very stiff, because if loading bends the device, there will be an outward pull. The ice around the piton or screw should be inspected during and after driving to see if it is unduly fractured. Brittle ice may fracture radially outwards from the point of driving as much as 1 ft (.3 m) or more, and the pin could fail by coming out with a large chunk of ice. Some recent tests (Ref. 1) have indicated holding powers as high as 3000 lbs (1400 kg) for the large screws in hard glacier ice, but the significance of these tests has been questioned (Ref. 2). The corkscrew types are generally considered to be too weak for any use but for aid climbing and opening wine bottles.

Several of the devices should be used together to form a rescue anchor. They should be placed well apart (3 ft or 1 m or more) to prevent fracture lines extending from one to the next and should be joined with an equalizing anchor system (Ch. 25).

If the anchor point is loaded heavily for a period of more than a few minutes, the device will tend to ooze through the ice and be pulled out. This phenomenon must be watched for. Also, heat from the sun will warm the metal and cause the ice around it to soften and lose its grip. Burying the head of the device and carabiner with snow or ice will slow this process. Frequent inspection of each piton or screw is essential during rescue operations loading the device.

Recently there have been some developments in ice pitons which are of particular value in thin layers of hard ice. These are described in Ref. 3 and do not depend on holding in a solid position in ice but rather tend to hold better as they move, somewhat like a deadman in snow. They are too new to be of proven value in rescue but appear to have promise if an anchor is needed in thin hard ice.

The placement of ice pitons and screws requires a great deal of judgment on the part of the rescuer, much more so than for rock pitons, largely due to the highly variable nature of snow and ice. A solid rock anchor is normally preferred.

The above paragraphs are only a brief review of some snow and ice anchors. Experience is the best teacher.

ICE AX BELAYS

We describe below two convenient ice ax systems which combine the roles of anchor and brake and are the ones most commonly used for lowering or belaying. These should be known along with the anchors described above which may be used with any desired brake system for lowering a litter or akja, or as backup anchors for another system. The ice ax systems are quick to set up, but a great deal of practice is required before they could be considered reliable enough or suitable for routine rescue use. In all cases a small platform should be stamped out down to consolidated snow where the ax will be placed, and the belayer should kick steps for a solid stance. If the belayer needs a tie-in himself, he may use an anchor as above, most likely the unattended ice ax.

Boot-Ax Belays. The belayer stands with one foot uphill and ahead of the other, with the ax pushed vertically into the snow on the uphill side of the upper boot with the pick pointing into the slope thus orienting the shaft for greatest strength (see Fig. 29-6). The rope from the litter is passed over the instep on the toe side of the ax and then either a) around the ax shaft and boot heel (the "C" belay) to the belayer's downhill (braking) hand (Fig. 29-6b), or b) around the ax shaft and under the boot sole (no crampons) to the braking hand (Fig.

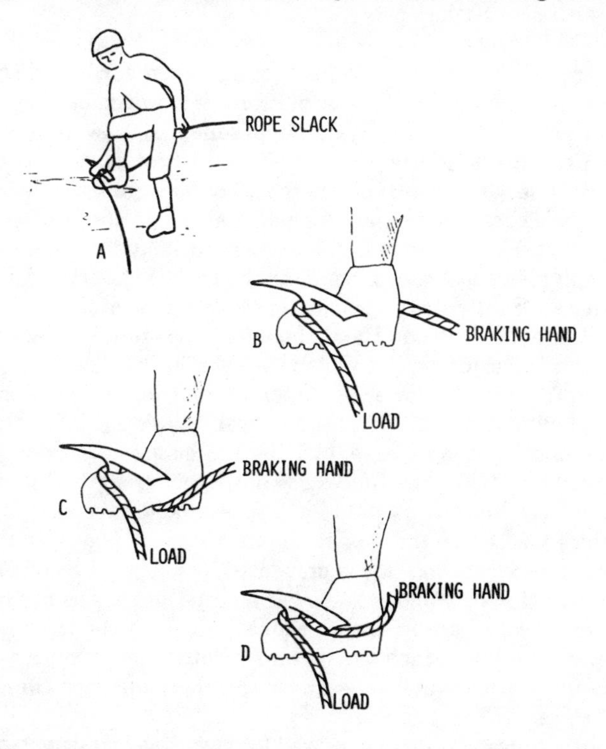

Fig. 29-6. Boot-ax belays. a) The stance. b), c), d) Showing several ways of wrapping the rope around the ax and boot.

29-6c), or c) around the ax shaft and back over the instep to the braking hand (Fig. 29-6d, the "S" belay) where the braking hand wraps the rope around the heel in an uphill direction to increase friction. The "S" belay is equally effective and easy with the downhill hand on the ax and uphill hand braking. In each case the belayer's hand on the ax head pushes downwards quite hard if the snow is hard enough that the head is not all the way down to the boot. The position is quite solid, in that the rope load tends to pull the ax against the uphill boot which is braced solidly into the slope, and the uphill hand also holds the ax in place.

Friction is controlled by the degree of wrap of the rope around the shaft and boot, and by tightness of grip on the rope; the "S" belay provides more friction than the "C." Gloves or mittens must be worn. Multiple turns of rope around the shaft give much more friction, generally too much for any situation except holding a purely static load, such as a backup belay.

"Stomper" Belay. This excellent ice ax system for lowering a litter on snow is shown in Fig. 29-7. A platform is stamped out in the snow, and the ax is placed vertically in the consolidated snow to its head. The brakeman stands securely with his uphill boot placed against the downhill side of the ax and on the rope. The rope from the litter passes under the boot, around the ax shaft and under the boot again, up across the brakeman's chest to his downhill shoulder, then behind to his uphill side and braking hand, as shown in Fig. 29-7a. An equally effective alternative is to pass the rope around the hips for a hip belay instead of across the chest and shoulder. The stance is very natural and is easier to do than to describe. The brakeman has excellent control of friction for lowering. Much of the friction comes on the ax and boot with some additional on the brakeman's body. For best resistance to motion, the ax head (pick) is pointed along the slope so that the broad face of the shaft faces downhill; the strength of the shaft is less this way, but any ax used for rescue should have a strong shaft.

If the snow is soft, the rope to the litter tends to cut into the snow and move down the ax; this is prevented by placing a second ax horizontally in the snow under the lowering rope just downslope from the main ax. Also, a backup anchor should be used if the snow is soft. A convenient way to attach the backup is with a carabiner around the shaft, and if the carabiner is under the rope, the rope cannot slide down the shaft into the snow.

The above system works very well for lowering, being more comfortable and less awkward for the brakeman to apply friction than with the "S" or "C" technique. However, the method is not good for belaying a load or climber coming up because it is difficult to take in the rope which passes around the body; the hip belay has less of a problem in this regard than the shoulder method. A simple change in the stance reduces the friction at the ax and boot and allows the rope to be taken up easily. The change from Fig. 29-7b is simply to put the toe of the boot on the ax adze instead of on the rope in front of the ax, as in Fig. 29-7c; the boot remains on the downslope side of the ax. This belay is somewhat less secure than the one in Fig. 29-7b because the shaft is not held upright so firmly, but it is quite adequate for belaying up a climber in most snow conditions.

No form of ice ax belay should be counted on to hold loads unless the technique has been practiced at length. This is particularly true for the "Stomper" belay since there is no direct control of the ax head by hand; the belay fails totally if the ax pulls out, and the belayer then has no ax in hand for self-arrest.

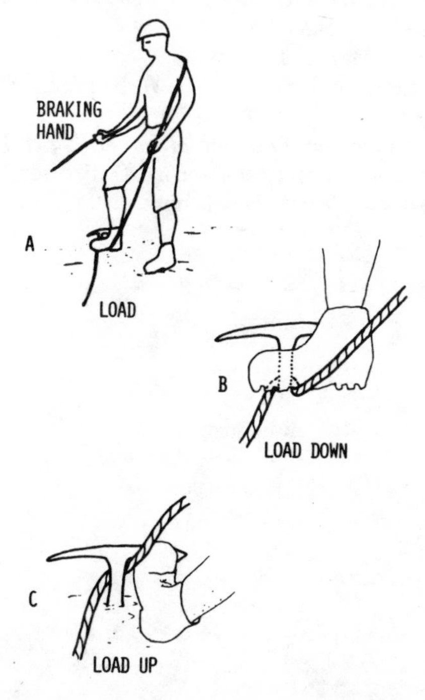

Fig. 29-7. "Stomper" belay. a) The stance. The rope can be placed around either shoulders or hips. b) Method of passing rope around boot and ax for lowering loads. c) A method of using the stomper belay for belaying a climber moving up towards the belayer.

Strength of the Ax. Some comment is in order regarding the intrinsic strength of the ax itself. Various tests have been performed under laboratory conditions to test the strength of the shaft (Mountain Safety Research, and Recreational Equipment Inc., both in Seattle, have test results available). The materials used for shafts, in order of increasing strength, are ash, hickory, and metal, with fiberglassing the shaft increasing its strength somewhat but causing some problems in belaying due to the rope cutting into the fiberglass. Strengths of various shafts are typically in the range 400-1000 lbs (180-450 kg). For mountain rescue use, it seems prudent to use the ax with the strongest shaft available, namely a metal shaft.

REFERENCES

1. a) "Testing Ice Pitons," Cal Magnusson, *Summit,* Oct. 1971, pp. 16-17. b) AAC *Accident Reports* 1968.

2. *Summit*, March, 1972, p. 42

3. "Innovations in Ice Pitons," H. W. Kendall, *Summit* July/August 1971, pp. 8-11.

4. *Mountaineering, Freedom of the Hills*, H. Manning.

5. *Manual of Ski Mountaineering,* D. Brower.

6. *Mountaineering,* A. Blackshaw.

CHAPTER 30

CREVASSE RESCUE

General Discussion. Any climbers moving on a crevassed glacier should be prepared for a crevasse rescue and be familiar with the appropriate rescue techniques. In preparation the party should be roped together with no slack between members. Also, everyone should have at least one prusik sling on the rope to aid in survival if he falls in and to aid rescue as described below should a ropemate fall in. At least one spare rope and pulley should be carried in the party for rescue purposes. Rescue gear should be distributed among two or more party members so that the one who falls in cannot have all the gear with him. Everyone should be dressed for survival in the cold encountered in the depths of a crevasse or at least have clothing readily accessible in the case of a fall in. The smaller the party the more important are these precautions and the more difficult will a crevasse rescue be.

Crevasse rescue takes various forms. The easiest situation occurs when a climber falls in perhaps thigh or waist deep, wallows around a bit and is the subject of laughter and insults from his partners before being given a helping hand to get out. More of a problem is the case where the victim falls in well over his head. If he is uninjured and able to aid in his own rescue, extrication is relatively easy. Much more serious is the situation in which the victim is injured and must depend completely on others for his rescue.

When one person falls into a crevasse, the others on the rope immediately drop into self-arrest. After the fall is stopped, those on top will, one at a time, use their prusik sling and ice ax to anchor the rope to allow their own freedom of movement.

Throughout rescue procedures, those on top must be careful to not knock snow down onto the victim. Only rescuers who need to be at the lip of the crevasse should be there.

The Victim Dangling from his Waist Loop. The first phase of a rescue of a fallen climber dangling from his waist loop is to relieve the constriction of the tie-in since blood circulation to the diaphragm may be cut off. The best method is to simply lower the victim to the bottom or to a platform (snowbridge) where he can wait comfortably. If this is not feasible and assuming that the climber is not badly injured and can help himself, he can tighten his prusik sling which should already be tied on the belay rope, place a boot in the sling loop, and stand or sit on this foot. When the victim is a middle man and has attached to his waist loop a slack rope which can be anchored, he can tie a clove hitch around a boot with this rope and stand or sit on this foot. Alternatively the victim could stand in a loop tied in the end of a spare belay rope lowered in by the rescuers.

If the victim has not dropped his ax (the wrist loop may be quite valuable once in a while), he may use it as a comfortable seat by the following simple procedure. He inverts himself for a moment so that his feet point up and his legs are parallel to the rope (and in this position the tie-in no longer constricts his breathing); he then puts the ax behind his legs but in front of the rope and rights himself. He is then sitting on the ax with the rope going from his waist loop down under the ax between his legs and back up as shown in Fig. 30-1. If the victim is wearing an independent waist loop so that the climbing rope is clipped or tied to the waist loop by a bowline, and if this bowline is tied leaving a foot (.3 m) or more of rope between the knot and the waist loop, then he can gain more comfort by placing his ax through the loop of the bowline. In this way, shown in Fig. 30-2, there is no downward pull on the waist loop, and the loading on the ice ax handle is reduced.

In the event that the victim has dropped his ax, a technique similar to that of Fig. 30-1 may be used, replacing the ax by a rather short sling formed into a Figure-of-Eight. The victim steps into this sling and places it on his thighs while inverted, and when he rights himself, the belay rope passes under the sling. If the sling is too long, the rope will not be directed downwards, and if too short, it cannot be placed on the legs. Webbing is much more comfortable than sling rope for this purpose.

The above techniques work easily if the victim is not wearing a heavy pack. It may be feasible and appropriate for the victim to use a spare sling as a prusik on the belay rope to clip on the pack to get it out of the way or to eliminate the backward pull on himself.

If the victim is unconscious or otherwise unable to help himself, the rescuers must waste no time in either lowering the victim to a ledge or in getting a man to the victim with a seat sling or belay seat or some

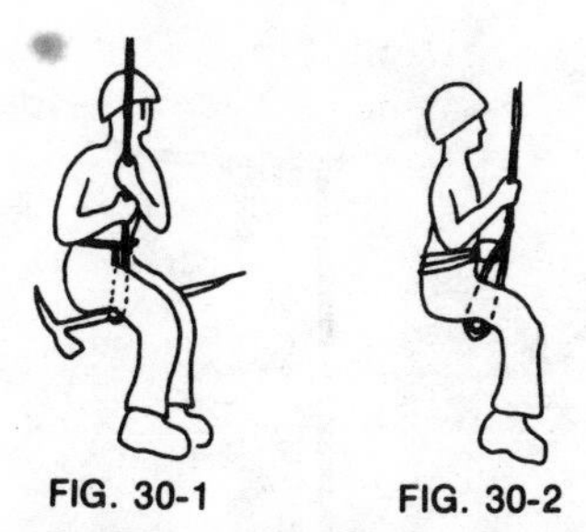

Fig. 30-1. Showing one method for a dangling victim to relieve constriction of the diaphragm. **Fig. 30-2.** Showing a more comfortable method.

other means of getting the tension off the waist loop. See Chapter 32 for third man techniques. Rescuers should remember that even though they may be sweating in the sun, the victim may be very cold in the crevasse and must be supplied with extra clothing.

Extrication. The victim may be able to perform self rescue either by climbing (chimneying or ice climbing) or by ascending the fixed line with prusiks or mechanical ascenders (see Ch. 19). Because the rope used on a glacier is apt to be wet and iced, ascending devices may not hold well, and prusik knots will be difficult to move. The devices which put a bend in the main rope work best, that is, Hieblers or Jumars loaded at the top would be used. The Gibbs ascenders also hold well.

At the lip of the crevasse the rope to the victim will cut deeply into the snow and might freeze in place. To prevent this, some item such as a summit pack or ski (with metal edge down) should be placed under the rope at the lip. An ice ax certainly could be used but may be much more useful as an anchor or elsewhere during the rescue. An anchor may be in order for whatever item is placed near the edge. This problem of the rope trenching into the snow and the resulting difficulty in getting the victim over the lip can be alleviated using the system shown in Fig. 30-3.

Near the top the victim may be able to work his way out using muscle, that is, hand over hand on the rope with feet against the crevasse wall, but more likely he will find exiting easier if anchored stirrups are lowered down. He also may be assisted using the technique shown in Fig. 30-3. If the trenching mentioned above is not prevented, exiting will be very difficult.

The simplest form of hauling to get a victim out is for the victim to extricate himself, by holding the rope in his hands and placing his feet against the wall and walking up and out. This will work only in the easiest of cases. With sufficient number of rescuers, a victim may be

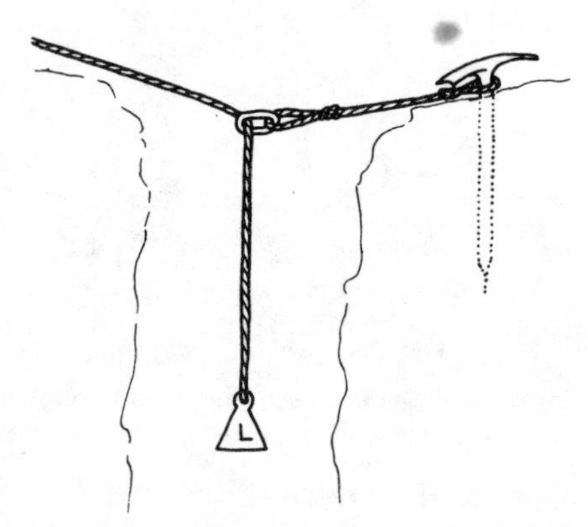

Fig. 30-3. Showing a means of alleviating the trenching problem at the lip of a crevasse.

pulled up with muscle (lots of it due to friction at the lip), and the victim steadies himself against the crevasse wall. Haulers must not pull him into an overhanging lip.

The double foot loop system is convenient if the victim is healthy and not in too deep. The technique, shown in Fig. 30-4, is basically very simple; two ropes are used, each with a loop in the end, one to each foot of the victim. One of the ropes is anchored temporarily, and the victim stands on that foot and raises the other. The second rope is pulled up taut and held firm, and the victim steps up on the second foot. The first rope, which is then slack, is pulled up taut, and so on. For safety the victim may attach a chest sling to one rope or be belayed by a third. The technique is effective only for short raises, say less than about 20 ft (6 m), because of stretch in the rope when loaded with the victim's weight. Good communication is essential to coordinate action of the victim and rescuers. Two different colored ropes may be useful. If the victim is dangling free and spinning, the twisting will be stopped if the ropes are moved apart at the top, or if the victim spreads the ropes with his hands.

There are a number of ways that the rescuers on top can handle the ropes of the double foot loop system. One man alone can perform the rescue by setting a prusik or mechanical device on each rope and anchoring each prusik sling to an ice ax. Two or more rescuers make the job much easier since then each rope can be taken up and anchored with multiple wraps around an ax or by a man using boot-ax belay or sitting hip belay with suitable tie-in.

If the victim is unable to help himself, a pulley hauling system (described in Ch. 26) will probably be needed to gain mechanical advantage. The friction of the rope passing over the lip is quite large. The simplest 2:1 system is to merely anchor one end of the rope on top, pass the rope down to a carabiner or pulley at the victim and back up, as was shown in Fig. 26-2a. A more complicated 2:1 system is shown in Fig. 30-5. When the prusik reaches either ax, the rope to the victim is held fast with the ax or a boot-ax belay while the prusik is slipped back to the edge of the crevasse. This is like Fig. 26-2b. Two rescuers

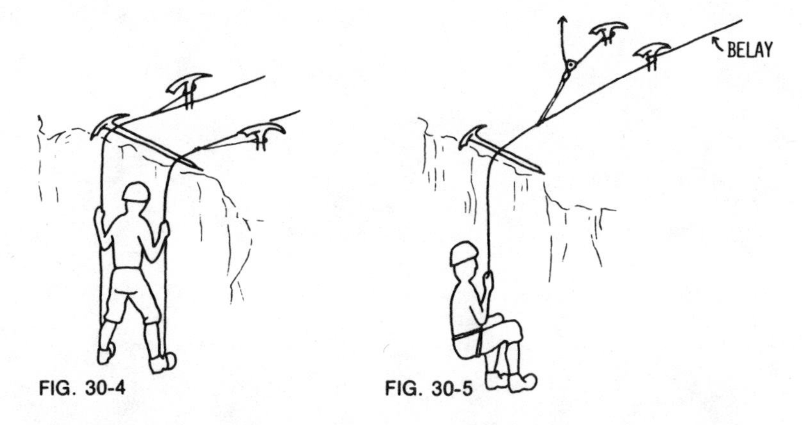

Fig. 30-4. Double foot loop system of crevasse rescue. **Fig. 30-5.** Crevasse rescue with two-to-one hauling system.

can lift about 200 lbs (90 kg) using this system. The anchors will usually make use of an ax which should never be left unattended. Certainly the more complex arrangements of Ch. 26 could be used, and a two or three pulley system will probably be needed to handle the case described below.

If the victim is injured or unconscious, a rescuer will have to go into the crevasse first to attend to first aid and warmth for the victim, then to arrange attachment of the hauling system, and finally to escort the victim back to the top. A convenient means to fix hauling lines to a not too seriously injured victim is with a belay seat or a three-loop bowline as described in Ch. 24. Some Third Man technique of Ch. 32 may be essential.

If the victim requires immobilization before evacuation, he may be lowered to a snowbridge or ledge in the crevasse to await further help or while a litter is improvised. Improvisation techniques may be done using skis or ice axes and clothing, or other techniques of Ch. 31.

REFERENCES

1. *Mountaineering: The Freedom of the Hills*, H. Manning, ed.
2. *Manual of Ski Mountaineering*, D. Brower.
3. *Mountain Rescue Techniques*, W. Mariner.

CHAPTER 31

IMPROVISATION TECHNIQUES

Improvisation techniques discussed in this chapter will find use in organized rescue operations; some of the schemes will also be used in self rescue or informal operations on expeditions. Third man techniques described in the next chapter are frequently used in conjunction with improvised rigging techniques and skills.

Lengthy experience and knowledge of mountaineering is the best guide to the individual in improvising. Mountaineering improvisation techniques such as making replacement sunglasses from cardboard with slots, or using a snowshoe as a shovel, will not be dealt with here but may be found discussed in books on mountain lore. However, there are some standard rescue improvisation techniques which mountain rescuers should know and which will be the main topics of this chapter. The skilled improviser will be imaginative in applying known techniques in unusual situations; he will have knowledge of the limitations of the techniques, and he will work confidently as close to these limits as necessary. In addition to the usual climbing hardware and rope, amazingly large quantities of parachute cord (550 lb or 250 kg test strength nylon line) and adhesive tape may be used in these improvisation schemes.

IMPROVISATION OF LITTERS

There are many ways to improvise litters other than the representative methods below, such as the travois drag and assembly of packframes with ice axes or tree limbs. Various references for general mountaineering lore often discuss such techniques at length.

Two-Man Trail Carry. The technique shown in Fig. 31-1 may be used whenever it is necessary to perform a carryout on a trail, but may be desirable even if a regular litter is available when the trail is very narrow in dense timber or on a sidehill. The side rails of the litter may be improvised from small-diameter tree trunks about 10 ft (3 m) long; at high elevation satisfactory timber will not be available, but in forests there should be no problem finding suitable materials. It is important that the packframes be of top quality with welded cross tubes since the loading on these frames is rather large. With hip straps on the packframes, moderate weight victims can be carried with surprising ease.

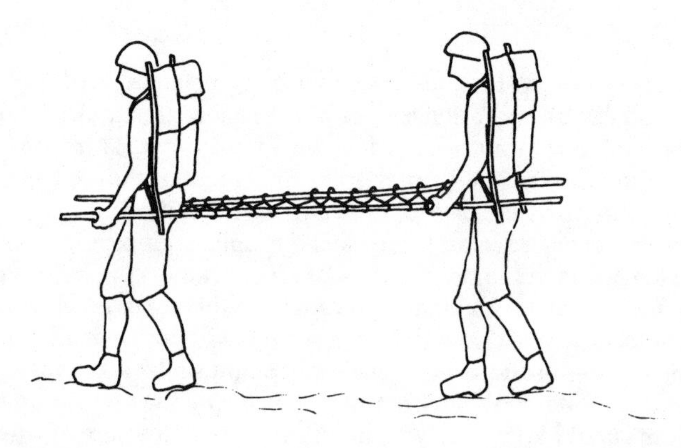

Fig. 31-1. Improvisation of a litter, especially useful on narrow trails and with only two litter bearers.

Rope Litters. A rope may be "crocheted" around a victim as shown in Fig. 31-2, and then slings are clipped from the rope loops to a horizontal pole which can be carried. Alternatively the "crocheting" may be done over the pole, which would then be about 1.5 ft (.5 m) over the victim. Care must be taken to provide adequate support under the victim's hips and shoulders, and a sling may be cinched around his feet. A belay seat clipped to a prusik sling makes an excellent support for his head. A litter such as this may be the most practical way of carrying a victim through thick brush.

Another form of rope litter is shown in Fig. 31-3. The small loops are tied about 3 ft (1 m) apart. This type of litter is less readily adjusted than the one of Fig. 31-2, but it is readily used by several "litter bearers" holding the loops to transport the victim without a separate pole.

Rope litters alone should never be used to transport the victim of a back injury.

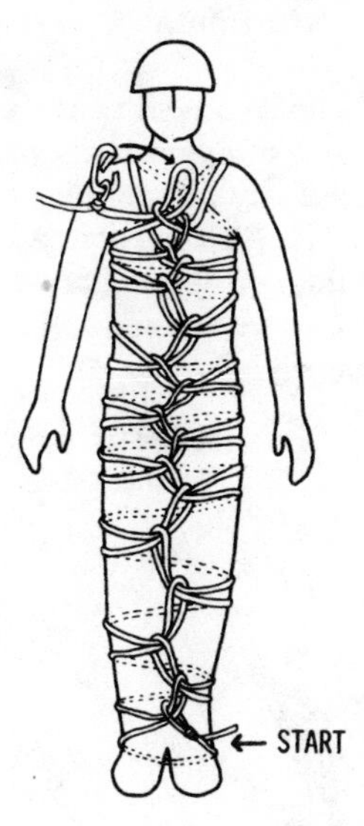

Fig. 31-2. Rope litter. The rope is laid out on the ground in serpentine fashion prior to "crocheting."

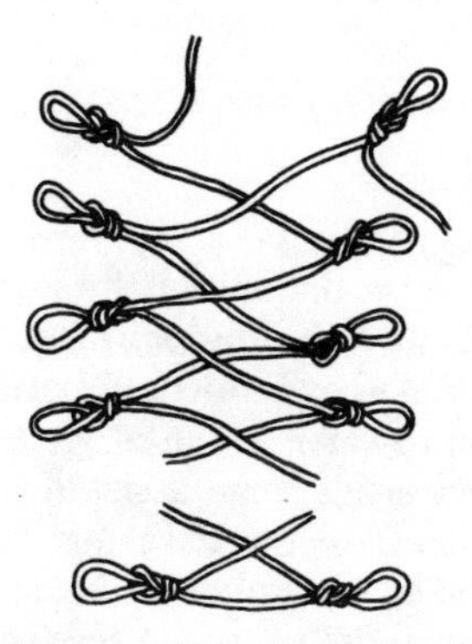

Fig. 31-3. Another rope litter easily used by several rescuers to move a victim a short distance.

Ski and Parka Stretcher. A similar form of litter may be improvised from skis (or small tree trunks). In its simplest form, the ski stretcher is put together by slipping skis through the sleeves of heavy parkas, and the parkas are zipped or buttoned shut with the sleeves inside. Any sharp metal edges on the skis should be taped over to prevent cutting the parka cloth.

ROPE SEATS

The commercially available Austrian tragsitz or Gramminger seat or its lighter equivalent made of nylon is very useful for lowering or carrying a victim with relatively minor injuries such as a sprained ankle—see Chs. 7, 22, and 24. An alternate approach is to specially build a set of rescuer's shoulder straps and provide a method of attachment of an improvised victim's seat as shown in Fig. 31-4. The victim's sling seat could also be suspended from a strong packframe.

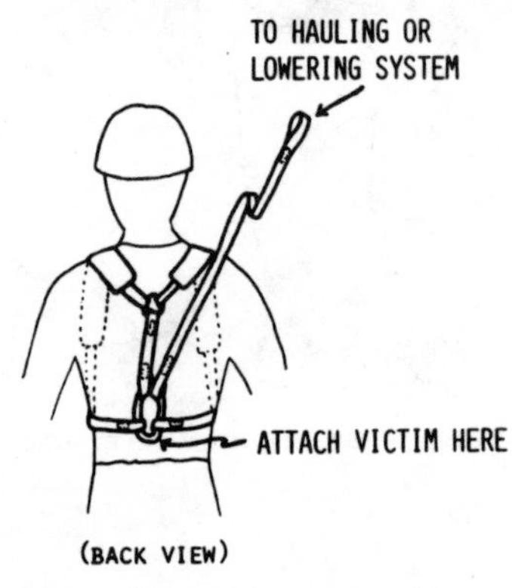

Fig. 31-4. Basic harness for improvising a tragsitz.

Triple Bowline Seat. The simplest seat for lowering an uninjured victim is a triple bowline on the end of the lowering rope with two loops longer for the legs, and a shorter loop for safety around the chest as in Fig. 31-5, or a double bowline could be used with a separate prusik sling on the main rope for the chest loop. If a victim on a wall is somewhat injured and needs some assistance from a rescuer, the rescuer may attach himself to the lowering rope with a prusik or Jumar and aid the victim as he would if using a tragsitz, with braking done at the anchor. The victim hugs the rescuer from the back.

The single strand leg loops as above are quite uncomfortable for extended use since they tend to cut circulation in the legs. If a victim is being lowered, he may be tied onto the lowering rope with the triple bowline but in addition have a belay seat attached to the rope with an adjustable prusik to take his weight and provide more comfort.

Rope Coil. For carrying a victim piggyback along a trail or for evacuation, a comfortable seat may be easily improvised from a rope

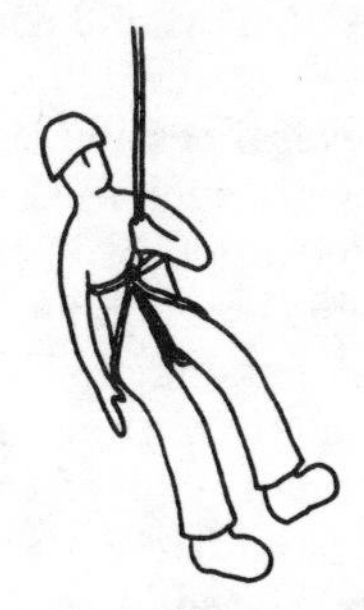

Fig. 31-5. Triple bowline for improvising a seat for the victim.

coil as shown in Fig. 31-6. The rescuer wears the coil as he would a pack. This technique, the "split-coil carry," is satisfactory for evacuating a lightweight victim by strong rescuers. For trail carry the victim is loaded onto the rescuer's back by the rescuer starting in a seated position, wearing the rope coil into which the victim gets seated. The rescuer rotates sideways onto his hands and knees, with the victim on the rescuer's back. The rescuer can then stand up easily.

Fig. 31-6. Split-coil seat. The rope coils are worn by the rescuer as a pack.

IMPROVISATION OF BRAKES

A brake for litter lowering must be solidly anchored and provide sufficient friction on the rope to reduce significantly the grip needed by the brakeman to hold the load and also be capable of dissipating the large amount of heat which is necessarily developed in the process of lowering the load. Some methods of improvising brakes when brake bars or brake plates are unavailable are discussed here. The general technique is to wrap the rope around something substantial.

Carabiner Brakes. Several possibilities are shown in Fig. 31-7. In general all gates should be in such a position that they will not accidentally open. The configuration of Fig. 31-7a is relatively safe because carabiners are doubled with gates opposed. The carabiners are easily assembled by first passing the loop of rope up through the carabiners as shown in Fig. 31-7b. Then the "brake bar" carabiners are clipped on at point P and finally clipped across the first carabiners into final position. Both safety and friction are reduced by using only two carabiners instead of four. For additional friction such brakes may be used in tandem.

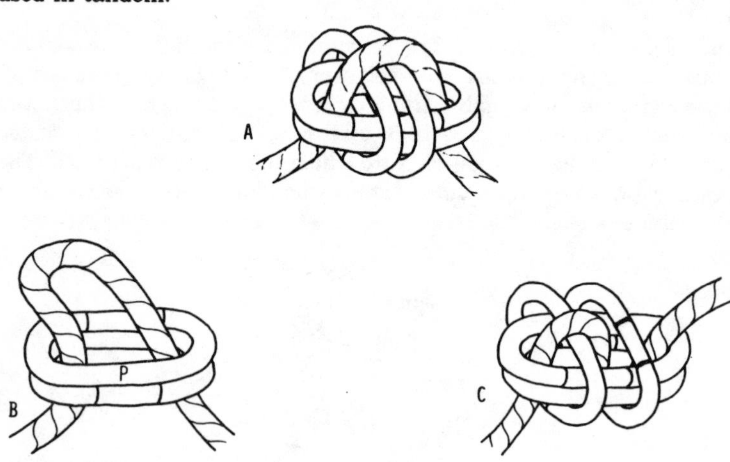

Fig. 31-7. Carabiner brakes. a) Basic brake, with doubled carabiners. b) Showing means of assembly. c) The S-brake.

Another configuration, Fig. 31-7c, called the S-brake, provides suitable friction for good control of lowering two people on a single rope and is about equivalent to three brake bars in series. The rescuer using this configuration must be aware of its dangers, since carabiner gates are not held shut.

Hammer-Handle Brake Bar. The use of this technique shown in Fig. 31-8 is obvious, and other items such as an ice ax handle could be used as well. A word of warning is appropriate: The handle can slip out, particularly if the load is reduced. This property is occasionally useful in situations requiring quick release of a brake, such as in rappels from a helicopter.

Piton Brake Bar. An angle piton may be substituted for a brake bar as shown in Fig. 31-9 but it must be used with caution since the carabiner gate is not locked shut as it would be with a regular brake bar.

Carabiner-Wrap. Two or three wraps of 7/16 in. Goldline as shown in Fig. 31-10 will provide friction about equal to the usual brake bar. More wraps of lighter sling rope will be needed for the same friction.

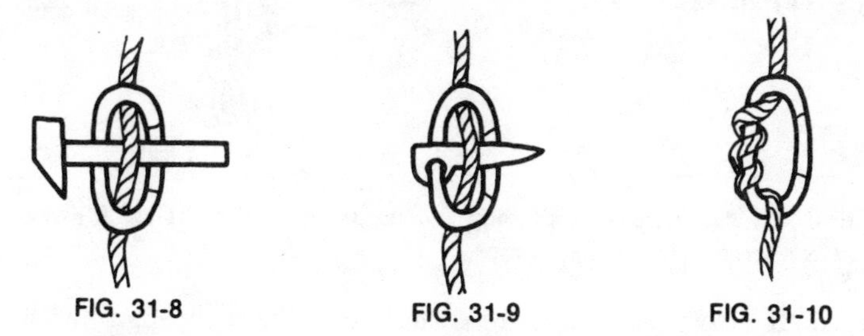

Fig. 31-8. Hammer handle instead of brake bar. **Fig. 31-9.** Piton instead of brake bar. **Fig. 31-10.** Carabiner-wrap brake.

As with all the techniques discussed in this chapter, the above schemes are not meant to form an all-inclusive list but are indicative of the general procedures of improvisation.

IMPROVISATION IN RAPPELLING

Brakes are not needed in rappelling since a body or dulfersitz rappel can always be done.

If it is necessary to make a series of rappels and recover the rope and if the rope is not long enough to be doubled to allow easy recovery, a single rope can be used as in Fig. 31-11 with light recovery cord; the latter can be parachute cord, spare slings, bootlaces, etc. If things are really desperate and even the light line is not available, the main line may be split into its three individual component strands and thus be nearly tripled in length but greatly weakened. Its strength will be much less than one third of the strength of the full rope because there is strength developed by having the strands twisted together. Rappelling will be difficult because of the reduced diameter rope.

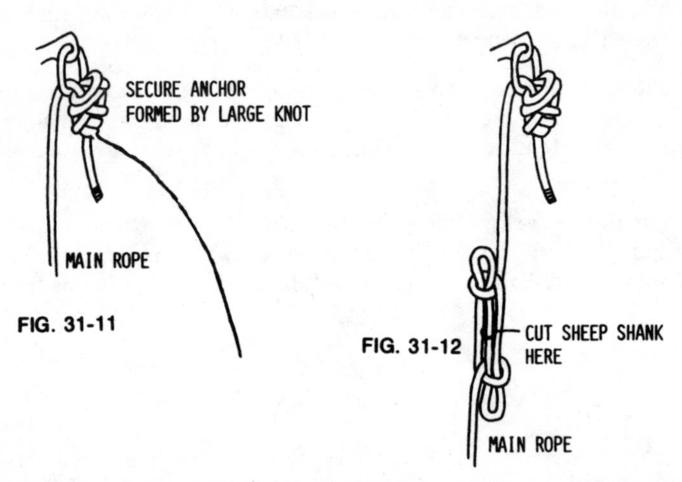

Fig. 31-11. A means of recovering the rappel rope. **Fig. 31-12.** A desperate means of recovering a rappel rope.

Another desperate measure is the use of the sheepshank with cut center strand (taped before cutting) as in Fig. 31-12. When the sheepshank is under load, it will hold well, but when tension is released and the main rope is shaken, the sheepshank will loosen and come apart, and most of the rope is recovered.

If neither hardware nor natural anchors are available, knots in webbing or rope can be jammed into cracks and used as nuts, sacrificing only the knot and a small hero loop around the knot.

KNOT PASS (ROPE CHANGE)

The normal technique of rope change could be used (Ch. 24) with the auxiliary brake improvised for convenience and simplicity using a long prusik sling in a multiple-wrap carabiner-wrap brake, Fig. 31-10.

Occasionally a knot gets jammed in a brake or pulley. A number of methods may be used to free the jammed knot. Perhaps best is to set up a hauling system with prusik on the rope to the load to provide about 6 in. (15 cm) of slack necessary to free the knot; if the hauling system is anchored to the same anchor as the brake (or pulley), stretch in the anchor will not have to be overcome by the hauling system. Only about 3 in. (7.5 cm) of slack is needed to unclip the brakes (or pulley) and thus provide sufficient slack to free the knot.

The following techniques may be used to free a jammed knot when a hauling system cannot be set up, but are potentially dangerous. In each case a well-anchored prusik is set firmly on the load-bearing rope. If this prusik can be anchored independently of the brakes (or pulley) in which the knot is jammed, then the original anchor may be released by cutting the anchor rope. If this is not an appropriate method, the prusik can be set solidly about 3 ft (1 m) below the brake (pulley). Then the knot might be untied if it is not too tightly jammed, or cut apart after taping to prevent unraveling. Both methods are potentially dangerous because the load-bearing rope could slip through the prusik. The knot is quickly retied on the load side of the brakes or pulley using the free ends.

A related method can be used for passing the knot, particularly past a pulley. This is to attach a second pulley or carabiner on the opposite side of the knot from the first pulley. This second pulley must be independently anchored with a secure shock resistant sling. Then the anchor rope to the first pulley is cut, and thus the load is suddenly transferred to the second pulley.

LITTER RIGGING

The recommended six-point rigging system (litter spiders) shown in Ch. 24 is quite convenient in high angle evacuations. The six points of attachment are useful for ease in loading of even a tall victim without distorting the victim to get him past the connection points. This rigging deliberately does not allow side-to-side tipping or leveling of the litter when all connections are used, since it is quickly discovered that rigging that allows leveling also allows dumping. Because carabiners used to clip the spiders onto the main rails are slightly larger than normal 'biners, improvised rigging materials may not include carabiners of large enough size, thereby requiring rope to be passed around these outer rails. Then the litter bearers must be quite careful to avoid completely letting the litter rail hit the rock; otherwise, the rope around the rail may be very seriously weakened by abrasion. Layers of tape on the rope at these critical spots will help ward off abrasion.

If slings are not available to improvise the litter spiders, the slings may be improvised by tying a triple bowline in the end of each lowering rope and using large carabiners to clip the rope loops to the rails. Alternatively a bowline on a coil may be tied directly around the rails. If loss of length of rope is critical, double bowlines could be used instead of triples, thereby reducing the number of connection points to four; better, a short anchor rope may be used to improvise the spiders. A minimum of 20 ft (6 m) of rope is required for a four-point system.

Litter bearer tie-ins are easily improvised by prusik slings attached to the main lowering ropes.

If there is only enough rope to use a single lowering rope and if the victim is to be kept in a horizontal position as is usually necessary from first aid considerations, then the suspension system shown in Fig. 31-13 may be used conveniently to allow end-to-end leveling of the litter. During initial setup it should be remembered that the head end is heavier when the victim is loaded.

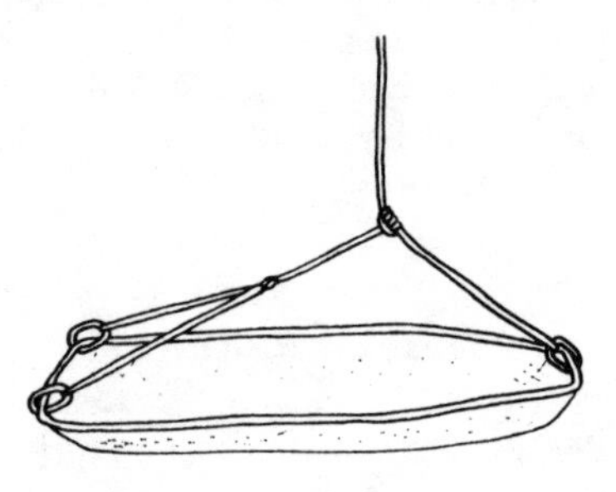

Fig. 31-13. Showing a method of using a single lowering rope for a high angle evacuation, adjustable for end-to-end tilt of the litter.

LOAD EQUALIZATION

If anchor points are weak, several should be used together with a self-equalizing system as described in Ch. 25. This system takes quite a bit of hardware, which may be unavailable. An equalizing method using fewer carabiners is shown in Fig. 31-14. This system may be set up easily for equal loads on each anchor point, but if one point fails, the system may not equalize fully due to the friction of the rope at the lower carabiner.

Often sufficiently strong slings will not be available for a particular job, and lighter weight materials need to be used with multiple turns. Rather than use an equalizing system, each turn would be tied so that each loop has essentially equal loading and so that if one turn fails, the entire system will not fail.

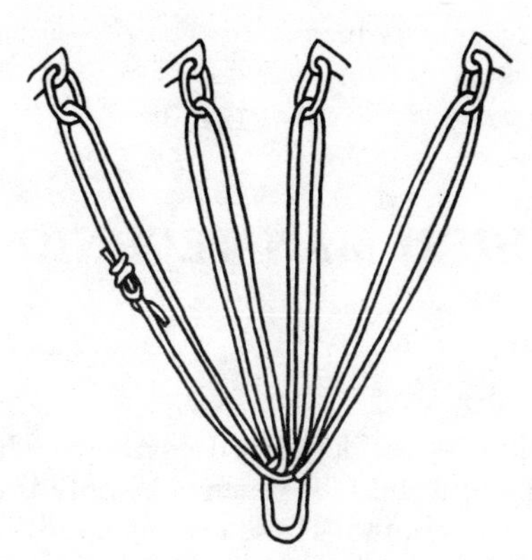

Fig. 31-14. Simple equalizing anchor. The knot can jam into the carabiners.

CHAPTER 32

THIRD MAN TECHNIQUES

If a serious climbing accident has occurred on a large technical rock face, the victim will usually be reached by only three rescuers before he is lowered to the ground. These are the two litter bearers and the so-called *Third Man*. The job of the third man is to make his way as soon as possible to the victim and render immediate first aid. Then he will prepare the rigging and victim for loading the victim into the litter and finally, upon arrival of the litter and litter bearers, perform the loading, assisted by the litter bearers. The well-trained third man is highly skilled, not only in all aspects of technical rescue and rock climbing, but also in first aid since he is usually the first rescuer to reach the victim in spite of the terminology *Third Man*. The process of loading a seriously injured victim without doing further damage to the victim (who for example has suffered back injuries) requires the greatest skills needed in technical rescue. Such skills are acquired only through extensive experience at free and aid climbing and rescue techniques and require a considerable ability to improvise expertly. We discuss below the classic third man technique and also some additional techniques sometimes needed by the third man in more complicated loading problems.

Third Man Loading Technique. The basic third man loading technique applies to the loading of a helpless victim into a litter on a vertical rock face when the litter may readily reach the victim using the standard high angle evacuation methods discussed in Ch. 24. We assume that there are no ledges which may be used to advantage by any of the rescuers on the face. The third man will be the first rescuer to arrive at the victim (by rappel most likely, or else by climbing). His first action will be to tie the victim to the wall or a secured rope, with a simple tie-in, to prevent the victim from falling further. First aid is then rendered. Then the rigging is set up for loading the victim as described here.

The loading process will always involve lifting the victim, since we assume that there is no lifting capability by the litter lowering system. If the litter is brought to just below the victim's level, the victim will have to be lifted to release his tie-in from the wall, and another brake system will have to be set up to lower the victim into the litter. (This tie-in could be cut thereby dropping the victim into the litter.) Alternatively, the litter could be lowered to just above the victim, and the victim is lifted into the litter with easy release of his tie-in to the wall. We will assume the latter, although the techniques discussed below may be used for either raising or lowering a victim smoothly, and are extensions of the basic techniques mentioned in Ch. 26.

The victim should be lifted with the least possible relative motion of his injured body parts as is desirable for any bone fracture and is essential in the case of a possible back injury. Such may be accomplished by improvising a rope and sling litter used only to transfer the victim into the rigid (Stokes) litter. Most of the victim's weight is nicely taken by a belay seat around his midsection with other slings going to his chest, head, and legs. The lengths of these ties are adjusted carefully and are brought to preferably one point several feet above the victim. A hammock could be used if it has a sufficient number of ties along its sides so that the victim is not jack-knifed when lifted. We now assume that the victim can be safely lifted by one carabiner, but this is not a requirement, as below.

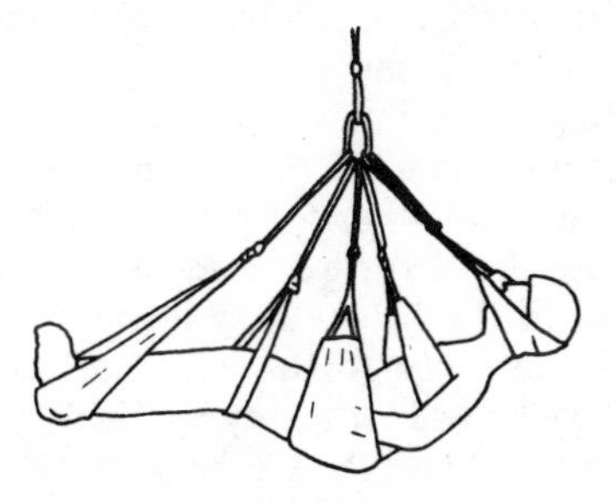

Fig. 32-1. Typical rigging on a victim for lifting. Considerable support is needed around the hips and shoulders. A foot sling may need to be secured at the boots.

The victim is now ready to be lifted and transferred to the litter using a raising system essentially the same as the Yosemite haul technique (Ch. 26). A short rope (20 ft or 6 m) goes from the victim's lifting point up to an anchored pulley and down to a foot of the third man who puts his full weight on this rope, thereby counterbalancing the weight of the victim. If the third man is somewhat lighter than the victim, he easily raises the victim by merely lifting the rope at the victim with a hand; the third man can easily lift a person 50 lbs (23 kg) heavier than himself. Alternatively, of course, if the victim is much lighter, the third man pulls down on the rope to the victim.

The anchor for the pulley of the victim's raising system may be either on the wall or on the third man's rappel rope. Because of rope stretch, the anchor should be at least 10 ft (3 m) above the victim and litter. With the anchor on the wall, the third man may end up high above the victim after loading, and if the anchor point is on the rappel rope, rope stretch may cause the point to drop to just above the litter when the victim's weight comes on the rope. At this time the third man will no longer be tied to his rappel rope but will have a rather long safety tie-in allowing adequate mobility.

The litter, assumed horizontal, is brought down by two litter bearers and is stopped about 1 ft (.3 m) above the center of gravity of the victim. The lowering ropes may stretch a little with time, dropping the litter slightly even though the brakeman does not allow any rope to feed out. The problem of rope stretch is a major one. Obviously the litter will go down when the weight of the third man or victim is added, and it will rise if a litter bearer transfers some of his weight off the lowering rope onto the rock, for example by standing on a small ledge. The litter bearers must be fully aware of this phenomenon and be prepared for the reaction of the litter to changing loading.

The litter bearers unclip one or both inside spider connections as necessary for loading the victim without distorting him. At this point the litter bearers must be alert to prevent the litter from tipping inward. They should be standing or squatting on the ends of the litter or perhaps standing in stirrups clipped to the litter rail, ready to position the victim in the litter. They cannot be much help when suspended by their seat slings. As the third man starts the movement, the victim should be clipped for safety to the litter system and *then* unclipped from the wall. Once the victim is in the litter, he should be securely strapped in, and the inside spider connections replaced.

At this point, the formal job of the third man is over, but he will have to clear the wall of gear, and he may assist the victim's partner off the rock. It is preferable that he not ride the litter down because of resulting high stresses on the evacuation system, thus he should rappel or Jumar.

Some Complications. It should be clear from the above that the third man needs a large amount of equipment and skill. Even more is needed for the techniques below.

If the victim is in an awkward position, the raising may require additional degrees of freedom not assumed above. The third man may set up two pulleys for raising the victim, for example with slings around the victim's head and trunk going to one rope, pulley and one of the third man's feet, and the victim's leg slings through the second pulley to the third man's other foot. Then the third man raises the victim using both feet independently; he tries to keep his hands free for use as necessary. Occasionally a second third man may be needed to assist in a particularly difficult loading problem, but too many rescuers at the scene on a vertical wall will get in each other's way.

A common possibility is for the victim to be under an overhang such that the litter cannot be lowered directly to the victim. We assume now that the third man can get to both the victim and to the litter as it approaches the scene. Either of two techniques may be used to bring the litter and victim together: the litter is pulled in to the victim, or the victim is lowered out to the litter. In the first method, when the litter is hauled in, an anchor and pulley are placed beyond the victim; a rope from the litter goes through the pulley and back to another pulley on the litter spider. A ratchet may be used if desired. The litter bearers can use this system to pull the litter and themselves in to the victim. One of the litter bearers can stand in a sling hitched with Jumar or prusik to the rope through the pulleys and use his body weight to advantage. See Fig. 32-2. The litter bearers will have to judge carefully the point at which the brakeman should stop lowering. With good placement of the pulley beyond the victim, it should be possible to lower the victim directly into the litter. Then the third man can rig a simple brake system to ease the litter back out from under the overhang.

The alternative approach, that of bringing the victim out from under the overhang to the litter, may be rigged in a variety of ways. One of these is to set up a Tyrolean suspension system (see Ch. 27) with one anchor on the wall and the other set with a Jumar on a litter lowering rope well above the victim. The anchor on the wall may be replaced by a brake system so that the suspension rope can be released under control, lowering the victim into the litter.

Useful Skills. *Rappelling Past a Knot.* This technique might be needed by a third man on a long evacuation, either to get to the victim or to free a jammed knot on a litter lowering rope. We assume that the third man has Jumars (but prusiks could be used) and that rappelling is with a brake bar. The steps to rappel past a knot are: a) The third man places a Jumar on the rope and clips into this, letting the Jumar

Fig. 32-2. A method of evacuating a victim from under a large roof.

take his weight when there is at least 6 in. (15 cm) of rope between the brake bar and the knot. b) The brake bar is removed from the rope and placed below the knot as the third man hangs from the Jumar. c) A second Jumar is placed on the rope above the brake bar and below the knot, and a sling loop is clipped to the Jumar (and clipped to a separate carabiner to the seat sling for extra safety). d) The third man stands in this sling loop, relieving his weight from the upper Jumar. e) The upper Jumar is removed. f) Finally he leans back and eases body weight off the lower Jumar onto the brake bar. The use of the lower Jumar may be eliminated by the expedient of standing in a clove hitch tied around a boot.

If a brake system for the rappel rope can be easily set up and operated by a brakeman, the following technique may be used to eliminate the need for the third man having to rappel past a knot. Instead of having the rappel ropes (joined with a knot) tied off at the top, the upper rope is placed in the brakes with the knot immediately below the brakes. The third man then starts his rappel below the knot. Now the brakeman lowers the third man until enough of the upper rope is out that the lower rope reaches the bottom of the rappel. The third man then continues his rappel to the bottom.

Improvised Techniques. Many of the sort of techniques described in the previous chapter will be needed from time to time by the third man. The key to success in any of these advanced techniques is the ability to improvise. Each problem will be different from the previous one, and only extensive experience will be a good guide to the rescuer in the various techniques to be applied.

CHAPTER 33

LONG FACE EVACUATIONS

This chapter will discuss problems encountered in long evacuations over technical terrain, specifically faces involving say over 1000 ft (300 m) of vertical or overhanging sections.

Such evacuations can be approached in two ways. The first of these might be called the Himalayan style approach involving considerable preplanning, abundant personnel and specialized equipment. It operates generally from a fixed point and either lowers the victims all the way to the bottom from a single anchor or raises them to the anchor. Perhaps the finest example of this type is the rescue of Corti from the North Face of the Eiger. This effort shows not only the scale of operations which can be undertaken but also the magnitude of the problems which must be foreseen and the efficiency or lack thereof which this size of operation almost necessarily entails. This approach has built into it a wide margin of safety. In spite of the great dangers and severe conditions on the Eiger, the rescuers suffered only minor injuries. The time lost in the organizational and buildup stages, however, may have cost Longhi his life.

The second approach to the long evacuation is seen in the rescue of a climber from the North Face of the Grand Teton by a few men with a minimum of equipment (see AAC Accident Reports, 1968). This was done in what can be called the Alpine style. It generally involves a small team, self-sufficient and detached, bringing a victim to safety by a series of short evacuations. It sacrifices most of the resources of the Himalayan style and may cut the objective margin of safety thinner. It often gains speed, which may be a key factor in overall safety.

Both of these styles have much to recommend them, as well as many drawbacks. The severity of the face involved will often dictate to a great extent the basic style of the rescue. Individual circumstances will affect the compromises which must be made among various advantages and drawbacks. It is imperative, however, that any rescue organization which proclaims its capability to perform a major face operation must be prepared to use either style and to combine elements of both without hesitation to meet whatever circumstances arise.

The potential for this kind of evacuation is by no means limited to the well-known faces of the Tetons, Longs Peak or Yosemite. Similar problems can occur on countless peaks in more remote areas of the United States or Canada. An evacuation in these areas would present problems which could easily be more severe than those met on more accessible faces.

Personnel. Persons going over the edge on a long evacuation should ideally be highly qualified in three areas. They must first be completely trained in all rescue techniques involving the litter, its loading, communications (both radio and alternative systems), the brake system, and group operating procedures. This can come only through years of practice in mountain rescue and preferably, specialization in litter handling and rock evacuation. Second, they should be highly qualified at first aid with specialized training beyond the advanced first aid level. Such additional training ought to include that leading to certification and registry as an Emergency Medical Technician or its equivalent. Last but not least, they ought to be climbers capable of extricating themselves from any position in which circumstances, foreseen or otherwise, might leave them. It would be rare to have always available two or more persons combining all three of these qualifications.

Of equal importance with the litter team is the group handling the brakes. Personnel for this job should have extensive rescue experience and intimate knowledge of every detail of all braking systems which could conceivably be used in any situation.

Equipment. Assuming an easy route to the top, almost unlimited equipment can be used if there is time. A team going over a face could be equipped with two radios, full bivouac gear, a full set of whatever climbing hardware is required to get off the face, various specialized gadgets and a large first aid kit. There is, however, no single piece of this equipment which is absolutely necessary for a rescue, and no effort should be abandoned or delayed because of one missing or faulty bit of hardware. An Alpine style evacuation will be done with much less equipment. The "software" of the trained rescuer's mind must be able to improvise with the material at hand and circumvent any given lack of "hardware."

Two radios for a litter team is an ideal. There should be no hesitation to go over the edge with only one, and if necessary, most evacuations could be completed without radios. Hardware requirements might run as high as 50 pitons and 80 free carabiners with aid slings, Jumars, two climbing ropes, and belay seats. Bivouac gear could run from one down jacket to hammocks, half bags, bivouac sacks and anything else necessary to sit out a blizzard while nailed into a wall. Food and water requirements will vary considerably with the season, terrain and probable time limits of the evacuation.

A good deal of special equipment is available for particular problems which could be encountered. Such items as rope throwing guns, poles with open carabiners mounted on the end, flare guns, pulleys, and winch equipment may be advisable if time and terrain permit a full scale Himalayan style buildup.

Technique. The possibility of having a knot jam several hundred feet down a face gives pause to anyone involved in this type of operation. If the Himalayan style is used, it may be possible to run the entire evacuation on single lengths of rope, off 1200 ft (360 m) coils. If many shorter ropes must be used, the rescue team must be prepared to send a man down on rappel to free a knot or have a litter bearer Jumar up to the jam. Either procedure is preferably avoided. Extreme care is necessary on the part of the litter team to avoid potential jams. Tests should be conducted to find out if such knots as the tucked double sheet bend will resist jams more than untucked knots, whether taped safeties can replace overhand knots and whether knots such as the ring knot (however hard it may be to untie) can eliminate the need for safeties.

If the victims are in the recess of an overhanging wall, the evacuation team may be hanging free many feet from the wall when they get to the proper height. Such gadgets as carabiner poles and rope guns may be necessary here until pulleys are developed for mountain rescue which can reliably pass a knot, allowing the rescuers to hold themselves into a wall. In some cases, the use of 1200 ft (360 m) ropes may solve this problem.

In any evacuation, but particularly when using the Himalayan style, great care must be taken to position the litter so that it will be lowered directly over the victims. This error cost hours on the Eiger. If weather permits, a spotter with a plumb bob at some distance from the face can radio specific instructions.

In a long evacuation using nylon rope, the rope stretch problem was once thought to present a major obstacle in loading a victim. However, experience on long evacuations has shown that loading does not require secondary anchors and brakes at the loading site. In particular on an evacuation with the litter hanging free for 400 ft (120 m), the addition of a victim (200 lbs, 90 kg) caused a drop of the litter of only

2 ft (.6 m), and similar evacuations free for 800 ft (240 m), had 10 ft (3 m) of extra rope stretch. These small stretch figures are accounted for by two factors. One is that most of the rope had been stretched for some time and had taken a set. The other is that the litter can be moved not only from side to side (easily about five litter lengths to each side of the fall line with 700 ft or 210 m of rope out) but also up and down a vertical face by simply "toeing" the rock to move the litter. There were no major litter handling problems on a nearly vertical evacuation using over 1500 ft (450 m) for each lowering rope.

The rescue of a climbing party off a big face may involve more than one victim. If both are to be taken up or down by the first litter team, we have the problem of double loading. An actual 500 ft (150 m) evacuation indicated that if the victim can sit up and use his legs, he should be placed in a belay seat above the litter and between the two lowering ropes. In this way he can see where he is placing his feet as he goes down and does not have to fight the litter in his lap. The psychological effect of being above the litter may be quite important with an injured man who has spent hours or days marooned on a face. If two victims require litter loading, they should be placed side by side. If back injuries require flat loading, the lighter victim will just have to be placed face down on top of the other. The alternative is a second litter. A large Himalayan buildup and good weather may permit this solution.

Experience has indicated that long vertical evacuations, done rapidly with minimal rope changes, can develop almost unacceptable heat levels in a carabiner-brake system. Brake plates are preferable for both heat dissipation and ease of handling to the usual carabiner brake system.

A problem requiring considerable physical effort to overcome when using new 7/16 in. Goldline taken directly off the spools is one of kinking. Kinks are developed at the rate of nearly one per foot (30 cm) of rope, and the spools must be spun to eliminate the kinking.

A particularly thought-provoking situation involves a face on which the best solution may be to lower a fully equipped self-sustaining four-man Alpine party off a 1000 ft (300 m) face. This party would pick up two victims on the way down and then rig a second anchor (or series of them) to descend a second 1000 ft (300 m) face to the bottom. Without extreme care this method could impose a load of as much as 1500 lbs (700 kg) on the primary brake and anchor system. This, of course, approaches the breaking strength of some components often used in brakes. The alternative Himalayan effort of setting up a single 2000 ft (600 m) evacuation is probably preferred. A fully Alpine effort using a series of short evacuations all the way down the face has more problems than either alternative.

First Aid. In any evacuation of this nature there will be considerable delay in getting to the victims. This delay could easily be as much as 36 hours. In remote areas, the figure might be three days or more. By and large we will not have to deal with hurry cases in the usual sense of the word. Shock, exposure, exhaustion and dehydration will constitute the immediate problems. These will require sleeping bags, food and water, and possibly heating units, IV fluids and pain-killing drugs. Beyond these, the problems that we can expect will include broken bones, head and internal injuries, and possibly pulmonary edema or other complications of altitude. In treating all of these with the exception of broken bones, the treatment of choice is a speedy evacuation. Even in the case of broken bones, if the possibility of fat embolism is present, speedy evacuation is indicated. It is at this point that the speed of an Alpine style effort may offset the slower but surer Himalayan style approach.

In a first aid kit designed for this type of rescue the emphasis ought to be on splinting materials, food and water, heat units, and pain-killing drugs. Bleeding control will probably be a minor factor. The inclusion of large amounts of oxygen would be good unless the weight leads to a significant delay in the arrival of the rescue team. In many cases, other drugs and IV fluids will be the treatment of choice. An advanced medical kit, used under the direction of a physician by rescue members specifically trained in its use, will be a key factor.

Weather. Any rescue effort on a large mountain face should expect to encounter bad weather. This may range from an afternoon squall to a full scale blizzard. Any of these conditions become more severe when met on an open face with little or no natural protection. The rescue from the Eiger and recent experience in winter climbs being done today show that it is possible to operate in or wait out on the mountain any weather conditions which we can expect to meet. In many locations lightning may be the major hazard. Lightning places severe limitations on the applications of cable equipment to mountain rescue in some areas. Put bluntly, no one should be on the same mountain with, much less hanging from the end of, a deployed steel cable when lightning is in the area. Opinions differ as to the potential danger to a team using rope. The brake location should be in as protected an area as can be found which still gives proper access to the fall line down the face. It should be possible to perform the evacuation to avoid times of maximum danger. When possible, an evacuation should begin no later than dawn. This means climbing the peak and setting up the entire system during the night, and starting the evacuation during the evening would generally be preferable to waiting through the night if the terrain of the face permits.

The rapidity with which the weather can change is another key factor in determining the basic style in which a rescue will be effected. If there is any question about the stability of a weather pattern, a Himalayan effort ought to be planned in such a way as to allow an Alpine team to be detached and continue the evacuation if speed suddenly becomes the primary consideration.

The Unexpected. There has been a good deal of dreaming, mostly nightmares, about this aspect of long evacuations. It has involved what happens when the helicopter with the rescue team crashes, what do you do if you unexpectedly find three climbers rather than two on the face, and inevitably, what if a rope breaks? The only answer lies in the selection of personnel for the evacuation. An Alpine effort must have a careful *balance* of skills with a clear delineation of responsibility. A Himalayan effort must have a consummate expert on the brakes and a litter team composed of persons who possess a *blending* of rescue, medical, and climbing skills which can be achieved only through experience. Anything less than this will mean that the unexpected may lead to disaster.

In reality, the call for this type of rescue is too likely to come when none of the people who have spent years developing the various systems involved are available. It will then have to be executed by persons who have not spent countless hours going over every detail of endless possible emergency situations which could develop. The rescue will be successful only insofar as there are mountaineers knowledgeable in the techniques and philosophy of modern climbing who have also trained in the procedures and discipline of rescue, and it will fail to the extent that there are climbers who do not rescue and rescuers who do not climb.

This chapter is adapted from an article written for the Mountain Rescue Association conference, Grand Teton National Park, June 1969, by J. S. Hough.

CHAPTER 34

AIRCRAFT ACCIDENTS

PRIORITIES AND LEGALITIES

The first priority is always to save lives. However, the job of the mountain rescuer at the scene of an airplane wreck is usually that of body removal. For wrecks large or small, there are legal aspects which mountain rescuers should know. In the case of a civilian plane crash, the National Transportation Safety Board (NTSB) will be in charge, with the Federal Aviation Administration (FAA) investigating some nonfatal light plane accidents. There will be an Investigator-in-Charge dispatched to the scene, along with a number of other personnel depending on the size of the accident. A military aircraft accident is a special case. The nearest military installation will promptly send personnel to handle most aspects of the crash and will certainly be the authority in charge, should local mountain rescue units be asked to assist. Except for the first priority of saving lives, including search in the wreckage, nothing will be done at the scene without the direction of the governmental authority in charge. In some cases, usually involving light planes, the legal authorities may not wish to go to the scene at all and will leave the entire job to the mountain rescuers, who will be given special jobs of reading numbers off instruments, etc., in addition to the problem of the evacuation.

CIVILIAN AIRCRAFT ACCIDENTS

In the case of civilian wrecks, once the survivors are cared for, there will be no great rush to get anything done, discounting other considerations such as impending bad weather, etc. The NTSB personnel will first give a general overall examination of the wreckage noting such things as directions of travel and locations of key items including wing sections and landing gear. If the aircraft was carrying US mail, the mail bags would be sought and safeguarded. The body removal is then performed. Photographs are taken to show locations of every body, and wreckage parts are moved only to extricate a body.

Once the human factors are taken care of, NTSB specialists will examine the remains of the aircraft structure and power plant. They want logs, instruments and cockpit controls. Of special interest also are worm gears which actuate any control surface or landing gear, firewall fuel shutoff valves, and the propeller hubs and prop governors. If a mountain rescuer finds such items, he should inform the NTSB personnel and should not alter the positions of any handles, knobs, or gears. If it is necessary to disturb such items, photographs should be taken prior to movement.

MILITARY AIRCRAFT ACCIDENTS

If a mountain rescue group does happen to be the first to the scene of a military aircraft wreckage, special procedures should be used. The first order of business is of course the saving of lives. After that, or simultaneously, the nearest military installation should be notified. The wreckage should be searched carefully for survivors, and nothing should be disturbed unless absolutely necessary. Special precaution should be taken in moving anything. External tanks or pods or any armament may carry explosives and should not be touched.

Escape hatches and exits are marked by orange-yellow or red on the outside of the aircraft. On aircraft with ejection seats, there will be a warning sign. Controls painted yellow and black operate these seats and should never be touched. Once all survivors have been found and cared for, the wreckage should be undisturbed and guarded until authority is taken by the military. The assistance of the mountain rescuer may then be no longer desired since the military may handle the entire problem alone, especially if the aircraft involved classified information in some way.

LEADERSHIP

Coordination with the NTSB or FAA inspectors may be a large and significant job on a large plane wreck, perhaps occupying one mountain rescue leader full time, in obtaining local assistance, etc. There also should be an overall leader of the mountain rescue field work overseeing technical aspects and personnel assignments for various tasks.

THE MOUNTAIN RESCUE UNIT AT THE SCENE

The work of the mountain rescue unit will always be in full cooperation with and under the direction of the NTSB Investigator-in-Charge. This may involve movement of equipment to and from the site of the wreckage, if helicopters cannot be used. Since most officials and newsmen getting to the scene are not mountain climbers, they will need to be guided and assisted by the rescue personnel. A good, easy, well-marked path should be chosen, and rescuers who are doing the guiding will need to move very slowly because the average official is not used to the mountain elevations. The state patrol or other law enforcement agency will be at the nearest roadhead and may come to the scene for security and crowd control. Military personnel will handle this job for military aircraft accidents. The rescuer should point out key items of scattered wreckage which may not be visible to the NTSB people. At the scene, the mountain rescuers may handle bodies under the direction of the coroner. All aspects of the evacuation from the wreckage will be under the direction of the NTSB.

Equipment. The normal rescue gear such as ropes, litters, etc., will be needed, but there are additional useful items. Obviously, a sufficient supply of body bags must be available, and these may be supplied by the rescue unit or by the local authorities. The type of bag used is somewhat significant. For example, the usual type from local agencies is a very heavy-duty rubberized canvas bag with handles useful to carry the remains from the wreckage itself to the point of beginning the evacuation. But these bags are heavy, about eight pounds each, and constitute a large load to be carried in the case of a large plane wreck. However, the lightweight plastic bags (actually body bag liners) are much less durable and may tear during an evacuation. Also, for personnel directly handling the bodies, rubber gloves and face masks may be useful (see below). Various tools may be desirable, including pliers, wrenches, prybars, and tree saws and hacksaws with spare blades, to name a few.

Handling Bodies. The bodies are handled by rescuers wearing rubber or other impervious gloves which will always be taken along with the body bags. If surgeons' gloves are used, they need to be protected by some other heavy gloves. Steamfitters' gloves are excellent, and rubber or plastic gloves need to be protected by some insulating layer such as cotton work gloves if there was a fire and the wreckage is still hot. In any case the gloves may be disposed of by leaving in a body bag. In the case of strong odors, a face mask with filter may help; such a mask can be improvised from a triangular bandage. Embalming chemicals should never be used because the NTSB may wish to perform pathological or toxicological examinations. The personnel involved with the direct handling of bodies should be carefully chosen, and their number held to a minimum. A few minutes of looking around before starting to work in the wreckage may help some people adjust their minds to the unpleasant task.

In both large and small wrecks, those involved should note location of any personal effects of the dead and be sure that such belongings are placed in the bag with the other remains. Such items are exceedingly helpful in identification of the bodies. Records should be kept of locations, and the remains numbered for future identification.

Technical Aspects of Evacuation. Ideally a helicopter can fly directly to the scene, and bagged bodies can be placed on board. Even if the helicopter cannot land, it may be able to sling-load a body out; the heavy duty body bag with handles can be easily rigged for suspension from one point on the chopper. Frequently in the mountains an evacuation involving carrying litters over technical and nontechnical terrain will be needed. The general techniques are discussed in other chapters, but some special considerations for large airplane wrecks are given here. First, bagged bodies cannot be lowered directly down a slope, even at 80°, without getting hung up on ledges or projections. Thus a standard litter evacuation or high line suspension system (Tyrolean) will be needed. The latter, put together from steel cable, is convenient for lowering loads several hundred feet. A sturdy body bag with handles may be clipped directly to the pulleys on the static line, or the bag may be secured in a litter. In either case, a hauling or brake line will be needed for control. Pulleys may be necessary to hold this hauling line off the ground and up to the static line.

If a long carryout is necessary with so few rescuers that repeated trips will be necessary for each, litter bearers should perhaps cover a relatively short distance many times rather than a longer distance a few times. This way they become familiar with the terrain and can perform the evacuation faster, and they get frequent rest going back without carrying a heavy load.

Some Aspects of Large Scale Rescue and Evacuation. An accurate count of the number of victims at a disaster scene must be kept. Tags marked with an identifying number and other information should be tied to each victim and a map made showing location of each. Means must be worked out to assure that all victims have been counted with no double counting. If the situation requires triage, color coding using surveyor's flagging on each victim may be found useful.

The chances are that only a few Stokes litters will be available to the mountain rescuers but that many Army stretchers can be obtained. Victims should be transferred from the Stokes to Army litters upon completion of evacuation off terrain where the Stokes is more suitable, allowing Stokes litters to be reused.

CHAPTER 35

HELICOPTER OPERATIONS

Helicopters are becoming almost commonplace in mountain rescue. The first part of this chapter gives a general discussion of conditions under which a chopper can and cannot be flown, and the remainder of the chapter includes loading and safety procedures which should be known by all mountain rescue team personnel who might be involved in a helicopter operation.

HELICOPTER OPERATIONS

As useful as helicopters might be in mountain rescue, leaders should give considerable thought to requesting the assistance of a chopper. The ships are very expensive to operate ($2 to $8 per *minute* for the usual ones used in mountain rescue, including military), somewhat prone to malfunction, and cannot be used in many conditions of weather and terrain. Their use is most often justified in lifesaving operations, namely evacuation of the seriously injured, less often for transport of rescue personnel and equipment and for search.

This section gives background information on which rescue leaders may base a decision to request helicopter assistance. Chapter 15 should be reviewed.

Sometimes even if a helicopter might be available, it would not be called because of victim injuries. For example, if the victim is in a litter and continuous first aid is required and if the only ship available is a small one, the victim would have to be loaded on the outside of the helicopter making first aid impossible.

A point worth emphasizing is that helicopters are complex mechanical devices which do have breakdowns and which are not useful under all conditions. In short, helicopters should not be depended on 100 percent. Even if a helicopter is on the way to do an evacuation, ground troops should be going in on foot and not waiting around, because the chopper may never get there.

General Discussion. Helicopters usually will not land or take off vertically but use some sort of a landing zone, perhaps hundreds of feet long. At the high elevations encountered in the mountains, they should have either a ground cushion (that is, be within about 30 ft, 10 m, of the ground) or have some forward motion, since a helicopter hovering say 100 feet (30 m) from the ground cannot land safely in the event of engine failure, which is most likely to occur on takeoff due to high engine stresses. In mountain flying, a pilot must be very careful to observe maximum load limitations in order to maintain a reasonable margin of safety. The effective elevation, known as the "density altitude," varies with temperature (and to a lesser extent with humidity), and a hot summer day is poor for high altitude flying. A helicopter may not have instrument flight capability, and then the pilot must have sight of the ground at all times. Also, landings and takeoffs are made easier in the presence of a light steady breeze (say 10 knots or 20 km/hr) than in still air, but a pilot is likely to choose not to take off or land in a wind greater than 45 knots (80 km/hr) or with a gust spread of over 15-20 knots (25-35 km/hr). Thus only if weather conditions and terrain are suitable, can a chopper be used, and only some types of ships will operate at high elevations. The range of the helicopter may be a serious limitation, 200 mi (320 km) total being typical.

Techniques such as winch loading or rappelling from a hover are feasible at sea level but may be unsafe or impossible at high mountain elevations due to severe stresses placed on the usual aircraft available for mountain rescue. Reliability of a ship operating at maximum power for more than a few seconds may be uncomfortably low. A military pilot is generally less willing to stress his ship heavily than is a commercial pilot. Rescuers should get instructions from the pilot prior to attempting these techniques. Cargo to be sling-loaded should be rigged for suspension from a single point. Loads slung from the cargo hook are often dropped accidentally.

A mountain rescuer aboard a chopper may have a difficult time following the course of the ship on a map in unknown territory, particularly when prominent landmarks such as high peaks may be obscured by clouds, due to the rather high speed of the aircraft.

Sources. The availability of helicopters varies from place to place and time to time. The usual source of a chopper for mountain rescue is the military, with requests going through appropriate authorities in the state. The military will normally respond in a life or death situation with time an important factor, but a helicopter may not be sent as a convenience for evacuation of a known fatality or for transport of rescuers, unless there are extenuating circumstances.

Other sources of choppers include large city police departments, a few radio stations, and some public utilities. Again for life-and-death cases these helicopters may be available free. Commercial services may be hired at their usual rates and are not likely to be free since costs are very high, $125 per hour and up.

Information Needed for a Request. The military will desire to know the name, age, sex, address and number of victims, nature of injuries, first aid information, and destination of the victim upon evacuation. Commercial services probably will not ask all these questions.

Any pilot will want to know the location of the accident site or proposed Landing Zone (LZ). If the LZ is a good one and located clearly, the chopper may proceed directly there; otherwise it will go to the rescue base camp and pick up a team leader who can direct the pilot to the LZ. The location should be specified clearly, giving reference to road maps, geographic coordinates specifying the location to within a mile, or magnetic bearings and mileage from some very prominent and identifiable landmarks, and preferably a combination of these. Pilots do not have the usual 7.5' USGS quadrangle maps used by ground rescue teams.

The landing zone should also be described. It may be an empty parking lot at base camp, but more likely it will be in the mountains, and the general nature of the terrain should be stated (mountains, desert . . .). Its elevation is important, as is its site and general condition (canyon bottom, ridge top or saddle, slope, surface condition such as tundra, rocky . . .). Any obstructions to landing must be clearly given stating height and proximity (distance and bearing: "100 foot tower 300 ft SSE of LZ"); trees, cliffs, etc., are significant, but most important are aerial wires, which are difficult for a pilot to see.

Finally weather conditions should be described. The ceiling is stated in feet above the ground to the bottoms of the lowest clouds. Visibility is given in miles, and the nature of the limitation is stated (fog, haze). Temperature, stating °C or °F, is important. An estimate of the wind velocity, direction and gust spread is given. If smoke grenades are available, the pilot will be pleased.

Landing Zone. The ideal mountain LZ is a flat strip 100 ft (30 m) wide and 300 ft (90 m) or more long on a flat ridge or saddle such that the pilot can "fall off" the end in takeoff. A 65 ft (20 m) diameter flat spot is the minimum for the usual small ship. The strip should face into the wind and not be on a lee slope with downdrafts likely. Ideally there should be no trees (at worst low topped ones), cliffs, walls, or wires (very dangerous) nearby. The LZ should be level, with 8° preferred maximum slope. Since the main rotor stirs up an 80 knot (150 km/hr) wind, the LZ surface should be free of small stuff that can be kicked up. Tall dry grass and shrubs should be avoided to prevent possible damage to the tail rotor. Tree stumps should be less than 1 ft (.3 m) high. A lake frozen through (at least 12 in. or 30 cm of sound ice on water) or firm snow makes a good LZ, but if the LZ is snow the pilot will need some objects such as markers or packs, etc., on the snow to provide depth perception.

It is very important to provide some form of wind indicator. Several pieces of highly visible surveyor's tape or flagging at each end of the LZ make good indicators, as does a smoke bomb set off as the ship first approaches or when requested by the pilot.

The LZ can be defined by brightly colored panels or crepe paper weighted down adequately to withstand the strong winds, or heavy packs. At night the area is defined by the rescue team members' headlamps held on and aimed steadily without wavering. But many pilots are very unhappy about night flying in unknown mountain terrain.

Communications with the Pilot. Ideally the pilot can easily find his way and land at base camp. A rescue team member with a radio is ferried by chopper to the LZ in the field, directing the pilot, and providing communications to the ground teams as necessary. However, due to noise inside the ship it is hard for the ground teams to understand what is said, since the usual rescue team radio is not equipped with a noise cancelling microphone. Some military choppers have emergency communications on channels available on ground radios. Occasionally commercial ships can bring packsets for ground use.

The pilot will have his destination described to within a mile (1.6 km) when he leaves his home base. If communications are good, he can be "talked in" when the ship is audible or visible. Otherwise a Very pistol flare is quite effective (but not in timber where there is fire danger), with the little pengun flares a good second choice.

Wind indicators and landing obstacles should be pointed out as the ship approaches. If a person is giving hand signals, the pilot should be told where this person is and what he is wearing.

Final Approach and Landing. Normally the pilot will make a high level pass over the LZ for observation of obstacles and wind indicators (smoke grenades are preferred) and then will come in at low level to feel out the site. During this approach all personnel not in the LZ should look away to avoid being hit in the face by debris kicked up by the prop wash. All ground troops should hold down any loose gear.

A rescue team leader is designated as man in charge and will handle all communications between ship and team members. The team members should be briefed on actions before arrival of the chopper and be prepared to act quickly and efficiently upon signal.

During final approach only one person at most should be in the LZ. With the helicopter some distance away, the touchdown point is indicated by a person upwind standing with his back to the wind and arms up facing towards the desired landing spot. There is a set of useful arm signals, but the pilot will probably ignore these not knowing whether he can trust them or not. Most important is the wave off, hands up and crisscrossed repeatedly overhead.

PERSONNEL LOADING AND SAFETY PROCEDURES

In general every rescuer involved in a helicopter operation must know precisely what to do, because of both safety and expense. Personnel transported into the field must be prepared to walk out, since flying conditions can deteriorate quickly. Passengers on any military aircraft may be required to sign a civilian release form.

Loading Procedures. A number of safety precautions must be taken during loading a helicopter while the rotors are moving. Only one person will approach the ship upon its landing, and he will approach only when signaled by the pilot or crew chief. This one person will give all signals to the other rescuers, and no one approaches the ship unless specifically told to do so. If the situation should arise that one must approach without a crew member signalling, the approach should be made from the front after getting a crew member's attention, and then the person points to the ship. Also, there should be no smoking within 100 feet (30 m) of the helicopter during landing, loading, or takeoff procedures.

All loading or unloading must be on the downhill side of the ship, since the rotor blade may be as close as 5 feet (1.5 m) to the ground in many models even when the aircraft is on level ground. Also, loading should be from within 60° of the front to be visible by the pilot. The tail rotor is to be avoided. This rotor is not visible when turning at high speed, and cases are known where personnel have walked into the rotor and a) damaged the rotor and b) were decapitated. The pilot must see personnel within reach of the tail rotor so that he will not turn the tail around in that direction.

Personnel should be ready to load or board when the ship arrives, but no one is to approach the helicopter until specifically told to do so by the team leader in charge of loading. Everyone should be wearing a hardhat with chin strap secured, goggles or glasses affixed with safety strap, and should have clothing buttoned up since each person will be in winds of up to 80 knots (150 km/h) under the main rotor. The rescuers' packs should be carried by hand, not worn, and no gear such as skis, snowshoes, ice ax or crampons should be attached to the outside of the pack.

When told to board, the ground team members keep their heads low (stooping) and run to the ship from the front, carrying their gear. Any gear to be stowed on an outside rack must be very securely lashed in place, perhaps by a person who is not about to board the aircraft, to save time. If the helicopter is a large one, the first man to the ship will place his pack inside, then move in all the way leaving room for those behind. He will probably be told by the pilot or crew chief specifically where to sit. He then fastens his seat belt and holds his pack between his feet. If he has an ice ax, it should have protective guards in place and be stowed where designated. If the helicopter is hovering rather than resting on the ground, the individual getting on should stand by the ship on the ground until specifically told to step aboard. Then he should move slowly and evenly; the pilot has to compensate for the added load made by the passenger and must be given time to do so.

The details of placing a victim in a litter on board will of course depend on the particular helicopter used. But in every case the victim must be securely placed in the litter and well covered to prevent being hit by debris from prop wash during loading. He should be told what is happening before loading. In the case of a small ship the litter will be secured on the outside opposite the pilot, and the victim should be completely covered and insulated from the 100 knot (180 km/hr) winds. First aid is impossible in this case. If the victim is quite heavy, a counterbalancing weight will be needed on the pilot's side. On bigger military ships set up for first aid, the victim's litter will be placed on top of a litter in the helicopter and secured by the normal victim tie-in straps of the underneath litter. A Stokes litter does fit on a standard Army stretcher.

Unloading the helicopter requires the same general safety precautions as loading. To reiterate, all personnel will exit downhill towards the front of the ship, never towards the tail, keeping head low, and should leave the chopper only when specifically told to do so. The first man out should refasten his seat belt so that the belt cannot fall outside and bang against the fuselage. He should make his exit and be handed his pack by the second man out who also hands his own pack to the first man. If any equipment is thrown out while the helicopter is moving, this gear should be well tagged with strips of flagging. Equipment secured to the outside of the ship should be removed as quickly as possible.

Special precautions should be taken during exiting from a hovering aircraft. No one should jump off until given the nod by the pilot or crew chief because the ship may be moving rapidly or the pilot may not be prepared. The jump should be gentle, not done with a spring. Rappelling out is dangerous and if absolutely necessary should be done with a very quick releasing rappel system.

Safety. Many items of safety were mentioned above. Here we reiterate procedures to be followed:

1) As the helicopter makes its landing approach or takeoff, stay out of its path and hold down loose items which could be blown in the prop wash.

2) In spite of the great tendency to watch, look away as the helicopter approaches to avoid being struck in the face by debris.

3) If using a smoke bomb, set it off where there is no fire danger.

4) No smoking.

5) If the main rotor is in motion, stay out of the Landing Zone unless specifically told to be in it.

6) Approach only from the front of the ship, when a crew member sees you.

7) Approach and exit only on the downhill side.

8) When approaching the ship, wear a hardhat with chin strap secured, and zip up your parka.

9) Wear goggles or glasses attached with a safety strap.

10) Keep your head low because the rotor could be as low as 5 feet (1.5 m) off level ground.

11) Stay away from the tail rotor.

12) Once inside the ship, fasten your seat belt securely, hold your pack and stow your ice ax safely.

13) Obtain permission from a crew member to "paw over" the parked ship. There are some critical parts which should not be touched, including the tail rotor and drive shaft.

Emergency Procedure. When power is lost, the pilot will put in negative pitch in the main rotor, and the helicopter will descend at perhaps 1800 feet/minute (540 m/min), with the rotor turning rapidly. As the ship approaches the ground, the pilot will add pitch, checking the descent. He has 5 to 10 seconds to land the chopper under control in this process known as autorotation.

Passengers should do the following: Tighten seat belts and check chin strap on hardhat. Hold pack and ice ax securely. Note location of exits and door handles. Stay out of the way of controls. It is possible that the pilot will want heavy items thrown out if time permits. Do nothing else until told to by the pilot, including exiting upon landing.

REFERENCES

The following are military training films concerning helicopter operations of particular value to mountain rescue. These may be borrowed by contacting an Air Force film library.

1) "Helicopter Mountain Operations" (25 min.) AF TF-1-5102B or Army MF46-8902.

2) "Helicopter Arctic Operations" (29 min.) AF TF-1-5102A or Army MF46-9029.

APPENDIX A

MOUNTAIN RESCUE STOKES LITTER

Splitting a Stokes Litter. A Stokes litter for mountain rescue will be split into two pieces for ease of carrying. The split should be made at a place such that the nested halves are matched in length. The rails of one of the pieces will be fitted with rods which mate with the rails of the other piece. Because of variations in location of the small cross ribs from one Stokes to another, the splitting will be such that on some litters, the inner of the nested pieces will have the male fittings, and the outer for others. Extra cross ribbing will be needed for support, and reinforcements should be put on the rails to avoid damaging the rail ends.

When the halves are mated, it is very important that they be mechanically held together, with a simple, foolproof and rugged system. There should be no separate parts or tools to get lost. One way of doing this is with a turnbuckle as shown in Fig. A-1, placed on the two bottom rails such that the litter rests on the rails rather than on the turnbuckles. To secure the turnbuckles while the litter halves are separated, the second welded projection is used as shown. An improvised method of securing the litter halves is simply to lash the pieces together with webbing, perhaps that used to attach the litter to its packframe.

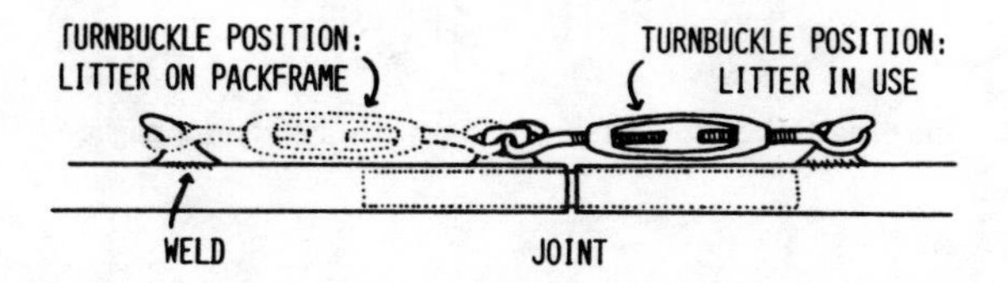

Fig. A-1. Showing turnbuckles as a simple method of securing litter halves.

Packing the Stokes Litter. When the litter is disassembled, the two pieces are nested together along with a rescue sleeping bag with the stuff sack placed open end down to prevent entry of rain or snow. The parts are lashed to a packframe with the head and foot ends up and the under side of the litter towards the packframe. The frame should be low on the litter; if the frame is too high, the litter rides uncomfortably low in carrying. The lowest crossrail of the litter half can be conveniently rested on the bottom cross bar of the packframe. The lashing may be accomplished with a length of narrow webbing, one end tied to a corner of the frame. The webbing is passed across the litter and around lashing studs on opposite sides of the frame, back and forth several times from stud to stud and terminated in a buckle, as shown in Fig. A-2. The webbing should be passed between the outer and next to outer rails of the litter, *not* around the outside rail, to prevent damage by abrasion to the webbing, and not through the chicken wire. The entire assembly should be cinched down very tightly to prevent it from working loose during carrying.

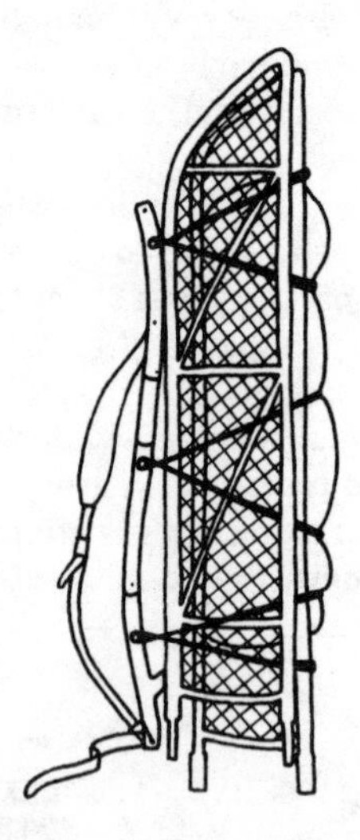

Fig. A-2. Showing the Stokes litter packed with a sleeping bag.

APPENDIX B

ASCENDER STRENGTH TESTS

Device	Conditions	Results
Jumar on 7/16" Goldline	*a) Pull on 5/16" Jumar sling	Sling broke 1250 lbs
	*b) Pull on 1" web	Broke opposite cam, 1700 lbs
	c) Pull on 1" web	Cam broke 1189 lbs
Bachmann knot	a) 5 doubled wraps 9/16" web on 11 mm perlon	Slipped at 185 lbs
	*b) 7 mm perlon on 7/16" Goldline	Sling broke 2700 lbs
Prusik knot	a) 3-wrap 5/16" on 7/16" Goldline	Holds over 1200 lbs
	b) 2-wrap 5/16" on 7/16" Goldline	Holds over 800 lbs
	c) 3-wrap 7 mm on 11 mm perlon	Slips at 1700 lbs
Hiebler	*a) On 7/16" Goldline	Bent and pulled rivet, 1200 lbs
	b) On 7/16" Goldline	Slipped at 850 lbs

*Tests by California Region MRA, 2-3 May, 1970.
Others by Rocky Mountain Rescue Group, Boulder.

INDEX